the incredibly indispensable
WEB DIRECTORY

the incredibly indispensable
WEB DIRECTORY
4th edition

CLIVE & BETTINA ZIETMAN

Published by:
Kogan Page

In association with:

BT wholesale

Publisher's note

Every possible effort has been made to ensure that the information contained in this book is accurate at the time of going to press, and the publishers and authors cannot accept responsibility for any errors or omissions, however caused. No responsibility for loss or damage occasioned to any person acting, or refraining from action, as a result of the material in this publication can be accepted by the editor, the publisher or any of the authors.

First published in 2000
Second edition 2001
Third edition 2002
Fourth edition 2003

Apart from any fair dealing for the purposes of research or private study, or criticism or review, as permitted under the Copyright, Designs and Patents Act, 1988, this publication may only be reproduced, stored or transmitted, in any form, or by any means, with the prior permission in writing of the publisher, or in the case of reprographic reproduction in accordance with the terms of licences issued by the Copyright Licensing Agency. Enquiries concerning reproduction outside those terms should be sent to the publishers at the undermentioned addresses:

Kogan Page Limited
120 Pentonville Road
London N1 9JN

Kogan Page (US) Limited
22883 Quicksilver Drive
Sterling VA 20166–2012
USA

Kogan Page website: www.kogan-page.co.uk

BT Wholesale website: www.btwholesale.com
BT Broadband website: www.bt.com/broadband

© Clive and Bettina Zietman, 2003

The right of Clive and Bettina Zietman to be identified as the authours of this work has been asserted by him in accordance with the Copyright, Designs and Patents Act 1988

British Library Cataloguing-in-Publication Data

A CIP record for this book is available from the British Library

ISBN 0 7494 3943 2

Typeset by Saxon Graphics Ltd, Derby
Printed and bound in Scotland by Scotprint, Haddington, East Lothian

THOMSON
Directories™

Need to track down a business in a hurry?

around britain

around the world

arts & entertainment

business

children

education, training & research

environment

food & drink

government

healthcare

help

hobbies & leisure

living

museums, libraries & information

news & information

personal finance

professional bodies & trade associations

science & nature

shopping

sport

contents

technology

travel

preface to the 3rd edition

This edition has been considerably revised and expanded and now covers over 11,000 household names on the web, allowing you to save hours of fruitless searching and surfing.

Thanks must go to Beth Druce. Your assistance has been invaluable.
Thank You.

the top household names on the internet

clive & bettina zietman

People who surf the web seem to enjoy the mere process of wandering aimlessly through different websites. Although surfing can be a fun hobby, this book has been written for people who know that the information or institution is out there, they want to go straight to it but do not know how. In other words, it is designed to give those who are frustrated and fazed by the Internet a portable, friendly guide through the maze. For anyone who has spent hours on their computer getting nowhere with the simplest search, this non-technical and straightforward directory is the answer.

This directory is different from all others. It is aimed at all UK users who are frustrated with the Web generally, in particular the failing of search engines. It is ideal for beginners, non-surfers, families, researchers and business users. It is a cherry-picked selection of household names on the Web, chosen from an essentially British perspective. Be it Tom Cruise or the Inland Revenue, the BBC or Nesquik, this book contains them all. It is a neat and crystal-clear list of official household names, familiar to everyday UK users.

For those who wish to go directly to the sites for Buckingham Palace, Aintree Racecourse or British Airways this book will be incredibly indispensable. It is not cluttered with the weird or the obscure. It is not dominated by American sites, nor does it contain anything but official sites supported by well-known companies and institutions. The Tate Gallery, Battersea Dogs Home and Tesco are in. The Utah Elvis Appreciation Society and the Klingon Dictionary are out. The websites listed are self-explanatory and thus the book does not contain commentary or descriptions. Roald Dahl, Oxford University, 10 Downing Street and Barclays Bank need no introduction.

searching the web

People who have just bought a computer may not be familiar with the mystique, language and workings of the Internet. Because the Internet was born and has grown in an unstructured and largely unregulated fashion it can be very difficult to navigate. Most people search the Web by inserting keywords into search engines. The search engines produce lists of websites (often in no particular order) which are triggered by the selected word. Say, for example, you are looking for the Imperial War Museum's website. By inserting the words "imperial", "war" and "museum" into a search engine, you may, with luck, be led in the right direction. Often however you will be led astray. Why?

There is a skill in using search engines. This is a skill which mere mortals don't necessarily possess. People who spend their lives working with computers assume that everyone in the world thinks like they do. The truth is that they don't.

Even the most powerful and sophisticated search engines only cover about 15 per cent of all websites.

Search engines are not human brains. They therefore do not think like the human brain, in particular they do not think like yours. Although you know what you are looking for, the search engine may well have very different ideas.

It is so easy to set up a website that the Web has already become full to the point of overflowing with websites of dire quality. The search engines find it hard to sift the wheat from the chaff.

Different search engines have different rules about refining searches. To use a particular search engine properly you have to learn the rules.

Even the choice of search engine is overwhelming. There are scores of search engines and some are better at searching particular subjects. At the last count, there were approximately 4000 in existence. Which search engine to use can be mystifying.

Although the Web is a wonderful source of information and search engines can do the trick, there is an alternative. If you know the precise company or institution you are looking for, it is far easier and quicker to go straight to it by typing in the web address. All computers linked to the Internet have an address box. Type in the address, press enter on your keyboard and you will be taken directly to your chosen destination. YOU DO NOT NEED TO USE A SEARCH ENGINE. This book enables you to circumvent the search engines completely if the website you are looking for is listed here.

Please note that not every famous name has a website. For example, only new films seem to have official websites. Films that pre-date the Internet do not. Similarly, many large institutions have not yet caught up with the Internet age. Some have sites under construction and others may well have changed their website address between the time this book was compiled and the date of publication. When companies are taken over or merge, this also tends to affect the website address. To some extent this book is aiming at a moving target and future editions will incorporate as many additions and changes as possible.

If for any reason you feel that a household name deserves inclusion in the next edition of the book – or if you have any other comments – please email your suggestions to update@householdnames.co.uk

brilliant broadband

Cherish your current conventional dial-up Internet connection, because it'll soon belong in a museum. In a few years your children will ask how you ever managed to use the Internet in its current incarnation, just like we wonder how the Wright brothers ever got off the ground in 1903. In fact, slow Internet speeds are already a thing of the past for many individuals. As more people become aware of the benefits of Broadband, thousands are upgrading every week.

Once you have Broadband, you can begin to use the Internet as a natural extension of your computer. Rather than going through the tedious process of dialling up your service provider via your modem and paying for the time you are online, with Broadband you typically pay a flat rate per month and your Internet access is 'always on' –similarly to electricity– so you will be instantly connected.

With Broadband access, all the Internet hype you've been bombarded with over the last few years finally starts to make sense. You can properly download high-quality music, videos and movie trailers in just a few minutes. Like that new Britney video? Download it. A new PC game? Grab the demo.

Even working from home becomes a real possibility, as accessing your company network will be quick and easy. You can also use the Internet as a stereo and listen to digital radio all day. Thousands of radio stations all over the world now broadcast on the web, so armed with a fast Internet connection you can listen to jazz from Senegal, live festivals from Reykjavik, or whatever else takes your fancy.

More services will develop for Broadband as more users switch over, but there are plenty of sites out there already. This guide has been compiled to demonstrate what you could be enjoying with a Broadband connection. There's just one question you have to ask yourself-are you ready for the future? Because the future is already here.

welcome to broadband

The Internet can be described as a 'virtual library' holding information and entertainment from all over the world. You can gain access to this library using a telephone line and a computer.

The speed at which the information flows from the library into your computer depends largely upon the type of line or connection you own. At present many Internet users find that it takes too long. That's why the World Wide Web is sometimes referred to as the World Wide Wait!

One easy way to get better Internet connection is via Broadband. As it works over your normal telephone line. Thousands of people are already enjoying the benefits. Having Broadband means getting information at up to 10 times the rate of an old-fashioned connection.

what is broadband?

With Broadband your connection is 'always on' which means there is no waiting to 'log on' to the Internet. Just sit down at your computer and your are reading to surf the Internet.

As if that wasn't enough, as a Broadband user, you will typically pay a flat monthly rate for your connection. This means no surprise costs and no restrictions on when you can go online and for how long. You'll find that you start to use the Internet in a new and different way. With Broadband once you're online, you can move swiftly from website to website, page to page, and all in a fraction of the time that a traditional connection used to take.

All the time you used to waste waiting for connections to establish and pages to download can now be saved. Many Broadband owners actually end up engaging in more leisure pursuits thanks to the time savings they enjoy.

Finally, Broadband means you can make and receive normal telephone calls, while using the Internet, as you no longer use the phone line with the modem.

who is using broadband?

tony tortise

'As a family, our experience of Broadband ADSL has been terrific,' says Tony Tortise, a manager from Birmingham. Tony's family includes Rita and their two children.

Rita's habits have changed thanks to Broadband 'Before Broadband I'd use the paper version of *The Yellow Pages* to find a local service like a plumber. It's now much easier and quicker to find the number online with the likes of Yell.'

Emma, Tony's 9-year-old daughter, enjoys visiting kids' sites. With Broadband she can surf these sites in no time and get the most out of their graphics and animation. And what about Tony himself? 'I love listening to radio stations from around the world using the Internet, something that wasn't really possible before Broadband.'

When James Tortise, 15, isn't using the Internet to revise for his forth-coming GCSEs he enjoys downloading music for his MP3 player. With an old-fashioned modem this took forever, but with Broadband he downloads a song in a fraction of the time.

transforming business

Before Broadband, Medivet Veterinary Group was struggling with its dial-up connection to transfer patient data between its 27 sites across Greater London. Not only was there a delay while they dialled up, but if staff tried to contact more than two sites the connection would hang up.

Once Broadband was installed, the first thing staff noticed was their ability to transfer data much faster. Furthermore, the new Intranet stream-lined communications between practices, enabling Medivet's 200 staff to keep up to date on the latest news, request drugs from other practices, and agree rotas. As a result, business efficiency increased dramatically. On one occasion, a vet in another practice needed specialist advice during a complex operation. Digital pictures were taken at each stage of the operation and sent down the network, enabling the specialist to give accurate advice which save the life of the patient.

deborah luffman

Deborah Luffman, of Croydon, was attracted to Broadband by the promise of faster Internet, fixed costs and telephone freedom. Deborah explains:

'Because I pay a flat rate each month I am not subject to surprise bills. This means that access to the Internet does not need to be confined to off-peak hours, and I can use it during the day. Now when my nephew comes to stay, he can go online for fun and study at any time.'

Broadband allows Deborah to use her phone line for calls and Internet access at the same time. 'Before Broadband it was frustrating not being able to receive and make calls when I was online. Being able to do both is a major advantage.'

Sending and receiving images is a fun way for Deborah's family to keep in touch from different parts of the UK. What might have taken 20 minutes with a standard line has been reduced to just a couple of minutes thanks to Broadband.

paul cooper

'I had Broadband installed almost a year ago and it's fantastic, it's so fast it's frightening. I work from home so I use the Internet for both business and pleasure. For the type business I'm in, speed is of the essence and Broadband does the job,' says executive Paul Cooper.

Before Broadband, Paul was restricted when working from home, and could not use some of the online programs important to his work. Since connecting to Broadband Paul is reaping the benefits. He says:

'Because I am permanently online emails just instantly appear in my inbox-letting me respond immediately to customers or suppliers. I can now access my company's Customer Relationship Management computer program from home. In fact, it's even quicker than working in the company office!'

And when Paul isn't working, he finds plenty of other uses for his fast connection-"I enjoy watching movie trailers and TV programmes from around the world. Before Broadband it just wasn't practically possible. My wife, who is from Hong Kong, also uses the Broadband connection to keep in touch with her family via webcam."

andrew wicks

Andrew Wicks is a self-confessed lover of computer games. He uses the Internet mainly for playing an online game called Everquest. This is currently one of the world's most popular online games with hundreds of thousands of subscribers.

Before Broadband, Andrew had problems. 'With a modem, I suffered from poor connection speeds and timeouts. For me this would sometimes make the game unplayable.'

But Broadband has changed all that. 'It's much more reliable than traditional dial-up access and I enjoy the game more. I now benefit from always on, fast, email and web browsing'.

how do I get broadband?

If you want to join the thousands of people who have already said yes to Broadband, or just want to know more about what Broadband can do for you, then visit **www.bt.com/broadband**

what's hot when you've got broadband?

Over the following pages you can find a selection of websites. Some of these sites feature video and audio, animation and interaction, and some contain massive amounts of data. With conventional access these features might present problems, but with Broadband they're a breeze to get into and enjoy.

Let your surfing pleasure commence

Around Britain

castles

Alnwick Castle
www.alnwickcastle.com

Auckland Castle
www.auckland-castle.co.uk

Balmoral Castle
www.balmoral-castle.co.uk

Caerlaverock Castle
www.aboutscotland.com/caer/caer.html

Castle Cornet
www.museum.guernsey.net

Dundas Castle
www.dundascastle.co.uk

Glamis Castle
www.glamis-castle.co.uk

Hedingham Castle
www.hedinghamcastle.co.uk

Kelburn Castle
www.kelburncountrycentre.com

Leeds Castle
www.leeds-castle.co.uk

Lulworth Castle
www.lulworth.com

Muncaster Castle
www.muncastercastle.co.uk

Powderham Castle
www.powderham.co.uk

Sherborne Castle
www.sherbornecastle.com

Skipton Castle
www.skiptoncastle.co.uk

Thirlestane Castle
www.thirlestanecastle.co.uk

Tower of London
www.camelot-group.com/tower

Warwick Castle
www.warwick-castle.co.uk

Windsor Castle
www.royal.gov.uk/

cathedrals & churches

Bradford Cathedral
www.bradford.anglican.org/cathedral

Canterbury Cathedral
www.canterbury-cathedral.org

Chester Cathedral
www.chestercathedral.org.uk

Christchurch Cathedral, Oxford
www.chch.ox.ac.uk/cathedral

Coventry Cathedral
www.coventrycathedral.org

Durham Cathedral
www.durhamcathedral.co.uk

Ely Cathedral
www.ely.org.uk

Exeter Cathedral
www.exeter-cathedral.org.uk

Glastonbury Abbey
www.glastonburyabbey.com

Lincoln Cathedral
www.lincolncathedral.com

Liverpool's Anglican Cathedral
www.merseyworld.com/cathedral

Liverpool's Roman Catholic
www.rcal.org.uk

Ripon Cathedral
www.riponcathedral.org.uk

Salisbury Cathedral
www.salisburycathedral.org.uk

St Alban's Cathedral
www.stalbansdioc.org.uk/cathedral

St Paul's Cathedral
www.stpauls.co.uk

Westminister Cathedral
www.westminstercathedral.org.uk

Westminster Abbey
www.westminster-abbey.org

Winchester Cathedral
www.win.diocese.org.uk/cathedral.html

Worcester Cathedral
www.cofe-worcester.org.uk/cathedral

York Minster
www.yorkminster.org

historic railways

Alford Valley
www.alford.org.uk

Aln Valley
www.avrs.co.uk

Avon Valley
www.avonvalleyrailway.co.uk

Beamish
www.countydurham.com/beamish

Bowes
www.bowesrailway.co.uk

Bridgnorth Cliff
www.pendry.demon.co.uk

Bure Valley
www.bvrw.co.uk

Chinnor & Princes Risborough
www.cprra.co.uk

Churnet
www.churnet-valley-railway.co.uk

Colne Valley
www.cvr.org.uk

Dartmoor
www.dartmoorrailway.co.uk

East Lancashire Light
www.east-lancs-rly.co.uk

Eastleigh Lakeside
www.steamtrain.co.uk

Ffestiniog
www.festrail.co.uk

Flying Scotsman
www.flyingscotsman.com

Foxfield
www.foxfieldrailway.co.uk

Gloucestershire Warwickshire Steam
www.gwsr.plc.uk

Great Central
www.gcrailway.co.uk

Great Little Trains of Wales
www.whr.co.uk/gltw

Isle of Wight Steam Railway
www.iwsteamrailway.co.uk

Keighley & Worth Valley
www.kwvr.co.uk

Lappa Valley
www.lappa-railway.co.uk

Leighton Buzzard
www.buzzrail.co.uk

Llangollen
www.llangollen-railway.co.uk

Lynton & Barnstaple
www.lyntonbarnstaple.ndirect.co.uk

Mid Norfolk
www.mnr.org.uk

Middleton
www.middletonrailway.org.uk

Mid-Hants 'Watercress'
www.watercressline.co.uk

Nene Valley
www.internetlink.co.uk/nvr.htm

North Norfolk
www.nnrailway.co.uk

North Yorkshire Moors
www.nymr.demon.co.uk

Northampton & Lamport
www.nlr.org.uk

Peak Rail
www.peakrail.co.uk

Ravenglass
www.ravenglass-railway.co.uk

Ribble
www.dockrail.org.uk

Romney Hythe & Dymchurch
www.rhdr.demon.co.uk/rhdr.html

Royal Scotsman
www.royalscotsman.com

Severn Valley
www.svr.co.uk

Snowdon
www.snowdonrailway.co.uk

South Devon
www.southdevonrailway.org

Swanage
www.swanrail.demon.co.uk

Talyllyn
www.talyllyn.co.uk

Tanfield
www.tanfield-railway.co.uk

Welshpool & Llanfair
www.wllr.org.uk

West Somerset
www.west-somerset-railway.co.uk

Wyvernrail
www.wyvernrail.co.uk

monuments & historic buildings

10 Downing Street
www.number-10.gov.uk

Albert Dock
www.merseyworld.com/albert

Althorp
www.althorp.com

Auckland Castle
www.auckland-castle.co.uk

Baden Powell House
www.scoutbase.org.uk

Beaulieu
www.beaulieu.co.uk

Blenheim
www.blenheimpalace.com

Bolton Abbey
www.boltonabbey.com

Bowood House
www.bowood-estate.co.uk

Broadlands
www.broadlands.net

Buckingham Palace
www.royal.gov.uk

Burghley House
www.stamford.co.uk/burghley

Callendar House
www.falkirkmuseums.demon.co.uk

Castle Howard
www.castlehoward.co.uk

Chatsworth House
www.chatsworth-house.co.uk

Coventry Cathedral
www.coventrycathedral.org

Cutty Sark
www.cuttysark.org.uk

Duncombe Park
www.duncombepark.com

Durham Cathedral
www.dur.ac.uk/~dla0www/c_tour/tour.html

Ely Cathedral
www.ely.org.uk

Exeter Cathedral
www.exeter-cathedral.org.uk

Fountains Abbey
www.fountainsabbey.org.uk

Fursdon House
www.eclipse.co.uk/fursdon

Hadrian's Wall
www.hadrians-wall.org

Hampton Court Palace
www.hrp.org.uk/hcp

Harewood
www.harewood.org

Historic Royal Palaces
www.hrp.org.uk

Houses of Parliament
www.parliament.uk

Kensington Palace
www.royal.gov.uk/output/page563.asp

Kentwell
www.kentwell.co.uk

Kilmartin House
www.kht.org.uk

Longleat
www.longleat.co.uk

Mount Stuart
www.mountstuart.com

Newby Hall
www.newbyhall.co.uk

Owlpen Manor
www.owlpen.com

Penshurst Place
www.penshurstplace.com

Port Lympne
www.howletts.net

Royal Mews
www.royal.gov.uk/output/page556.asp

Sewerby Hall
www.bridlington.net/sewerby

Somerleyton Hall
www.somerleyton.co.uk

Stanford Hall
www.stanfordhall.co.uk

Stonehenge
www.stonehenge.co.uk

Sulgrave Manor
www.stratford.co.uk/sulgrave

Tower Bridge
www.towerbridge.org.uk

Traquair House
www.traquair.co.uk

Wilton House
www.wiltonhouse.com

parks, gardens & arboreta

Arley Arboretum
www.arley-arboretum.org.uk

Athelhampton
www.athelhampton.co.uk

Auchgourish Gardens
www.auchgourishgardens.com

Batsford Arboretum
www.batsford-arboretum.co.uk

Birmingham Botanical Gardens
www.bham-bot-gdns.demon.co.uk

Bodenham Arboretum
www.bodenham-arboretum.co.uk

Bowood House
www.bowood-estate.co.uk

Bradenham Hall Garden & Arboretum
www.bradenhamhall.co.uk

Bramham Park
www.yorkshirenet.co.uk/bramham/

Castle Bromwich Gardens
www.cbhgt.swinternet.co.uk

Castle Howard
www.castlehoward.co.uk

Chatsworth House
www.chatsworth-house.co.uk

Duncombe Park
www.duncombepark.com

Elsham Hall Country & Wildlife Park
www.plus44.com/local/lincs/elsham.html

Exbury Gardens
www.exbury.co.uk

Finlaystone Country Estate
www.finlaystone.co.uk

5

Fishers Farm Park
www.fishersfarmpark.co.uk

Garden Visit & Travel Guide
www.gardenvisit.com

Harewood
www.harewood.org

Kelburn Castle & Country Centre
www.kelburncountrycentre.com

Kew Gardens
www.rbgkew.org.uk

Knoll Gardens
www.knollgardens.co.uk

Lulworth Castle
www.lulworth.com

Mount Stuart House & Gardens
www.mountstuart.com

National Memorial Arboretum
www.nationalmemorialarboretum.co.uk

North Devon Farm Park
www.farmpark.co.uk

Odds Farm Park
www.oddsfarm.co.uk

Painswick Rococo Gardens
www.beta.co.uk/painswick

Penshurst Place & Gardens
www.penshurstplace.com

Royal Parks
www.royalparks.gov.uk

Sir Harold Hillier Gardens & Arboretum
www.hillier.hants.gov.uk

Somerleyton Hall & Gardens
www.somerleyton.co.uk

Walsall Arboretum
www.walsallarboretum.co.uk

Westonbirt Arboretum
www.westonbirtarboretum.com

regions

About Scotland
www.aboutscotland.com

Ambleside
www.ambleside.u-k.org

Ayrshire
www.ayrshire-arran.com

Brecon Beacons
www.breconbeacons.org

Chilterns
www.chilterns.net

Cumbria
www.gocumbria.com

Dartmoor
www.dartmoor-npa.gov.uk

Derbyshire
www.thisisderbyshire.co.uk

Devon
www.devon.gov.uk/econeuro/tourism

Durham
www.durham.gov.uk

Edinburgh & Lothians
www.edinburgh.org

Exmoor
www.apgate.com/exmoor/index.htm

Fort William & Lochabar
www.fort-william.net

Hebrides
www.hebrides.com

Highlands of Scotland
www.host.co.uk

Isle of Bute
www.isle-of-bute.com

Isle of Skye
www.skye.co.uk

Isle of Wight
www.isle-of-wight-tourism.gov.uk

Isles of Scilly
www.rosevear.demon.co.uk

Jersey
www.jersey.co.uk

Lake District
www.lake-district.gov.uk

Merseyside
www.merseyside.org.uk

Norfolk
www.broadland.com

North York Moors
www.northyorkmoors-npa.gov.uk

Northumbria
www.ntb.org.uk

Orkney
www.orknet.co.uk/tourism

Pembrokeshire Coast National Park
www.pembrokeshirecoast.org

South Devon
www.southdevon.org.uk

South East England
www.southeastengland.uk.com

Southern England
www.gosouth.co.uk

Staffordshire
www.thisisstaffordshire.co.uk

West Country
www.westcountry.net

Yorkshire Dales
www.yorkshirenet.co.uk/visinfo/ydales

tourist attractions

Anglesey Sea Zoo
www.aquariauk.com/anglsy.html

BBC Experience
www.bbc.co.uk/experience

Bekonscot
www.bekonscot.org.uk

Blue Planet Aquarium
www.blueplanetaquarium.com

Bournemouth Oceanarium
www.oceanarium.co.uk

Cadbury World
www.cadbury.co.uk

Deep Sea World
www.deepseaworld.com

Jorvik Viking Centre
www.jorvik-viking-centre.co.uk

Kielder Water Bird of Prey Centre
www.discoverit.co.uk/falconry

London Aquarium
www.londonaquarium.co.uk

London Dungeon
www.thedungeons.com

London Eye
www.londoneye.com

Madame Tussaud's
www.madame-tussauds.com

Monkey World
www.monkeyworld.co.uk

Mother Shipton's Cave
www.mothershipton.co.uk

Original Bus Tour Company
www.theoriginaltour.com

Wookey Hole
www.wookey.co.uk

World of Beatrix Potter
www.hop-skip-jump.com

tourist information

24 Hour Museum
www.24hourmuseum.org.uk

Blue Badge Guides
www.blue-badge.org.uk

British Hotel Reservations Centre
www.bhrc.co.uk

British Tourist Authority
www.visitbritain.com

Edinburgh and Lothians Tourist Board
www.edinburgh.org

English Tourism Council
www.englishtourism.co.uk

Evening Standard
www.thisislondon.com

Good Guide to Britain
www.goodguides.com

Highlands of Scotland Tourist Board
www.host.co.uk

Information Britain
www.information-britain.co.uk

London Tourist Board
www.londontown.com

Northern Ireland Tourist Board
www.ni-tourism.com

Northumbria Tourist Board
www.ntb.org.uk

Perthshire Tourist Board
www.perthshire.co.uk

Scottish Tourist Board
www.visitscotland.com

South East England Tourist Board
www.southeastengland.uk.com

Travel England
www.travelengland.org.uk

Wales Tourist Board
www.visitwales.com

West Country Tourist Board
www.westcountryholidays.com

Yorkshire Tourist Board
www.ytb.org.uk

towns & cities

Abergavenny
www.abergavenny.co.uk

Aberystwyth
www.dewin.net/aberystwyth

Abingdon & District
www.oxlink.co.uk/abingdon

Ashbourne
www.ashbourne-town.com

Aylesbury
www.aylesburyvale.net

Ballymena
www.ballymena.gov.uk

Bath
www.bath.co.uk

Beaconsfield
www.beaconsfield.co.uk

Bedford
www.bedfordonline.co.uk

Bicester
www.bicester.net

Biggin Hill
www.bigginhill.co.uk

Blackpool
www.blackpooltourism.com

Blackpool Southshore
www.southshore.co.uk

Bournemouth
www.bournemouth-info.com

Bradford
www.bradford-net.com

Brighton
www.brighton.co.uk

Bristol
www.brisindex.co.uk/tourism

Bury St Edmunds
www.stedmunds.co.uk

Buxton
www.buxtonuk.com

Cambridge
www.cambridge.gov.uk/leisure

Canterbury
www.canterbury.co.uk

Cardiff
www.totalcardiff.com

Chelmsford
www.chelmsfordcityinthemaking.co.uk

Cheltenham
www.cheltenham.uk.com

Chepstow
www.chepstow.co.uk

Chesham
www.chesham.org

Chester
www.chester.org

Chichester
www.chichesteruk.co.uk

Chinatown London
www.chinatown-online.co.uk

Cirencester
www.cirencester.co.uk

Colchester
www.qlink.co.uk/Colchester

Coventry
www.cwn.org.uk

Derby
www.derbycity.com

Didcot
www.didcot.com

Donington
www.donington.com

Dover
www.dover.uk.com

East Grinstead
www.egnet.co.uk

Edinburgh
www.edinburghonline.org.uk

Egham
www.egham.co.uk

Epsom
www.epsom.townpage.co.uk

Exeter
www.thisisexeter.co.uk

Fakenham
www.fakenham.org.uk

Falkirk
www.falkirkweb.co.uk

Farham
www.farnham.co.uk

Filey
www.filey.co.uk

Fort William
www.fort-william.net

Glastonbury
www.glastonbury.co.uk

Glossop
www.glossop.com

Guildford
www.guildford.org.uk

Henley-on-Thames
www.henley-on-thames.org.uk

Kidderminster
www.kidderminster.org.uk

Leominster
www.leominster.co.uk

Lindisfarne
www.lindisfarne.org.uk

London
www.londontown.com

Manchester
www.manchesteronline.co.uk

Mansfield
www.mansfieldpages.co.uk

Morpeth
www.morpethnet.co.uk

Plymouth
www.plymouthcity.co.uk

Portmeirion
www.virtualportmeirion.com

Redditch
www.redditch.com

Rugby
www.rugbytown.co.uk

Rye
www.rye-tourism.co.uk

Scarborough
www.scarborough.co.uk

Sheffield
www.sheffieldcity.co.uk

Southport
www.visitsouthport.org.uk

Stratford
www.stratford.co.uk

Swansea
www.swansea.com

Thames Ditton
www.thamesditton.com

Virginia Water
www.virginiawater.co.uk

Ware
www.ware-herts.co.uk

West Wickham
www.west-wickham

Whitby
www.whitby.co.uk

York
www.york-tourism.co.uk

attractions

Australia
Art Gallery of New South Wales
www.artgallery.nsw.gov.au

Australian Museum
www.austmus.gov.au

Australian National Parks
www.atn.com.au/parks

Museum of Contemporary Art
www.mca.com.au

National Gallery of Australia
www.nga.gov.au

National Gallery of Victoria
www.ngv.vic.gov.au

Powerhouse Museum
www.phm.gov.au

Sydney Opera House
www.soh.nsw.gov.au

Austria
Schönbrunn Palace
www.schoenbrunn.at

Spanish Riding School of Vienna
www.spanische-reitschule.com

Vienna Boys Choir
www.wsk.at

Vienna Kunsthistorisches Museum
www.khm.at

Belgium
Brussels Expo
www.bruexpo.be

Flanders Opera
www.vlaamseopera.be

Royal Museums of Fine Arts
www.fine-arts-museum.be

Canada
Calgary Stampede
www.calgary-stampede.com

Canada's Wonderland, Toronto
www.canadas-wonderland.com

Canadian National Parks
http://parkscanada.pch.gc.ca/np/np_e.htm

CN Tower, Toronto
www.cntower.ca

Niagra Falls
www.city.niagarafalls.on.ca

Skydome, Toronto
www.skydome.com

Denmark
Legoland
www.legoland.dk

Tivoli
www.tivoligardens.com

Egypt
Suez Canal
www.suezcanal.com

France
Disneyland, Paris
www.disneylandparis.com

Eiffel Tower, Paris
www.tour-eiffel.com

Festival de Marseille
www.festivaldemarseille.com

Louvre
www.louvre.fr

National Museum of Modern Art
www.cnac-gp.fr

Palace of Versailles
www.chateauversailles.fr

Parc Asterix
www.parcasterix.com

Pompidou Centre
www.centrepompidou.fr/english

Germany
Berlin Wall
www.wall-berlin.org

Phantasialand
www.phantasia.de

Greece
Acropolis
www.culture.gr

Epigraphical Museum
www.culture.gr

National Archaeological Museum of Athens
www.culture.gr

New Acropolis Musem
www.culture.gr

Israel
Caesarea
www.caesarea.co.il

Dead Sea
www.deadsea.co.il

Masada
www.masada.com

Italy
Leaning Tower of Pisa
http://torre.duomo.pisa.it/index_eng.html

Sistine Chapel
www.christusrex.org

Teatro alla Scala
www.lascala.milano.it

Uffizi Gallery, Florence
www.uffizi.firenze.it

Vatican
www.vatican.va

Japan

Disneyland
www.tokyodisneyresort.co.jp

Expoland
www.expoland.co.jp/eng

Kenya

National Museums of Kenya
www.museums.or.ke

Netherlands

Anne Frank Museum
www.annefrank.nl

Efteling
www.efteling.nl

Euromast
www.euromast.nl

Rijksmuseum
www.rijksmuseum.nl

Van Gogh Museum
www.vangoghmuseum.nl

Norway

Museumnet Norway
www.museumsnett.no/engelsk

Oslo Opera House
www.alsoparchitects.com/culture/oslo.html

Russia

Lenin Mausoleum
www.lenin.ru

Russian National Museums
www.museum.ru/defengl.htm

State Heritage Museum, St Petersburg
www.hermitagemuseum.org

South Africa

South African National Parks
www.ecoafrica.com/saparks

Sweden

Astrid Lindgren's World
www.alv.se

Kolmarden Zoo, Norrkoping
www.kolmarden.com

Nationalmuseum, Stockholm
www.nationalmuseum.se

Nordiska Museet, Stockholm
www.nordm.se

Postmuseum, Stockholm
www.posten.se/museum

Royal Palace, Stockholm
www.royalcourt.se

Skansen, Stockholm
www.skansen.se

Switzerland

Olympic Museum
www.museum.olympic.org

USA

Andy Warhol Museum, Pittsburgh
www.warhol.org

Busch Gardens, Florida
www.buschgardens.com

Disneyland California
www.disney.co.uk/usa-resorts/disneyland

Disneyworld Florida
www.disneyworld.co.uk

Dollywood, Tennessee
www.dollywood.com

Empire State Building, New York City
www.esbnyc.com

Golden Gate Bridge, San Fransisco
www.goldengate.org

Graceland, Memphis
www.elvis.com/graceland

Guggenheim, New York
www.guggenheim.org

J Paul Getty Museum, California
www.getty.edu

Knotts Berry Farm, California
www.knotts.com

Library of Congress, Washington
www.loc.gov

Los Angeles Museum of Art
www.lacma.org

Metropolitan Museum of Art, New York
www.metmuseum.org

Mount Rushmore, South Dakota
www.nps.gov/moru

Museum of Fine Arts, Boston
www.mfa.org

Museum of Modern Art, New York
www.moma.org

National Museum of American Art, Washington
www.nmaa.si.edu

Norman Rockwell Museum, Massachusetts
www.nrm.org

Sears Tower, Chicago
www.sears-tower.com

Seaworld
www.seaworld.org

Smithsonian Institution, United States
www.si.edu

Space Needle, Seattle
www.spaceneedle.com

Statue of Liberty, New York
www.nps.gov/stli

Universal Studios
www.universalstudios.com

Wet 'n' Wild, Florida
www.wetnwild.com

Yellowstone National Park, Wyoming
www.yellowstone.net

Yosemite National Park, California
www.nps.gov/yose

information

Angola
www.angola.org

Angola: Luanda
www.luanda.com

Antarctica (1)
www.antarctica.org

Antarctica (2)
www.south-pole.com

Antigua
www.antigua-barbuda.com

Argentina
www.info.gov.ar

Argentina: Buenos Aires
www.gba.gov.ar

Australia
www.australia-online.com

Australia: Canberra
www.nationalcapital.gov.au

Australia: Melbourne
www.melbourne.vic.gov.au

Australia: Sydney
www.sydney.visitorsbureau.com.au

Australia: Victoria
www.tourism.vic.gov.au

Australia: Western Australia
www.westernaustralia.net

Austria
www.austria-tourism.at

Austria: Graz
www.graztourism.at

Austria: Innsbruck
www.tiscover.com/innsbruck

Austria: Klagenfurt
www.info.klagenfurt.at

Austria: Salzburg
www.salzburginfo.at

Austria: Vienna
http://info.wien.at

Bahamas
www.bahamas.com

Bangladesh
www.bangladesh.com

Bangladesh: Dhaka
www.dhaka.com

Belgium
www.belgium-tourism.com

Belgium: Antwerp
www.antwerpen.be

Belgium: Bruges
www.brugge.be

Belgium: Brussels
www.brussel.irisnet.be

Belgium: Gent
www.gent.be

Belgium: Ostend
www.oostende.be

Bermuda
www.bermudatourism.com

Brazil
www.brazilinfo.com

Brazil: Sao Paulo
www.saopaulo.sp.gov.br

Cameroon: Duala
ww.duala.com

Canada
www.canadatourism.com

Canada: Alberta
www.travelalberta.com

Canada: British Columbia
www.hellobc.com

Canada: New Brunswick
www.TourismNewBrunswick.ca

Canada: Newfoundland & Labrador
www.gov.nf.ca/tourism

Canada: Northwest Territories
www.northernfrontier.com

Canada: Nova Scotia
http://destination-ns.com

Canada: Nunavut
www.nunatour.nt.ca

Canada: Ontario
www.ontario-canada.com

Canada: Prince Edward Island
www.peiplay.com

Canada: Saskatchewan
www.sasktourism.com

Canada: Yukon
www.touryukon.com

Cayman Islands
www.caymanislands.ky

Channel Islands: Alderney
www.alderney.gov.gg

Channel Islands: Guernsey
www.guernseymap.com/tourism.htm

Channel Islands: Herm
www.herm-island.com

Channel Islands: Jersey (1)
www.jerseyheritagetrust.org

Channel Islands: Jersey (2)
www.jtourism.com

China (1)
www.china.org.cn

China (2)
www.cnto.org

China: Beijing
www.beijing.gov.cn/english/index.htm

China: Hong Kong
www.hkta.org

Cyprus
www.cyprustourism.org

Cyprus: Limassol
www.limassolmunicipal.com.cy

Cyprus: Nicosia
www.nicosia.org.cy

Denmark
www.dt.dk

Denmark: Copenhagen
http://copenhagen.now.dk/english.html

Egypt
www.touregypt.net

Falkland Islands
www.tourism.org.fk

Fiji
www.fiji-online.com.fj

Finland
www.mek.fi

Finland: Helsinki
www.helsinki.fi

France
www.franceguide.com

France: Brittany
www.brittanytourism.com

France: Cannes
www.ville-cannes.fr

France: Cote d'Azur
www.coteazur.com

France: Courchevel
www.courchevel.com

France: Lyon
www.lyon-france.com

France: Nice
www.nice-coteazur.org

France: Paris
www.paris-france.org

Gambia
www.gambia.com

Germany
www.gnm.de

Germany: Berlin
www.berlin.de/home/English

Germany: Cologne
www.cologne.de

Germany: Frankfurt
www.frankfurt-online.de

Germany: Munich
www.muenchen.de

Germany: Nuremberg
www.nuernberg.de

Germany: Stuttgart
www.stuttgart.de

Ghana
www.ghana.com/republic

Gibraltar
www.gibraltar.gov.gi

Greece
www.gnto.gr

Greenland
www.greenland-guide.gl

Grenada
www.grenada.org

Hungary
www.hungarytourism.hu

Hungary: Budapest
www.budapest.hu

Iceland
www.icetourist.is

India
www.indiatouristoffice.org

India: Delhi
http://delhigovt.nic.in

India: Goa
www.nic.in/goa

India: Gujarat
www.gujaratindia.com

India: Himachal Pradesh
http://himachal.nic.in

India: Jammu & Kashmir
http://jammukashmir.nic.in

India: Punjab
http://punjabgovt.nic.in

India: Rajasthan
www.rajgovt.org

India: Uttar Pradesh
www.up-tourism.com

India: West Bengal
www.westbengal.gov.in

Ireland
www.shamrock.org

Ireland: Cork
www.corkcoco.com

Ireland: Donegal
www.donegal.ie

Ireland: Dublin
www.visitdublin.com

Ireland: Galway
www.galwaycoco.ie

Ireland: Kerry
www.kerrycoco.ie

Ireland: Limerick
www.limerickcorp.ie

Ireland: Waterford
www.waterfordcorp.ie

Israel
www.infotour.co.il

Israel: Haifa
www.haifa.gov.il

Israel: Jerusalem
www.jerusalem.muni.il

Israel: Tel-Aviv
www.tel-aviv.gov.il

Italy
www.enit.it

Jamaica
www.jamaicatravel.com

Japan
www.jnto.go.jp

Japan: Hiroshima
www.city.hiroshima.jp/index-E.html

Japan: Okinawa
www.virtualokinawa.com

Japan: Sapporo
www.global.city.sapporo.jp

Jordan
www.see-jordan.com

Kenya
www.kenyatourism.org

Korea
www.knto.or.kr

Lebanon
www.lebanon-tourism.gov.lb

Lebanon: Beirut
www.bse.com.lb

Liechtenstein
www.news.li/touri/index.htm

Liechtenstein: Vaduz
www.vaduz.li

Luxembourg (1)
www.luxembourg.co.uk

Luxembourg (2)
www.luxembourg-city.lu/touristinfo

Luxembourg: Beaufort
www.beaufort.lu

Malaysia
www.tourism.gov.my

Malaysia: Kuala Lumpur
www.klse.com.my

Maldives
www.visitmaldives.com

Malta
www.tourism.org.mt

Mauritius
www.mauritius.net

Mexico
www.mexico-travel.com

Monaco (1)
www.monaco.mc

Monaco (2)
www.monaco.monte-carlo.mc

Morocco
www.mincom.gov.ma

Nepal
www.welcomenepal.com

Netherlands
www.goholland.co.uk

Netherlands: Amsterdam
www.visitamsterdam.nl

Netherlands: Arnhem
www.arnhem.nl

Netherlands: Eindhoven
www.eindhoven.nl

Netherlands: Groningen
www.groningen.nl

Netherlands: Hague
www.denhaag.nl

Netherlands: Leiden
www.leiden.nl

Netherlands: Maastricht
www.maastricht.nl

Netherlands: Rotterdam
www.stadhuis.rotterdam.nl

Netherlands: Tilburg
www.tilburg.nl

Netherlands: Utrecht
www.utrecht.nl

Netherlands: Venlo
www.venlo.nl

New Zealand
www.nz.com

New Zealand: Auckland
www.akcity.govt.nz

New Zealand: Christchurch
www.ccc.govt.nz

New Zealand: Gisborne
www.gisborne.govt.nz

New Zealand: Wellington
www.wcc.govt.nz

New Zealand: Rotorua
www.rotoruanz.com

Norway
www.norway.org.uk

Pakistan
www.tourism.gov.pk

Philippines
www.tourism.gov.ph

Portugal
www.portugal.org

Portugal: Faro
www.cm-faro.pt

Portugal: Lisbon
www.cm-lisboa.pt

Puerto Rico
www.prtourism.com

Romania
www.rezq.com/ronto

Russia
www.russia-travel.com

Russia: Moscow
www.moscowcity.com

Russia: St Petersburg
www.stpete.org

Serbia
www.serbia-info.com/ntos

Seychelles
www.seychelles.uk.com

Singapore
www.travel.com.sg/sog

Solomon Islands
www.solomons.com

South Africa: Cape Town
www.ctcc.gov.za

South Africa: Durban
www.durban.gov.za

South Africa: Johannesburg
www.joburg.org.za

South Africa: Pietermaritzburg
www.pmbcc.gov.za

South Africa: Pretoria
www.pretoria.co.za

South Korea: Seoul
www.metro.seoul.kr

Spain
www.tourspain.co.uk

Spain: Barcelona
www.bcn.es

Spain: Bilbao
www.bilbao.net

Spain: Cadiz
www.cadizayto.es

Spain: Madrid
www.munimadrid.es

Spain: Palma
www.a-palma.es

Spain: Seville
www.sevilla.org

Spain: Valencia
www.ayto-valencia.es

Spain: Toledo
www.diputoledo.es

St Kitts & Nevis
www.interknowledge.com/stkitts-nevis

St Vincent & The Grenadines
www.svgtourism.com

Sweden (1)
www.kulturnat.org

Sweden (2)
www.swetourism.org.uk

Sweden: Göthenburg
www.goteborg.com

Sweden: Malmö
www.malmo.com

Sweden: Torsby
www.torsby.se

Switzerland
www.myswitzerland.com

Switzerland: Basel
www.baseltourismus.ch

Switzerland: Geneva
www.geneva-tourism.ch

Switzerland: Zurich
www.zurichtourism.ch

Tahiti
www.tahiti-tourisme.com

Thailand
www.tourismthailand.org

Tibet
www.tibet.com

Tunisia
www.tourismtunisia.co.uk

Turkey
www.turkey.org/turkey

Turkey: Ankara
www.ankara-bel.gov.tr

Turkey: Istanbul
www.ibb.gov.tr

UAE: Dubai
http://dubaitorism.co.ao

Uganda
www.ugandaweb.com

USA
www.go-unitedstates.com

USA: Boston
www.ci.boston.ma.us

USA: Dallas
www.ci.dallas.tx.us

USA: Denver
www.denvergov.org

USA: Detroit
www.ci.detroit.mi.us

USA: Honolulu
www.co.honolulu.hi.us

USA: Houston
www.ci.houston.tx.us

USA: Las Vegas
www.ci.las-vegas.nv.us

USA: Los Angeles
www.ci.la.ca.us

USA: Massachusetts
www.mass-vacation.com

USA: Memphis
www.ci.memphis.tn.us

USA: Miami
www.ci.miami.fl.us

USA: Minneapolis St Paul
www.ci.minneapolis.mn.us

USA: New York
www.ci.nyc.ny.us

USA: Orlando
www.go2orlando.com

USA: Philadelphia
www.phila.gov

USA: Salt Lake City
www.ci.slc.ut.us

USA: San Francisco
www.ci.sf.ca.us

USA: Seattle
www.ci.seattle.wa.us

USA: St Louis
http://stlouis.missouri.org

USA: Utah
www.utah.com

USA: Washington DC
www.trncwashdc.org

Venezuela
www.venezuela.com

Virgin Islands
www.usvi.net

Yugoslavia
www.putnik.co.yu

actors & actresses

Adam Sandler
www.adamsandler.com

Alicia Silverstone
www.alicia-silverstone.net

Alyssa Milano
www.alyssa.com

Anna Friel
www.netshopuk.co.uk/annafriel

Antonio Banderas
www.antoniobanderasfans.com

Arnold Schwarzenegger
www.schwarzenegger.com

Audrey Hepburn
www.audreyhepburn.com

Ava Gardner
www.avagardner.org

Ben Affleck
www.affleck.com

Bob Hope
www.bobhope.com

Boris Karloff
www.karloff.com

Bruce Lee
www.brucelee.org.uk

Burl Ives
www.burlives.com

Cameron Diaz
www.cameron-diaz.com

Carrie Fisher
www.carriefisher.com

Cary Grant
www.carygrant.co.uk

Catherine Zeta Jones
www.catherinezetajones.com

Cheryl Ladd
www.cherylladd.com

Christian Bale
www.christianbale.org

Claire Danes
www.clairedanes.com

Clint Eastwood
www.clinteastwood.net

Courteney Cox
www.courteneycox.net

Craig Charles
www.craigcharles.co.uk

Daniel Day-Lewis
www.danielday.org

David Schwimmer
www.davidschwimmer.net

Don Johnson
www.donjohnson.com

Doris Day
www.dorisday.com

Errol Flynn
www.errolflynn.net

Ewan McGregor
www.ewanspotting.com

Gail Porter
www.gail-porter-world.co.uk

George Clooney
www.georgeclooney.org

Gillian Anderson
www.gillian-anderson.co.uk

Gwyneth Paltrow
www.gwyneth.cjb.net

Halle Berry
www.hallewood.com

Harold Lloyd
www.haroldlloyd.com

Harrison Ford
www.harrison-ford.net

Helena Bonham-Carter
www.helena-bonham-carter.com

Ian McKellen
www.mckellen.com

Ingrid Pitt
www.pittofhorror.com

Jack Ryder
www.jackryder.dot.nu

Jim Carrey
www.jimcarreyonline.com

Jimmy Stewart
www.jimmy.org

Joseph Smith
www.joesmith.com

Kate Winslet
www.kate-winslet.org

Keanu Reeves
www.keanunet.com

Kelly Brook
www.kellybrookonline.com

Kevin Spacey
www.spacey.com

Leonard Nimoy
www.nimoy.com

Leonardo di Caprio
www.leonardodicaprio.com

Martin Lawrence
www.martin-lawrence.com

Matt Damon
www.mattdamon.com

Meg Ryan
www.megryan.net

Melanie Griffith
www.melaniegriffith.com

Melissa Joan Hart
www.melissa-joan-hart.com

Nicolas Cage
www.cage-cave.avalon.hr

Nicole Kidman
www.nicolekidman.org

Paul Nicholls
www.paul-nicholls.com

Peter Cushing
www.petercushingmuseum.com

Robson Green
www.robsongreen.com

Roy Rogers
www.royrogers.com

Sandra Bullock
www.sandra.com

Sheree J Wilson
www.shereejwilson.com

Stephen Collins
www.stephencollins.com

Thomas Dolby
www.thomas-dolby.com

Timothy Dalton
www.timothydalton.com

Tony Curtis
www.tonycurtis.com

Tony Hancock
www.tonyhancock.org.uk

Tori Spelling
www.tori-spelling.com

Val Kilmer
www.valkilmer.org

Wes Craven
www.wescraven.com

Will Smith
www.willsmith.net

William Shatner
www.williamshatner.com

art

Artists

Andy Warhol
www.warholstore.com

Clarice Cliff
www.claricecliff.co.uk

Cynthia Lennon
www.cynthialennon.co.uk

Escher
www.worldofescher.com

Gilbert & George
www.gilbertandgeorge.co.uk

Pablo Picasso
www.clubinternet.com/picasso

Tom Thomson
www.tomthomson.org

Associations

Arts Council
www.artscouncil.org.uk

Arts Council of Northern Ireland
www.artscouncil-ni.org

Arts Council of Wales
www.artswales.org.uk/home/location_e.asp

Association of Art Historians
www.gold.ac.uk/aah

Association of Illustrators
www.aoi.co.uk

Association of Photographers
www.aophoto.co.uk

Batik Guild
www.batikguild.org.uk

British Arts Festivals Association
www.artsfestivals.co.uk

British Society of Master Glass Painters
www.bsmgp.org.uk

Contemporary Art Society
www.contempart.org.uk

English Regional Arts Boards
www.arts.org.uk

Federation of British Artists
www.the-rba.org.uk/fba_index.htm

Institute of Contemporary Arts
www.ica.org.uk

London Arts Board
www.arts.org.uk/directory/regions/london

National Acrylic Painters' Association
www.artarena.force9.co.uk/napa/

National Art Library
www.nal.vam.ac.uk

National Portraiture Association
www.natportrait.com

North West Arts Board
www.arts.org.uk/directory/regions/north_west

Northern Arts Board
www.arts.org.uk/directory/regions/northern

Northern Ireland Film Commission
www.nifc.co.uk

Pastel Society
www.thepastelsociety.org.uk

Royal Society of Miniature Painters Sculptors & Gravers
http://royal-miniature-society.org.uk

RSA
www.rsa.org.uk

SAA Society for all Artists
www.saa.co.uk

Scottish Arts Council
www.sac.org.uk

Silk Painters Guild
www.silkpainters-guild.co.uk

Society of Equestrian Artists
www.equestrianartists.co.uk

Society of London Art Dealers
www.slad.org.uk

Society of Women Artists
www.society-women-artists.org.uk

South West Arts Board
www.swa.co.uk

Southern Arts Board
www.arts.org.uk/directory/regions/southern

Galleries & Exhibitions

Aberdeen Art Gallery
www.aagm.co.uk

Andrew Logan Museum of Sculpture
www.andrewlogan.com

Ashmolean
www.ashmol.ox.ac.uk

Birmingham Museum & Art Gallery
www.birmingham.gov.uk/bmag

Blackheath Gallery
www.blackheath-gallery.co.uk

Brantwood
www.brantwood.org.uk

City Art Gallery, Southampton
www.southampton.gov.uk/leisure/arts

Courtauld Institute
www.courtauld.ac.uk

Dean Gallery
www.natgalscot.ac.uk

Dove Cottage (The Wordsworth Museum)
www.dovecott.demon.co.uk

Edinburgh City Art Centre
www.edinburgh.gov.uk/cit_art_centre/web/cac

Guernsey Museum & Art Gallery
www.museum.guernsey.net

Hatton Gallery, Newcastle-upon-Tyne
www.ncl.ac.uk/hatton

Hayward Gallery
www.hayward-gallery.org.uk

Henry Moore Foundation
www.henry-moore-fdn.co.uk/hmf

Holburne Museum of Art
www.bath.ac.uk/holburne

Hunterian Art Gallery
www.gla.ac.uk/Museum

Hunterian Art Gallery, Glasgow
www.gla.ac.uk/Museum/ArtGall

Ikon Gallery, Birmingham
www.ikon-gallery.co.uk

Inverleith House, Edinburgh
www.rbge.org.uk/inverleith-house

Khalili Collections
www.khalili.org

Letchworth Museum & Art Gallery
www.letchworthgardencity.net/museum

Maidstone Museum & Art Gallery
www.museum.maidstone.gov.uk

Manchester City Art Galleries
www.manchestergalleries.org

Marlborough Fine Art
www.marlboroughfineart.com

Museum of Modern Art, Oxford
www.moma.org.uk

National Art Library
www.nal.vam.ac.uk

National Gallery
www.nationalgallery.org.uk

National Gallery of Scotland
www.natgalscot.ac.uk

National Museum of Photography, Film & Television
www.nmpft.org.uk

National Museums & Galleries of Wales
www.nmgw.ac.uk

National Portrait Gallery
www.npg.org.uk

Norwich Gallery
www.nsad.ac.uk/gallery

Photographers' Gallery
www.photonet.org.uk

Redfern Gallery
www.redfern-gallery.co.uk

Royal Academy
www.royalacademy.org.uk

Scottish Gallery, Edinburgh
www.scottish-gallery.co.uk

Serpentine Gallery
www.serpentinegallery.org

Tate Gallery
www.tate.org.uk

Tate Gallery, St Ives
www.tate.org.uk/stives

Tunbridge Wells Museum & Art Gallery
www.tunbridgewells.gov.uk/museum

Turner House Gallery
www.nmgw.ac.uk/thg

University Gallery, Leeds
www.leeds.ac.uk/gallery

Wallace Collection
www.the-wallace-collection.org.uk

White Cube Gallery
www.whitecube.com

Whitworth Art Gallery, Manchester
www.whitworth.man.ac.uk

William Morris Gallery
www.lbwf.gov.uk/wmg

York City Art Gallery
www.york.gov.uk/heritage/museums/art/

backstage

Casting Collective
www.castingcollective.co.uk

Lee Lighting
www.lee.co.uk

Panavision
www.panavision.co.uk

Terrie Tanaka Management
www.terrietanaka.com

Troupers
www.troupers.com

ballet

American Ballet Theatre
www.abt.org

Australian Ballet
www.australianballet.com.au

Birmingham Royal Ballet
www.brb.org.uk

Bolshoi Ballet
www.bolshoi.ru

Continental Ballet
www.continentalballet.com

Copenhagen International Ballet
www.koelpin.com

English National Ballet
www.ballet.org.uk

Frankfurt Ballet
www.frankfurt-ballett.de

Hamburg Ballet
www.hamburgballett.de

Hong Kong Ballet
www.hkballet.com

Kirov Ballet
www.kirovballet.com

London Junior Ballet
www.londonjuniorballet.cwc.net

Moscow Flying Ballet
www.flying-ballet.com

National Ballet of Canada
www.nationalballet.ca

New York City Ballet
www.nycballet.com

Northern Ballet Theatre
www.nbt.co.uk

Royal Ballet
www.royalballet.org

Royal Ballet School
www.royal-ballet-school.org.uk

Sadler's Wells
www.sadlers-wells.com

Scottish Ballet
www.scottishballet.co.uk

clubs

Cavern
www.cavernclub.co.uk

Jazz Café
www.jazzcafe.co.uk

Ministry of Sound
www.ministryofsound.co.uk

Nightclub Network
www.nightclub.com

Roadhouse
www.roadhouse.co.uk

Ronnie Scott's
www.ronniescotts.co.uk

Scala
www.scala-london.co.uk

Stringfellows
www.stringfellows.co.uk

comedy

Attila the Stockbroker
www.attilathestockbroker.com

BBC Comedy Zone
www.comedyzone.beeb.com

Ben Elton
www.ben-elton.com

Comedy Store
www.thecomedystore.co.uk

Comic Relief
www.comicrelief.org.uk

Dame Edna
www.dame-edna.com

Danny La Rue
www.dannylarue.com

Dilbert
www.dilbert.com

Eddie Izzard
www.izzard.com

Fascinating Aida
www.fascinating-aida.co.uk

French & Saunders
www.frenchandsaunders.com

George Formby
www.georgeformby.co.uk

Graham Norton
www.grahamnorton.co.uk

Jongleurs
www.jongleurs.com

Laurel & Hardy
www.laurel-and-hardy.com

Lee & Herring
www.leeandherring.com

Monty Python Online
www.pythonline.com

Morecambe & Wise
www.morecambeandwise.co.uk

Penn & Teller
www.sincity.com

Reeves & Mortimer
www.come.to/vicandbob

Rowan Atkinson
www.hsn.dk/rowan

events

Aldeburgh Productions
www.aldeburgh.co.uk

Art Basel
www.art.ch

Arts Worldwide
www.artsworldwide.org.uk

BAFTA Awards
www.bafta.org

Bath International Music Festival
www.bathfestivals.org.uk

Berlin International Film Festival
www.berlinale.de

Birmingham International Film & Television
Festival
www.film-tv-festival.org.uk

Blues & Roots Music Festival
www.bluesfest.com.au

Booker Prize
www.bookerprize.co.uk/home.asp

Brighton Festival
www.brighton-festival.org.uk

Brit Awards
www.brits.co.uk

British Arts Festivals Association
www.artsfestivals.co.uk

British Federation of Festivals for Music,
Dance & Speech
www.festivals.demon.co.uk

Buxton Festival
www.buxtonfestival.co.uk

Cambridge Folk Festival
www.cam-folkfest.co.uk

Cambridge Music Festival
www.cammusic.co.uk

Cannes Film Festival
www.festival-cannes.fr

Central London Festival of Baroque Music
www.artsfestivals.co.uk

Chelsea World of Sport
www.chelseaworldofsport.com

Cheltenham International Festival of Music
www.cheltenhamfestivals.co.uk

City of London Festival
www.colf.org

Covent Garden Festival
www.cgf.co.uk

Crufts Dog Show
www.crufts.org.uk

Dance Umbrella
www.danceumbrella.co.uk

Edinburgh Festival
www.edinburghfestivals.co.uk

Edinburgh Fringe Festival
www.edfringe.com

European Festivals Association
www.euro-festival.net

Fleadh Festival
www.fleadhfestival.com

Galaxen, Arvika
www.galaxen.se

Glasgow International Jazz Festival
www.jazzfest.co.uk

Glastonbury Festival
www.glastonbury-festival.co.uk

Glyndebourne
www.glyndebourne.com

Greenwich & Docklands Festival
www.festival.org

Grosvenor House Art & Antiques Fair
www.grosvenor-antiquesfair.co.uk

Hampton Court Palace Festival
www.hamptoncourtfestival.com

Henley Festival
www.henley-festival.co.uk

Hultsfredsfestivalen
www.rockparty.se

Ideal Home Show
www.idealhomeshow.co.uk

International Film Festival of Wales
www.iffw.co.uk

International Musical Eisteddfod
www.arik.co.uk/lime

International Workshop Festival
www.i-w-f.demon.co.uk

Jersey Battle of Flowers
www.battleofflowers.com

Just For Laughs – International Comedy
Festival (Montreal)
www.hahaha.com

Laurence Olivier Awards
www.olivierawards.com

Leeds International Film Festival
www.leedsfilm.com

Lichfield Festival
www.lichfieldfestival.org

London Art Week
londonart.co.uk

London Fashion Week
www.londonfashionweek.co.uk

London Festival of Chamber Music
www.londonfestivalofchambermusic.com

London Festival of Literature
www.theword.org.uk

London Film Festival
www.lff.org.uk

London International Festival of Theatre
www.lift-info.co.uk

London International Mime Festival
www.mimefest.co.uk

London Open House
www.londonopenhouse.org

London Parade
www.londonparade.co.uk

London String of Pearls Millennium Festival
www.stringofpearls.org.uk

Lord Mayor's Show
www.lordmayorsshow.org

Los Angeles Film Festival
www.laiff.com

Montreux Jazz Festival
www.montreuxjazz.com

Moscow State Circus
www.moscowstatecircus.co.uk

Motor Show
www.motorshow.co.uk

Music Festivals UK
www.aloud.com/festival.shtml

Music Festivals Worldwide
www.festivals.com

Notting Hill Carnival
www.nottinghillcarnival.net.uk

Oscars
www.oscar.com

Picnic Concerts
www.picnicconcerts.com

Promenade Concerts
www.bbc.co.uk/proms

Raindance Film Showcase
www.raindance.co.uk

Reading Festival
www.readingfestival.co.uk

Royal Highland Games
www.braemargathering.org

Stockholm Water Festival
www.waterfestival.se

Sundance Film Festival
www.sundance.org

T in the Park
www.tinthepark.com

Thames Festival
www.thamesfestival.org

Tony Awards
www.tonys.org

Toronto International Film Festival
www.bell.ca/toronto/filmfest

Welsh International Film Festival
www.iffw.co.uk

Whitbread Book Awards
www.whitbread-bookawards.co.uk

Womad
www.womad.org

fashion

Agnes B
www.agnesb.fr

Alberta Ferretti
www.albertaferretti.it

Alexander McQueen
www.alexandermcqueen.net

Armani
www.armaniexchange.com

Caprice
www.caprice-supermodel.com

Cartier
www.cartier.com

Cerruti
www.cerruti.net

Chanel
www.chanel.fr

Charles Jourdan
www.charles-jourdan.com

Chloe
www.chloesdesigns.com

Christian Lacroix
www.christian-lacroix.fr

Cindy Crawford
www.cindy.com

Cindy Margolis
www.cindymargolis.com

Claude Montana
www.claudemontana.net

Claudia Schiffer
www.claudiaschiffer.com

Dolce & Gabbana
www.dolcegabbana.it

Energie
www.energie.it

Escada
www.escada.com

Esprit
www.esprit.com

Fashion Café
www.fashion-cafe.com

Fashion UK
www.fuk.co.uk

Ferragamo
www.salvatoreferragamo.com

Fiorelli
www.fiorelli.com

Fiorucci
www.fiorucci.it

Fruit Of Loom
www.fruit.com

Ghost
www.ghost.co.uk

Gianfranco Ferre
www.gianfrancoferre.com

Givenchy
www.givenchy.fr

Gucci
www.gucci.com

Guess
www.guess.com

Helmut Lang
www.helmutlang.com

Hugo Boss
www.hugo.com

Iman
www.i-iman.com

Jean-Paul Gaultier
www.jpgaultier.fr

Jimmy Choo
www.jimmychoo.com

Joop
www.joop.com

Jordache
www.jordache.com

Kate Moss
www.facescafe.com

Kookai
www.kookai.fr

Krizia
www.krizia.net

La Perla
www.laperla.com

Lacoste
www.lacoste.com

Lancome
www.lancome.com

Louis Vuitton
www.vuitton.com

Maharishi
www.emaharishi.com

Mr Python
www.mrpython.com

Paul Smith
www.paulsmith.co.uk

Polo
www.polo.com

Prada
www.prada.com

Ralph Lauren
www.ralphlauren.com

Rodier
www.rodier.tm.fr

Samantha Fox
www.samfoxagency.com

Sergio Rossi
www.sergiorossi.com

Sisley
www.sisley.com

Sonia Rykiel
www.sonia-rykiel.com

Ted Baker
www.tedbaker.co.uk

Tommy Hilfiger
www.tommy.com

Trussardi
www.trussardi.it

Yves Saint Laurent
www.yslonline.com

Zandra Rhodes
www.zandrarhodes.com

film

Cinemas

ABC
www.abccinemas.co.uk

Apollo
www.apollocinemas.co.uk

Caledonian
www.caledoniancinemas.co.uk

Cinemark
www.cinemark.com

Cineworld
www.cineworld.co.uk

Circle
www.circlecinemas.co.uk

Empire
www.empireonline.co.uk

Imax
www.imax.com

Odeon
www.odeon.co.uk

Pathé
www.pathe.co.uk

Picture House
www.picturehouse-cinemas.co.uk

Queen's Film Theatre, Belfast
www.qub.ac.uk/qft

Reeltime
www.reeltime-cinemas.co.uk

Robins
www.robinscinemas.co.uk

Roxy
www.roxycinema.co.uk

Scott
www.scottcinemas.co.uk

Screen
www.screencinemas.co.uk

Showcase
www.showcasecinemas.co.uk

UCI
www.uci-cinemas.co.uk

Virgin
www.virgin.net/cinema

Warner
www.warnervillage.co.uk

West Coast
www.westcoastcinemas.co.uk

Organisations

Academy of Motion Picture Arts &
Sciences
www.oscars.org

American Film Institute
www.afionline.org

Association of Motion Picture Sound
www.amps.net

BAFTA
www.bafta.org

British Board of Film Classification
www.bbfc.co.uk

British Film Commission
www.britfilmcom.co.uk

British Film Institute
www.bfi.org.uk

British Films Catalogue
www.britfilms.com

British Universities Film & Video Council
www.bufvc.ac.uk

British Video Association
www.bva.org.uk

Cinema Organ Society
www.cinema-organs.org.uk

Cinema Theatre Association
www.cinema-theatre.org.uk

Directors' Guild of Great Britain
www.dggb.co.uk

London Film & Video Development Agency
www.lfvda.demon.co.uk

Moving Image Society
www.bksts.com

New Producer's Alliance
www.npa.org.uk

Producers Alliance for Cinema & Television
www.pact.co.uk

Production Companies & Studios

20th Century Fox UK
www.fox.co.uk

Bollywood
www.bollywood.org.uk

Buena Vista International
www.bvimovies.com

Castle Rock
www.castle-rock.com

Columbia Tristar
www.spe.sony.com/movies

Dimension Films
www.dimensionfilms.com

Disney
www.disney.com/disneypictures

Ealing – NTFS
www.ealingstudios.co.uk

Elstree
www.elstreefilmstudios.co.uk

FilmFour
www.filmfour.com

Fine Line Features
www.flf.com

Hollywood
www.hollywood.com

Leavesden
www.leavesdenstudios.com

Lucas Film
www.lucasfilm.com

MCA Universal
www.mca.com

MGM
www.mgm.com

Miramax
www.miramax.com

New Line
www.newline.com

October Films
www.octoberfilms.com

Orion
www.orionpictures.com

Paramount
www.paramount.com/motionpicture

Pathé
www.pathé.co.uk

Picture Palace Productions
www.picturepalace.com

Sony Pictures Entertainment
www.spe.sony.com

Steven Spielberg Dreamworks
www.spielberg-dreamworks.com

Teddington
www.teddington.co.uk

Three Mills Island
www.threemills.com

United International Pictures
www.uip.com

Universal
www.universalstudios.com

Universal Pictures
www.universalpictures.com

Walt Disney
www.disney.go.com/StudioOperations

Warner Brothers
www.warnerbros.com

West Freugh
www.backlot.co.uk/westfreugh

fireworks

Black Cat Fireworks
www.blackcatfireworks.ltd.uk

Explosive Industry Group
www.eig.org.uk

Fireworks Magazine
www.fireworks-mag.org

UK Firework Safety
www.fireworksafety.co.uk

funding, organisations & regulation

American Film Foundation
www.americanfilmfoundation.com

Arts Council for England
www.artscouncil.org.uk

Arts Council for Wales
www.ccc-acw.org.uk

Association of Professional Theatre for
Children & Young People
www.designer.co.uk

British Academy of Dramatic Combat
www.badc.co.uk

British Copyright Council
www.britishcopyright.org.uk

Broadcasting Standards Commission
www.bsc.org.uk

Community Development Foundation
www.cdf.org.uk

Community Media Association
www.commedia.org.uk

Copyright Licensing Agency
www.cla.co.uk

Crafts Council
www.craftscouncil.org.uk

Department for Culture, Media & Sport
www.culture.gov.uk

Digital Arts Development Agency
www.da2.org.uk

Foundation for Art & Creative Technology
www.fact.co.uk

Freeform Arts Trust
www.freeform.org.uk

Heritage Lottery Fund
www.hlf.org.uk

Independent Television Commission
www.itc.org.uk

Independent Theatre Council
www.itc-arts.org

International Arts Bureau
www.international-arts.org

International Thespian Society
www.etassoc.org

Media Trust
www.mediatrust.org

Millennium Commission
www.millennium.gov.uk

Museums & Galleries Commission
www.museums.gov.uk

National Campaign for the Arts
www.artscampaign.org.uk

National Council for Voluntary
Organisations
www.ncvo-vol.org.uk

National Endowment for Science,
Technology & the Arts (NESTA)
www.nesta.org.uk

National Foundation for Youth Music
www.youthmusic.org.uk

National Lottery Charities Board
www.nlcb.org.uk

New Opportunities Fund
www.nof.org.uk

Scottish Arts Council
www.sac.org.uk

literature

Anne Frank
www.annefrank.com

Arvon Foundation
www.arvonfoundation.org

Book Trust
www.booktrust.org.uk

Danielle Steel
www.daniellesteel.com

Douglas Adams
www.douglasadams.com

Ian Fleming
www.ianfleming.org

John Grisham
www.jgrisham.com

John Steinbeck
www.steinbeck.org

Ken Follett
www.ken-follett.com

London Review of Books
www.lrb.co.uk

Paulo Coelho
www.paulocoelho.com

PG Wodehouse (Fan Club)
www.serv.net/~camel/wodehouse

Poetry Book Society
www.poetrybooks.co.uk

Poetry Review
www.poetrysoc.com

Rudyard Kipling
www.kipling.org.uk

Shakespeare Birthplace Trust
www.shakespeare.org.uk

Stephen King
www.stephenking.com

magazines & websites

.Net Magazine
www.netmagazine.co.uk

Art Guide
www.artguide.org

Art Libraries of UK & Ireland
http://arlis.nal.vam.ac.uk

Art Review
www.art-review.co.uk

BBC Music
www.bbcworldwide.com/musicmagazine

BBC Music Magazine
www.bbcmusicmagazine.beeb.com

Boxing – Monthly
www.boxing-monthly.co.uk

Cable Guide
www.cableguide.co.uk

Circa
www.recirca.com

Dotmusic
www.dotmusic.com

Exe
www.exe.co.uk

FHM
www.fhm.co.uk

Fortean Times
www.forteantimes.com

Galleries Magazine
www.artefact.co.uk

Gramophone Magazine
www.gramophone.co.uk

G-Wizz
www.g-wizz.net

Hitchhikers Guide to the Galaxy
www.h2g2.com

International Directory of Art Libraries
http://iberia.vassar.edu/ifla-idal

International Movie Database
www.imdb.com

Internet Magazine
www.internet-magazine.com

Live Art Magazine
http://art.ntu.ac.uk/livemag

Melody Maker
www.ipc.co.uk/pubs/melodymake.htm

MP3
www.mp3.com

New Musical Express (NME)
www.nme.com

Official London Theatre
www.officiallondontheatre.co.uk

Opening Line
www.openingline.co.uk

Popcorn
www.popcorn.co.uk

Q
www.qonline.co.uk

Radio Times
www.radiotimes.co.uk

Radio Times
www.rtguide.beeb.com

Rolling Stone
www.rollingstone.com

Satellite World
www.satellite-world.net

SceneOne
www.sceneone.co.uk

Screen International
www.screendaily.com

Smash Hits
www.c3.vmg.co.uk

Spotlight Casting Directory
www.spotlightcd.com

Teletext
www.teletext.co.uk

The Spectator
www.spectator.co.uk

The Stage
www.thestage.co.uk

Theatre
www.uktw.co.uk/theatremag

Time Out
www.timeout.co.uk

Times Literary Supplement
www.the-tls.co.uk

TV Times
www.tvtimes.co.uk

Ultimate Band List
www.ubl.com

Warner ESP (Music Catalogue)
www.warneresp.co.uk

What Hi-Fi
www.whathifi.co.uk

World Wide Arts Resources
www.world-arts-resources.com

Royalty

Hereditary Titles
www.hereditarytitles.com

Prince of Wales
www.princeofwales.gov.uk

Royal Insight
www.royalinsight.gov.uk

Royal Palaces
www.hrp.org.uk

Royal Residences
www.royalresidences.com

Royal Websites
www.royalwebsites.co.uk

Royalty Magazine
www.royalty-magazine.com

The Royal Family
www.royalfamily.com

magicians

David Copperfield
www.dcopperfield.com

Magic by Post
www.magic-by-post.co.uk

Magic Interactive
www.magic-interactive.com

Magic Websites
www.magicwebsites.co.uk

Marvin's Magic
www.marvinsmagic.co.uk

Paul Daniels
www.pauldaniels.co.uk

Penn & Teller
www.sincity.com

The International Brotherhood of Magicians
www.magician.org

The Magic Arena
www.corporatemagic.co.uk

The Magic Circle
www.themagiccircle.co.uk

The Magic Company
www.magic.co.uk

Uri Geller Online
www.urigeller.com

Young Magicians Club
www.youngmagiciansclub.co.uk

model agencies

Elisabeth Smith
www.elisabethsmith.co.uk

Elite
www.elitepremier.com

Lookalikes
www.lookalikes.ltd.co.uk

Models 1
www.models1.co.uk

Scallywags
www.scallywags.co.uk

Storm
www.stormmodels.com

music

101cd
www.101cd.com

Audiostreet
www.audiostreet.infront.co.uk

Big Mouth
www.bigmouth.co.uk

Classical Net
www.classical.net

Click Music
www.clickmusic.co.uk

Hail Music
www.hailmusic.com

Look Music
www.lookmusic.com

Mal Ford Management Ltd
www.malford.com

Music Web
www.musicweb.uk.net

Music Websites
www.musicwebsites.co.uk

Music Week
www.dotmusic.com

Artists

A1
www.a1-online.com

Abba
www.abbasite.com

AC/DC
www.elektra.com/retro/acdc

Adam Ant
www.adam-ant.net

Aerosmith
www.aerosmith.com

A-ha
www.a-ha.net

Alanis Morisette
www.alanismorissette.com/main.html

Alice Cooper
www.alicecoopershow.com

All Saints
www.theallsaints.com

America
www.venturahighway.com

Animals
www.animals.mcmail.com

Anne Murray
www.annemurray.com

Another Level
www.anotherlevel.co.uk

Aqua
www.aqua.dk

Atomic Kitten
www.atomickitten.co.uk

Atomic Rooster
www.atomicrooster.com

Aztec Camera
www.killermontstreet.com

B 52's
www.theb52s.com

B*Witched
www.b-witched.com

Backstreet Boys
www.backstreetboys.com

Badly Drawn Boy
www.badlydrawnboy.co.uk

Bananarama
www.bananaramaweb.com

Barbra Streisand
www.barbra-streisand.com

Barclay James Harvest
www.bjharvest.co.uk

Barry Manilow
www.manilow.com

BB King
www.bbking.com

Beach Boys
www.beach-boys.com

Beastie Boys
www.beastieboys.com

Beatles
www.beatles.com

Beautiful South
www.beautifulsouth.co.uk

Be-Bop Deluxe
www.billnelson.com

Beck
www.beck.com

Bee Gees
www.beegees.net

Bellamy Brothers
www.bellamybros.com

Belle & Sebastian
www.jeepster.co.uk/belleandsebastian

Beth Orton
www.beth-orton.co.uk

Big Brother & the Holding Company
www.bbhc.com/BigBrother.htm

Big Country
www.bigcountry.co.uk

Billie Piper
www.billie.co.uk

Billy Idol
www.billyidol.com

Billy Joel
www.billyjoel.com

Bjork
www.bjork.co.uk/bjork

Bjorn Again
www.bjornagain.com

Black Sabbath
www.black-sabbath.com

Blondie
www.blondie.net

Blue
www.officialblue.com

Blur
www.blur.co.uk

Bob Dylan
www.bobdylan.com

Bob Geldof
www.bobgeldof.com

Bob Marley
www.bobmarley.com

Bob Seger
www.segerbob.com

Bon Jovi
www.bonjovi.com

Boy George
www.boy.george.net

Boyzone
www.boyzone.co.uk

Brandy
www.foreverbrandy.com

Britney Spears
www.britneyspears.co.uk

Bruce Springsteen
www.brucespringsteen.net

Bryan Adams
www.bryanadams.com

Buzzcocks
www.buzzcocks.com

Cardigans
www.cardigans.net

Cat Stevens
www.catstevens.co.uk

Catatonia
www.catatonia.com

Celine Dion
www.celineonline.com

Charlie Parker
www.charlieparker.com

Chemical Brothers
www.algonet.se/~inftryck/chemical

Cher
www.cher.com

Chicago
www.chirecords.com

Chopin
www.chopin.org

Chris De Burgh
www.cdeb.com

Chris Isaak
www.repriserec.com/chrisisaak

Christina Aguilera
www.christina-aguilera.com

Christina Milian
www.christinamilian.com

Clash
www.westwaytotheworld.com

Cleopatra
www.cleopatramusic.com

Cliff Richard
www.cliffrichard.org

Cocteau Twins
www.cocteautwins.com

Coldplay
www.coldplay.com

Corrs
www.the corrs-inblue.com

Crosby, Stills, Nash & Young
www.csny.net

Counting Crows
www.countingcrows.com

Craig David
www.craigdavid.co.uk

Cranberries
www.the-cranberries.net

Crash Test Dummies
www.crashtestdummies.com

Culture Club
www.cultureclub.net

Cure
www.thecure.com

Cyndi Lauper
www.cyndilauper.com

Dannii Minogue
www.dannii.com

David Bowie
www.davidbowie.com

David Cassidy
www.davidcassidy.com

David Essex
www.davidessex.com

David Gray
www.davidgray.com

David Knopfler
www.knopfler.com

Dean Friedman
www.deanfriedman.com

Deep Purple
www.deep-purple.com

Del Amitri
www.delamitri.com

Depeche Mode
www.depechemode.com

Des'ree
www.desree.co.uk

Destiny's Child
www.destinyschild.com

Diana Ross
www.dianaross.com

Divine Comedy
www.thedivinecomedy.com

Dixie Chicks
www.dixiechicks.com

Dolly Parton
www.dolly.net

Donny & Marie Osmond
www.donnyandmarie.com

Doobie Brothers
www.doobiebros.com

Doors
www.thedoors.com

Doves
www.doves.net

Duran Duran
www.duranduran.com

Dwight Yoakam
www.wbr.com/nashville/dwightyoakam

Elton John
www.eltonjohn.com

Elvis Costello
www.elvis-costello.com

Elvis Presley
www.elvis.com

Emerson Lake & Palmer
www.emersonlakepalmer.com

Eminem
www.eminem.com

Enigma
www.enigma4.com

Enya
www.repriserec.com/enya

Eric Clapton
www.repriserec.com/ericclapton

Everything But The Girl
www.ebtg.com

Fairport Convention
www.fairportconvention.co.uk

Faith Hill
www.faithhill.com

Fatboy Slim
www.normancook.cjb.net

Frank Sinatra
www.sinatra.com

Fugees
www.fugees.net

Gabrielle
www.gabrielle.co.uk

Garbage
www.garbage.com

Gareth Gates
www.ggates.co.uk

Gary Barlow
www.garybarlow.mcmail.com

Genesis
www.genesis-web.com

George Benson
www.georgebenson.com

George Harrison
www.allthingsmustpass.com

George Michael
www.aegean.net

Geri Halliwell
www.geri-halliwell.com

Gerry Marsden & the Pacemakers
www.gerrymarsden.com

Glen Campbell
www.glencampbellshow.com

Glen Miller Orchestra
www.glennmillerorchestra.com

Glitter Band
www.starguitar.mcmail.com

Gloria Estefan
www.gloriafan.com

Golden Earring
www.golden-earring.nl

Grateful Dead
www.dead.net

Greg Lake
www.greglake.com

Guns N' Roses
www.gnronline.com

Hall & Oates
www.hallandoates.org.uk

Hanson
www.hansonline.com

Harry Connick Jr
www.hconnickjr.com

Hawkwind
www.hawkwind.com

Hearsay
www.hearsay-popstars.net

Heaven 17
www.heaven17.com

Hollies
www.hollies.co.uk

Honeyz
www.honeyz.co.uk

Hootie & the Blowfish
www.hootie.com

Howard Jones
www.howardjones.com

Ian Dury
www.iandury.co.uk

Idlewild
www.idlewild.co.uk

Iron Maiden
www.ironmaiden.co.uk

Isaac Hayes
www.isaachayes.com

Isley Brothers
www.theisleybrothers.com

Jamiroquai
www.jamiroquai.co.uk

Janet Jackson
www.janet-jackson.com

Jean Michel Jarre
www.jeanmicheljarre.com

Jeff Beck
www.epicrecords.com/jeffbeck

Jennifer Lopez
www.jenniferlopez.com

Jethro Tull
www.j-tull.com

Jewel
www.jeweljk.com

Jimi Hendrix
www.jimi-hendrix.com

JJ 72
www.jj72.com

Jo Dee Messina
www.jodeemessina.com

Joan Armatrading
www.joanarmatrading.com

Joan Baez
www.baez.woz.org

Joe Brown
www.joebrown.co.uk

Joe Cocker
www.joediffie.com

Joe Jackson
www.joejackson.com

Johnny Cash
www.johnnycash.com

Jon Bon Jovi
www.jonbonjovi.com

Joni Mitchell
www.JoniMitchell.com

Judy Tzuke
www.tzuke.com

Julian Cope
www.juliancope.com

Julian Lennon
www.julianlennon.com

Julie Felix
www.herebedragons.co.uk

Julio Inglesias
www.julioiglesias.net

Kajagoogoo
www.kajagoogoo.com

KC & the Sunshine Band
www.heykcsb.com

Kd lang
www.kdlang.com

Kenny Rogers
www.kennyrogers.net

Kinks
www.raydavies.com

Kiss
www.kissonline.com

Korn
www.korn.com

Kula Shaker
www.kulashaker.co.uk

Kylie Minogue
www.kylie.com

LeAnn Rimes
www.rimestimes.com

Led Zeppelin
www.led-zeppelin.com

Lenny Kravitz
www.virginrecords.com/kravitz

Leonard Bernstein
www.leonardbernstein.com

Leonard Cohen
www.leonardcohen.com

Level 42
www.level42.com

Levellers
www.levellers.co.uk

Liberty X
www.libertyx.co.uk

Lighthouse Family
www.lighthousefamily.wildcardrecords.co.uk

Lightning Seeds
www.lightningseeds.com

Limahl
www.limahl.co.uk

Limp Bizkit
www.limpbizkit.com

Linkin Park
www.linkinpark.com

Lisa Stansfield
www.lisa-stansfield.com

Lou Reed
www.loureed.org

Luther Vandross
www.epicrecords.com/luthervandross

Macy Gray
www.macygray.com

Madness
www.madness.co.uk

Madonna
www.wbr.com/madonna

Mandy Moore
www.mandymoore.com

Manic Street Preachers
www.manics.co.uk

Mansun
www.mansun.co.uk

Marc Almond
www.marcalmond.co.uk

Mariah Carey
www.mcarey.com

Marillion
www.marillion.com

Marilyn Manson
www.marilynmanson.net

Mark Knofler
www.mark-knopfler-news.co.uk

Martine McCutcheon
www.martinemccutcheon.com

Mary Chapin Carpenter
www.sonynashville.com/MCC/index.html

Mary J Blige
www.mjblige.com

Massive Attack
www.massiveattack.co.uk

Mavericks
www.themavericks.com

Meat Loaf
www.meatloaf-oifc.com

Melanie C
www.northern-star.co.uk

Metallica
www.metclub.com

Michael Bolton
www.michaelbolton.com

Michael Jackson
www.mjnet.com

Michael Nyman
www.michaelnyman.com

Mike Oldfield
www.mikeoldfield.org

Miles Davis
www.miles-davis.com

Monkees
www.monkees.net

Moody Blues
www.moodyblues.co.uk

Morrissey
www.morrissey.co.uk

Natalie Imbruglia
www.natalie-imbruglia.co.uk

Neil Diamond
www.sonymusic.com/artists/NeilDiamond/

Neneh Cherry
www.nenehweb.com

Nitin Sawhney
www.nitinsawhney.com

Nitty Gritty Dirt Band
www.nittygritty.com

Norman Greenbaum
www.spiritinthesky.com

Oasis
www.oasisinet.com

Ocean Colour Scene
www.oceancolourscene.com

Olivia Newton John
www.onlyolivia.com/onj.html

Osmonds
www.osmond.com

Ozzy Osbourne
www.ozzy.com

Patsy Cline
www.patsy.nu

Paul McCartney
www.paulmccartney.com

Paul Young
www.paul-young.com

Paula Abdul
www.aet.cup.edu/~jakallis/paula

Pet Shop Boys
www.petshopboys.co.uk

Peter Gabriel
www.petergabriel.com

Peter Tork
www.petertork.com

PJ Harvey
www.pjh.org

Placebo
www.placebo.co.uk

Placido Domingo
www.placido-domingo.com

Pogues
www.pogues.com

Portishead
www.portishead.co.uk

Prince
www.love4oneanother.com

Prodigy
www.prodigy.com

Public Enemy
www.public-enemy.com

Puff Daddy
www.puffdaddy.com

Pulp
www.pulponline.com

Queen
www.queen-fip.com

Quincy Jones
www.wbr.com/quincyjones

Radiohead
www.radiohead.co.uk

Ramones
www.officialramones.com

Ray Charles
www.raycharles.com

REM
www.wbr.com/rem

Rick Astley
www.rickastley.co.uk

Ricky Martin
www.rickymartin.com

Ringo Starr
www.ringotour.com

Robbie Williams
www.robbiewilliams.co.uk

Rod Stewart
www.wbr.com/rodstewart

Roger Daltrey
www.rogerdaltrey.net

Roger Waters
www.roger-waters.com

Roger Whittaker
www.rogerwhittaker.com

Rolf Harris
www.rolfharris.com

Rolling Stones
www.the-rolling-stones.com

Ronan Keating
www.ronankeating.net

Roxy Music
www.roxymusic.co.uk

Roy Orbison
www.orbison.com

Roy Wood
www.roywood.com

S Club 7
www.sclub7.co.uk

Saint Etienne
www.saint.etienne.net

Sarah McLachlan
www.sarahmclachlan.com

Saw Doctors
www.sawdoctors.com

Seal
www.wbr.com/seal

Searchers
www.the-searchers.co.uk

Shakin Stevens
www.shaky.net

Shakira
www.shakira.com

Shania Twain
www.shania-twain.com

Sheena Easton
www.sheenaeaston.com

Sheryl Crow
www.sherylcrow.com

Shola Ama
www.shola-ama.com

Simon & Garfunkel
www.legacyrecordings.com/simonandgarfunkel

Simply Red
www.simplyred.co.uk

39

Sinead O'Connor
www.sinead-oconnor.com

Sixpence None the Richer
www.sixpence-ntr.com

Smashing Pumpkins
www.smashing-pumpkins.net

Smokey Robinson & the Miracles (Fan Club)
www.prism.net/smokey_miracles

Sparks
www.sparksofficialwebsite.com

Spice Girls
www.spicegirlsforever.co.uk

Spinal Tap
www.spinaltap.com

Squeeze
www.squeezefan.com

Status Quo
www.statusquo.co.uk

Stephen Sondheim
www.sondheim.com

Steps
www.stepsofficial.com

Stereophonics
www.stereophonics.co.uk

Stevie Nicks
www.nicksfix.com

Sting
www.stingchronicity.co.uk

Suede
www.suede.co.uk

Supergrass
www.supergrass.com

Supertramp
www.supertramp.com

Suzanne Vega
www.vega.net

Tammy Wynette
www.tammywynette.com

Tears for Fears
www.sonymusic.com/artists/TearsForFears

Texas
www.texas.uk.com

Tina Turner
www.tina-turner.com

Tom Jones
www.tomjones.com

Tom Petty
www.tompetty.com

Toni Braxton
www.tonibraxton.net

Tony Bennett
www.tonybennett.net

Toploader
www.toploader.com

Tori Amos
www.toriamos.com

Travis
www.travisonline.com

Tricky
www.trickyonline.com

Trisha Yearwood
www.mca-nashville.com/trishayearwood

Turtles
www.theturtles.com

U2
www.u2.com

UB 40
www.ub40.co.uk

Ultravox
www.ultravox.org.uk

Van Halen
www.van-halen.com

Vanessa Mae
www.vanessa-mae.org

Vengaboys
www.vengaboys.com

Verve
www.the-raft.com/theverve

Victoria Beckham
www.victoriabeckham.mu

Village People
www.villagepeople-official.com

Westlife
www.westlife.co.uk

Whitney Houston
www.whitney-houston.co.uk

Will Smith
www.willsmith.net

Will Young
www.wyoung.co.uk

Wishbone Ash
www.wishboneash.com

Wyclef
www.wyclef.com

Internet

Audiogalaxy
www.audiogalaxy.com

Kazaa
www.kazaa.com

MP3
www.mp3.com

Napster
www.napster.com

Magazines

Fly!
www.fly.co.uk

People Sound
www.peoplesound.com

Opera

English National Opera
www.eno.org

Grand Opera House Belfast
www.goh.co.uk

La Scala
www.teatroallascala.org

London Opera Players
www.operaplayers.co.uk

Royal Opera House
www.royaloperahouse.org

Welsh National Opera
www.wno.org.uk

Orchestras

Adelaide Symphony Orchestra
www.aso.com.au

Ambache
www.ambache.co.uk

Association of British Orchestras
www.abo.org.uk

BBC Philharmonic Orchestra
www.bbc.co.uk/orchestras/philharmonic

BBC Symphony
www.bbc.co.uk/orchestras/so

Berlin Philharmonic
www.berlin-philharmonic.com

Birmingham Contemporary Music Group
www.bcmg.org.uk

Boston Symphony
www.bso.org

Chicago Symphony
www.chicagosymphony.org

City of Birmingham Symphony
www.cbso.co.uk

Glasgow Chamber Orchestra
www.gco.org.uk

Irish Chamber Orchestra
www.icorch.com

Israel Philharmonic
www.ipo.co.il

Kensington Symphony Orchestra
www.kso.org.uk

Liverpool Philharmonic
www.rlps.co.uk

London Metropolitan
www.lmo.co.uk

London Philharmonic
www.lpo.co.uk

London Symphony
www.lso.co.uk

Los Angeles
www.laphil.org

National Association of Youth Orchestras
www.nayo.org.uk

National Youth Orchestra
www.nyo.org.uk

New Edinburgh Orchestra
www.ndirect.co.uk/~williams/neo/

New York Philharmonic
www.nyphilharmon.org

New Zealand Symphony Orchestra
www.nzso.co.nz

Northern Sinfonia
www.ndirect.co.uk/~nsinfonia

Philadelphia Orchestra
www.philorch.org

Philharmonia
www.philharmonia.co.uk

Royal Philharmonic
www.rpo.co.uk

Royal Scottish National
www.scot-art.org/rsno

Seattle Symphony
www.seattlesymphony.org

Toronto Symphony
www.orchestratoronto.org

Ulster Studio Symphony Orchestra
http://sso.musicpage.com

Vienna Philharmonic
www.vienna.at/philharmoniker/vph

Vienna Symphony
www.wiener-symphoniker.at

Organisation

British Music Information Centre
www.bmic.co.uk

British Phonographic Industry
www.bpi.co.uk

Music Industries Association
www.mia.org.uk

National Foundation for Youth Music
www.youthmusic.org.uk

Performing Rights Society
www.prs.co.uk

Sonic Arts Network
www.sonicartsnetwork.org

Record Companies

21st Century Music
www.21stcentury.co.uk

A&M
www.amrecords.com

Arista
www.aristarec.com

Atlantic
www.atlantic-records.com

Beggars Banquet
www.beggars.com

Chandos
www.chandos-records.com

Columbia
www.columbiarecords.com

Creation
www.creation.co.uk

Decca
www.decca.com

ECM
www.ecmrecords.com

EMI Chrysalis
www.emichrysalis.co.uk

Epic
www.epicrecords.com

Geffen
www.geffen.com

HMV
www.hmv.co.uk

Hyperion
www.hyperion-records.co.uk

Island
www.mercuryrecords.com

Legacy Recordings
www.legacyrecordings.com

MCA
www.mcarecords.com

Mercury
www.mercuryrecords.com

Ministry of Sound
www.ministryofsound.co.uk

Naxos & Marco Polo
www.hnh.com

Nimbus
www.nimbus.ltd.uk

Parlophone
www.parlophone.co.uk

Polydor
www.polydor.co.uk

Polygram
www.polygram.com

QED Productions
www.qed-productions.com

Sony
www.sonymusic.co.uk

Sony Classical
www.sonyclassical.com

Telstar
www.telstar.co.uk

Tower
www.towerrecords.co.uk

Universal Music Group
www.umusic.com

Virgin
www.virgin.com

Warner Brothers
www.wbr.com

Studios

Abbey Road Studios
www.abbeyroad.co.uk

RAK Recording Studios
www.rakstudios.co.uk

promotors & directors

Directors' Guild of Great Britain
www.dggb.co.uk

Raymond Gubbay
www.raymond-gubbay.co.uk

Robert Stigwood Organisation
www.rsogroup.com

Steven Berkoff
www.east-productions.demon.co.uk

radio
Africa

Angolan National Radio
www.rna.ao

Egypt Government Information Service
www.sis.gov.eg

SAFM (Johannesburg)
www.safm.co.za

Antarctica

Anetstation
www.anetstation.com

Asia

China Radio International (Beijing)
www.cri.com.cn/english

Radio Nepal
www.catmando.com/news/radio-nepal

RTHK (Hong Kong)
www.rthk.org.hk

Australasia

873 2GB (Sydney)
www.2gb.com

Australian Broadcasting Corporation
www.abc.net.au

Fresh FM (Adelaide)
www.freshfm.com.au

Radio Australia (Melbourne)
www.abc.net.au/ra

Europe

Pioneer (Munich)
www.radiopioneer.com

Radio Sweden
www.stfturist.se

Radio Vlaanderen International
www.rvi.be

Stockholm
www.radiosweden.com

Vatican Radio
www.vatican.va/news_services/radio

Voice of Russia
www.vor.ru/index_eng.html

XFM (Dublin)
www.isis.ie/xfm

Programmes

Archers (Fan Club)
www.archers-addicts.com

UK

Aire FM (Leeds)
www.yourleeds.com

Atlantic
www.atlantic252.com

Bath FM
www.bathfm.uk.com

BBC Asian Network
www.bbc.co.uk/england/asiannetwork

BBC Essex
www.bbc.co.uk/england/essex

BBC GMR (Manchester)
www.bbc.co.uk/england/gmr

BBC Hereford & Worcester
www.bbc.co.uk/england/herefordworcester

BBC Local Radio
www.bbc.co.uk/england/radindex.shtml

BBC Radio 1
www.bbc.co.uk/radio1

BBC Radio 2
www.bbc.co.uk/radio2

BBC Radio 3
www.bbc.co.uk/radio3

BBC Radio 4
www.bbc.co.uk/radio4

BBC Radio 5
www.bbc.co.uk/radio5

BBC Radio Berkshire
www.bbc.co.uk/england/thamesvalley

BBC Radio Bristol
www.bbc.co.uk/england/radiobristol

BBC Radio Cambridgeshire
www.bbc.co.uk/england/radiocambridgeshire

BBC Radio Cleveland
www.bbc.co.uk/england/radiocleveland

BBC Radio Cornwall
www.bbc.co.uk/england/radiocornwall

BBC Radio Coventry & Warwickshire
www.bbc.co.uk/england/coventrywarwickshire

BBC Radio Cumbria
www.bbc.co.uk/england/radiocumbria

BBC Radio Cymru
www.bbc.co.uk/cymru

BBC Radio Derby
www.bbc.co.uk/england/radioderby

BBC Radio Devon
www.bbc.co.uk/england/radiodevon

BBC Radio Gloucestershire
www.bbc.co.uk/england/radiogloucestershire

BBC Radio Guernsey
www.bbc.co.uk/england/radioguernsey

BBC Radio Humberside
www.bbc.co.uk/england/radiohumberside

BBC Radio Jersey
www.bbc.co.uk/england/radiojersey

BBC Radio Kent
www.bbc.co.uk/england/radiokent

BBC Radio Lancashire
www.bbc.co.uk/england/radiolancashire

BBC Radio Leeds
www.bbc.co.uk/england/radioleeds

BBC Radio Leicester
www.bbc.co.uk/england/radioleicester

BBC Radio Lincolnshire
www.bbc.co.uk/england/radiolincolnshire

BBC Radio Merseyside
www.bbc.co.uk/england/radiomerseyside

BBC Radio Newcastle
www.bbc.co.uk/england/radionewcastle

BBC Radio Norfolk
www.bbc.co.uk/england/radionorfolk

BBC Radio Northampton
www.bbc.co.uk/england/radionorthampton

BBC Radio Nottingham
www.bbc.co.uk/england/radionottingham

BBC Radio Sheffield
www.bbc.co.uk/england/radiosheffield

BBC Radio Shropshire
www.bbc.co.uk/england/radioshropshire

BBC Radio Solent
www.bbc.co.uk/england/radiosolent

BBC Radio Stoke
www.bbc.co.uk/england/radiostoke

BBC Radio Suffolk
www.bbc.co.uk/england/radiosuffolk

BBC Radio Wales
www.bbc.co.uk/wales

BBC Radio WM
www.bbc.co.uk/england/radiowm

BBC Radio York
www.bbc.co.uk/england/radioyork

BBC Somerset Sound
www.bbc.co.uk/england/radiobristol

BBC Southern Counties
www.bbc.co.uk/england/southerncounties

BBC Three Counties Radio
www.bbc.co.uk/england/threecounties

BBC Wiltshire Sound
www.bbc.co.uk/england/wiltshiresound

BBC World Service
www.bbc.co.uk/worldservice

Beacon FM (Shropshire)
www.beaconfm.co.uk

Beacon FM (Wolverhampton)
www.beaconfm.co.uk

BRMB FM (Birmingham)
www.brmb.co.uk

Cambridge Red
www.redradio.com

Capital FM (London)
www.capitalfm.com

Capital Gold (London)
www.capitalgold.co.uk

Caroline
www.radiocaroline.co.uk

Century 105 (North West)
www.centuryfm.co.uk

Channel 103FM (Channel Islands)
www.103fm.itl.net

City FM (Liverpool)
www.liverpool.fm

Classic FM
www.classicfm.co.uk

Classic Gold
www.classicgold828.co.uk

Classic Gold Amber
www.amber.radio.co.uk

Clyde
www.radioclyde.co.uk

Cool FM (Belfast)
www.coolfm.co.uk

County Sound (Surrey)
www.countysound.co.uk

Forth FM (Edinburgh)
www.radioforth.co.uk

Fox FM (Oxford)
www.foxfm.co.uk

Fresh Air FM
www.freshairfm.co.uk

Galaxy 105 (Yorkshire)
www.galaxy105.co.uk

Galaxy Radio
www.galaxyradio.co.uk

GWR FM
www.gwrfm.musicradio.com

Hallam FM (Sheffield)
www.hallamfm.co.uk

Invicta FM (Kent)
www.invictafm.com

Island FM (Guernsey)
www.islandfm.guernsey.net

Isle of Wight Radio
www.iwradio.co.uk

Jazz FM (London)
www.jazzfm.com

Kiss FM (London)
www.kissonline.co.uk

Lantern FM (Devon)
www.lanternnet.co.uk

LBC (London)
www.lbc.co.uk

Lincs FM (Lincolnshire)
www.lincsfm.co.uk

Magic AM (Yorkshire)
www.magicam.co.uk

Manx Radio
www.manxradio.com

Medway FM (Kent)
www.medwayfm.com

Metro FM (Newcastle)
www.metroradio.co.uk

New Atlantic 252
www.atlantic252.co.uk

News Direct (London)
www.newsdirect.co.uk

Ocean FM
www.oceanfm.com

Operadio
www.operadio.com

Orchard FM
www.orchardfm.co.uk

Oxygen FM
www.oxygen.demon.co.uk

Pirate FM
www.piratefm102.co.uk

Power FM
www.powerfm.com

Radio Caroline
www.radiocaroline.co.uk

Radio City 96.7 (Liverpool)
www.yourliverpool.com

Red Dragon FM (Cardiff)
www.reddragonfm.co.uk

Shot FM
www.shoutfm.com

Signal Radio FM
www.signalradio.com

Spire FM
www.spirefm.co.uk

Talk Radio
www.talk-radio.co.uk

Talk Sport
www.talksport.net

Victory FM (Portsmouth)
www.radiovictory.co.uk

Virgin Radio
www.virginradio.com

Voice of America
www.voa.gov

XFM
www.xfm.co.uk

USA

KIIS FM (Los Angeles)
www.kiisfm.com

Mountain 103.7 (Washington)
www.kmtt.com

New Orleans Channel
www.southernmusic.net/orleansthisweek.htm

WFNX (Boston)
www.fnxradio.com

WNYC (New York)
www.wnyc.org

stadia & concert halls

Aberdeen Exhibition & Conference Centre
www.aecc.co.uk

Aberystwyth Arts Centre
www.aber.ac.uk/~arcwww

Barbican
www.barbican.org.uk

Birmingham Hippodrome
www.hippodrometheatre.co.uk

Birmingham NEC
www.nec.co.uk

Bridgewater Hall, Manchester
www.bridgewater-hall.co.uk

Brighton Centre
www.brightoncentre.co.uk

Earls Court Olympia
www.eco.co.uk

Hackney Empire
www.hackneyempire.co.uk

London Arena
www.londonarena.co.uk

Manchester G-Mex
www.gmex.co.uk

Mean Fiddler
www.meanfiddler.com

National Indoor Arena
www.nia-birmingham.co.uk

Ocean Music Venue
www.ocean.org.uk

Royal Albert Hall
www.royalalberthall.com

Royal Festival Hall
www.rfh.org.uk

Royal Opera House
www.royaloperahouse.org

Sheffield Arena
www.sheffield-arena.co.uk

South Bank Centre
www.sbc.org.uk

Wembley
www.wembley.co.uk

television

Channels

ABC
www.abc-tv.net

Anglia
www.angliatv.co.uk

BBC
www.bbc.co.uk

Border
www.border-tv.com

Bravo
www.bravo.co.uk

Carlton
www.carltontv.co.uk

Carlton Select
www.carltonselect.com

Central
www.centraltv.co.uk

Challenge TV
www.challengetv.co.uk

Channel 4
www.channel4.co.uk

Channel 5
www.channel5.co.uk

Channel Television
www.channeltv.co.uk

Christian Channel
www.godnetwork.com

CNN
www.cnn.com

Discovery
www.discovery.com

Disney Channel
www.disneychannel.co.uk

Euro TV
www.eurotv.com

Film Four
www.filmfour.com

Golf Channel
www.thegolfchannel.com

Grampian
www.grampiantv.co.uk

Granada
www.granada.co.uk

Granada Plus
www.gplus.co.uk

Granada Sky
www.gsb.co.uk

HTV
www.htv.co.uk

ITV
www.itv.co.uk

Living
www.livingtv.co.uk

LWT
www.lwt.co.uk

Meridian
www.meridiantv.co.uk

MTV
www.mtv.co.uk

NBC
www.nbc.com

ONDigital
www.ondigital.co.uk

S4C (Wales)
www.s4c.co.uk

Sci-Fi Channel
www.scifi.com

Scottish Television
www.scottishtv.co.uk

Sky
www.sky.com

UTV (Ulster)
www.utvlive.com

Web TV
www.webtv.com

West Country
www.westcountry.co.uk

Critics

Victor Lewis-Smith
www.lewis-smith.com

Organisation

Emmys (Academy of Television Arts & Sciences)
www.emmys.org

Producers Alliance for Cinema & Television
www.pact.co.uk

Royal Television Society
www.rts.org.uk

Personalities

Cilla Black
www.cillablack.com

David Copperfield
www.dcopperfield.com

Des O'Connor
www.des-oconnor.com

Graham Norton
www.grahamnorton.co.uk

Jonathan Dimbleby
www.jonathandimbleby.co.uk

Nick Ross
www.nickross.co.uk

Zoe Ball
www.zoeball.net

Production Companies

Aardman Animations
www.aardman.com

Addictive Television
www.addictive.com

Ginger Media Group
www.ginger.com

Hat Trick Productions
www.hat-trick.co.uk

Mentorn
www.mentorn.co.uk

Mersey Television Company
www.merseytv.com

Programmes

Alan Partridge
www.alan-partridge.co.uk

Babylon 5
www.babylon5.com

Baywatch
www.baywatchtv.com

BBC Schools
www.bbc.co.uk/education/schools

Beverly Hills 90210
www.helicon7.com/90210

Bewitched
www.bewitched.net

Big Brother
www.channel4.com/bigbrother

Brookside
www.brookie.com

Buffy the Vampire Slayer
www.buffyslayer.com

Bugs
www.bugs.co.uk

Changing Rooms
www.bbc.co.uk/changingrooms

Charlie's Angels
www.charliesangels.com

Chicago Hope
www.cict.com/programs/chicgo.htm

Cold Feet
www.coldfeetonline.co.uk

Coronation Street
www.coronationstreet.co.uk

Dawson's Creek
www.dawsons-creek.com

Dempsey & Makepeace
www.dempseyandmakepeace.de

Dr Quinn Medicine Woman
www.drquinn.com

Due South
www.duesouth.com

Eastenders
www.bbc.co.uk/eastenders

Ed Sullivan Show
www.edsullivan.com

Emmerdale
www.emmerdale.co.uk

ER
www.ertv.com

Frasier
www.frasier.mcmail.com

Gardeners' World
www.gardenersworld.beeb.com

GMTV
www.gmtv.co.uk

Have I Got News For You
www.hignfy.net

Hawaii Five-O
www.mjq.net/fiveo

Hill Street Blues
www.net-hlp.com/hsb

Holby City
www.bbc.co.uk/holbycity

Hollyoaks
www.hollyoaks.com

Home & Away
www.homeandaway.seven.com.au

Horizon
www.bbc.co.uk/horizon

Jerry Springer Show
www.jerryspringer.com

Knight Rider
www.knight-rider.com

League of Gentlemen
www.roystonvasey.co.uk

London Tonight
www.londontonight.co.uk

Lost in Space
www.lostinspacetv.com

Men Behaving Badly
www.menbehavingbadly.com

Monty Python
www.montypython.net

Mr Bean
www.mrbean.co.uk

Neighbours
www.neighbours.com

NYPD Blue
www.nypdblue.com

Oprah Winfrey
www.oprahshow.com

Peak Practice
www.peakpractice.co.uk

Planet of the Apes
www.foxhome.com/planetoftheapes

Red Dwarf
www.reddwarf.co.uk

Seinfeld
www.seinfeld.com

South Park
www.southpark.co.uk

Space 1999
www.space1999.net

Star Trek
www.startrek.com

Starsky & Hutch
www.spe.sony.com/tv/shows/sgn/sh

Talk TV
www.talktv.co.uk

TFI Friday
www.tfifriday.com

The Bill
www.thebill.com

The Prisoner
www.the-prisoner-6.freeserve.co.uk

The Sweeney
www.thesweeney.com

This Morning with Richard & Judy
www.g-wizz.net/thismorning

Today's the Day
www.mentorn.co.uk/tdd

Tomorrow's World
www.bbc.co.uk/tw

Top Gear
www.topgear.beeb.com

Top of the Pops
www.totp.beeb.com

Who Wants to be a Millionaire?
www.phone-a-friend.com

Wish You Were Here?
www.wishyouwerehere.com

World at War
www.theworldatwar.com

X-Files
www.thex-files.com

theatre

Companies

NTC Touring Theatre Company
www.ntc-touringtheatre.co.uk

QuicksilverTheatre Company
www.quicksilvertheatre.org

Rocket Theatre Company
www.rockettheatre.co.uk

Soho Theatre Company
www.sohotheatre.com

Tara Arts
www.tara-arts.com

Productions

An Inspector Calls
www.aninspectorcalls.com

Buddy Holly Story
www.buddythemusical.com

Cats
www.reallyuseful.com/cats

Chicago
www.chicagothemusical.com

Doctor Dolittle
www.doctordolittle.co.uk

Evita
www.thenewevita.com

Fosse the Musical
www.fosse.uk.com

Jekyll & Hyde
www.jekyll-hyde.com

Les Miserables
www.lesmis.com

Lord of the Dance
www.lordofthedance.com

Mamma Mia!
www.mamma-mia.com

Miss Saigon
www.miss-saigon.com

My Fair Lady
www.tcfhe.com/myfairlady

Notre Dame de Paris
www.notredameusa.com

Phantom of the Opera
www.thephantomoftheopera.com

Riverdance
www.riverdance.com

Rocky Horror Picture Show
www.rockyhorror.com

Saturday Night Fever
www.nightfever.co.uk

Spend, Spend, Spend
www.spendspendspend.net

Starlight Express
www.starlight-xpress.co.uk

Tap Dogs
www.tapdogs.com

The King and I
www.kingandi.co.uk

Theatres

ADC Theatre, Cambridge
www.adc-theatre.cam.ac.uk

Almeida
www.almeida.co.uk

Bloomsbury Theatre
www.thebloomsbury.com

Brighton Centre
www.brightoncentre.co.uk

Bristol Old Vic
www.bristol-old-vic.co.uk

Chapter, Cardiff
www.chapter.org

Chichester Festival Theatre
www.cft.org.uk

Citizens Theatre, Glasgow
www.citz.co.uk

Compass Theatre Company
www.compasstheatrecompany.com

Corn Exchange, Cambridge
www.cornex.co.uk

De Montfort Hall, Leicester
www.demontforthall.co.uk

Derngate Theatre, Northampton
www.northamptontheatres.com

Donmar Warehouse
www.donmar-warehouse.com

Drill Hall Theatre
www.drillhall.co.uk

Empire Theatre, Sunderland
www.empiretheatre.co.uk

Everyman Theatre, Cardiff
www.everymantheatre.co.uk

Everyman Theatre, Cheltenham
www.everyman.u-net.com

Everyman Theatre, Liverpool
www.everymanplayhouse.com

Festival Theatre, Chichester
www.cft.org.uk

Festival Theatre, Edinburgh
www.eft.co.uk

Gaiety Theatre Isle of Man
www.iom.com/gaietytheatre

Gateway Theatre, Chester
www.gateway-theatre.org

Gilded Balloon, Edinburgh
www.gilded-balloon.co.uk

Grand Opera House, Belfast
www.goh.co.uk

Grand Theatre, Leeds
www.leeds.gov.uk/GrandTheatre

Grand Theatre, Wolverhampton
www.grandtheatre.co.uk

Hackney Empire
www.hackneyempire.co.uk

Hampstead Theatre
www.hampstead-theatre.co.uk

Haymarket, Basingstoke
www.haymarket.org.uk

Hexagon, Reading
www.readingarts.com

Hippodrome, Birmingham
www.birmingham-hippodrome.co.uk

Hoxton Hall
www.hoxtonhall.dabsol.co.uk

Kenneth More Theatre, Ilford
www.kenneth-more-theatre.co.uk

Komedia Theatre, Brighton
www.brighton.co.uk/listings/komedia

Landmark, Ilfracombe
www.northdevontheatres.org.uk/landmark

Library Theatre, Manchester
www.libtheatreco.org.uk

Lyric Studio Theatre
www.lyric.co.uk

Lyric Theatre, Belfast
www.lyrictheatre.co.uk

Mayflower
www.mayflower.org.uk

Milton Keynes Theatre & Gallery
www.mktgc.co.uk

Minack Theatre, Porthcurno
www.minack.com

New Victoria Theatre, Stoke on Trent
www.uktw.co.uk/info/newvic.htm

North Wales Theatre, Llandudno
www.nwtheatre.co.uk

Nuffield Theatre, Lancaster
www.lancs.ac.uk/users/nuffield

Open Air Theatre Regent's Park
www.open-air-theatre.org.uk

Pavilion Theatre, Glasgow
www.paviliontheatre.co.uk

Phoenix Arts, Leicester
www.phoenix.org.uk

Pitlochry Festival Theatre
www.pitlochry.org.uk

Playhouse Theatre, Derby
www.derbyplayhouse.co.uk

Playhouse Theatre, Oxford
www.oxfordplayhouse.co.uk

Playhouse, Nottingham
www.nottinghamplayhouse.co.uk

Really Useful Theatres
www.rutheatres.com

Regent, Ipswich
www.ipswich-ents.co.uk/regent

Royal Centre, Nottingham
www.royalcentre-nottingham.co.uk

Royal Exchange Theatre, Manchester
www.royalexchange.co.uk

Royal Lyceum Theatre, Edinburgh
www.infoser.com/infotheatre/lyceum

Royal National Theatre
www.nationaltheatre.org.uk

Royal Shakespeare Company Theatre
www.rsc.org.uk

Royal Theatre, Northampton
www.northamptontheatres.com

Sadler's Wells
www.sadlers-wells.com

Scarlet Theatre
www.scarlettheatre.co.uk

Shakespeare's Globe
www.shakespeares-globe.org

Stephen Joseph Theatre, Scarborough
www.sjt.uk.com

Stoll Moss Theatres
www.stoll-moss.com

Theatre Royal, Bury St Edmunds
www.theatreroyal.org

Theatre Royal, Glasgow
www.theatreroyalglasgow.com

Traverse Theatre, Edinburgh
www.traverse.co.uk

Tron Theatre, Glasgow
www.tron.co.uk

Unicorn Theatre for Children
www.unicorntheatre.com

Warehouse Theatre, Croydon
www.live-uk.com/warehouse_theatre

Watford Theatre
www.watfordtheatre.co.uk

West Yorkshire Playhouse, Leeds
www.wyp.co.uk

Wimbledon Theatre
www.wimbledontheatre.co.uk

York Theatre Royal
www.theatre-royal-york.co.uk

Yvonne Arnaud Theatre, Guildford
www.yvonne-arnaud.co.uk

tickets

Albemarle of London
www.albemarle-london.com

Aloud
www.aloud.com

BBC Ticket Unit
www.bbc.co.uk/tickets

First Call
www.first-call.co.uk

Global Tickets
www.globaltickets.com

Group Line
www.groupline.com

Hot Tickets Direct
www.hotticketsdirect.com

Keith Prowse
www.keithprowse.co.uk

Lashmars
www.londontheatre.co.uk/lashmars

Lastminute.com
www.lastminute.com

London Theatre Bookings
www.londontheatrebookings.com

Society of Ticket Agents & Retailers
www.s-t-a-r.org.uk

Theatre Tokens
www.theatretokens.com

Ticket Select
www.stoll-moss.com

Ticketmaster
www.ticketmaster.co.uk

Tickets Online
www.tickets-online.co.uk

Ticketselect
www.stoll-moss.com

Ticketweb
www.ticketweb.co.uk#

Wayahead
www.wayahead.com

Wembley
www.wembleyticket.com

West End Theatre Bookings
www.uktickets.co.uk

What's On Stage
www.whatsonstage.com

THOMSON
Directories™

Need to track down a business in a hurry?

Business

THOMSON
Directories™

www.thomsonlocal.com

53

advertising

Abbott Mead Vickers
www.amvbbdo.co.uk

Addison Wesley Longman
www.awl.com

Advertising Age
www.adage.com

Bartle Bogle Hegarty
www.bbh.co.uk

Bates Dorland
www.bates-dorland.co.uk

Beer Davies
www.beerdavies.co.uk

BMP DDB
www.bmp.co.uk

Charles Barker
www.cbarker.co.uk

Dewynters
www.dewynters.com

DMBB
www.dmbb.com

Dryden Brown
www.dryden.co.uk

Duckworth Finn Grub Waters
www.dfgw.co.uk

FCB
www.fcb.com

Grey
www.grey.co.uk

HHCL
www.hhcl.com

J Walter Thompson
www.jwtworld.com

Joslin Shaw
www.joshaw.co.uk

Leo Burnett
www.leoburnett.com

McCann Erickson
www.mccann.com

Paling Walters Targis
www.palingwalters.com

Poulter
www.poulter.co.uk

RDW
www.rdw-advertising.co.uk

Saatchi & Saatchi
www.saatchi-saatchi.com

Young & Rubicam
www.yandr.com

automotive

Dennis
www.dennis-group.co.uk

Henlys
www.henlys.com

Inchcape
www.inchcape.com

Kwik-Fit
www.kwik-fit.com

Lex Service
www.lex.co.uk

Motor Vehicle Repairers' Association
www.mvra.com

Retail Motor Industry Federation
www.rmif.co.uk

aviation

Aviation Industry Group
www.ai-group.co.uk

Aviation Today
www.aviationtoday.com

chambers of commerce
British

Aberdeen
www.aberdeenchamber.co.uk

Bedfordshire
www.beds-luton-business.co.uk

Birmingham
www.bci.org.uk

Bradford
www.bradfordchamber.co.uk

British
www.brainstorm.co.uk/bcc

Cambridge
www.cambridgechamber.co.uk

Central & West Lancashire
www.lancschamber.co.uk

Central Scotland
www.central-chamber.co.uk

Dorset
www.wdi.co.uk/dcci

East of England
www.go-eastern.gov.uk

Exeter
www.exeter-chamber-of-commerce.co.uk

Guernsey
www.industry.guernsey.net

Liverpool
www.liverpoolchamber.org.uk

Manchester
www.mcci.co.uk

North Derbyshire
www.derbyshire.org/chamber

Northern Ireland
www.nicci.co.uk

Oxford
www.oxlink.co.uk/coc

Plymouth
www.plymouth-chamber.co.uk

Rotherham
www.rccte.org.uk

Shropshire
www.shropshire-chamber.co.uk

Somerset
www.somerset.businesslink.co.uk

Southern Derbyshire
www.sdchamber.co.uk

Suffolk
www.suffolkchamber.co.uk

Thames Valley
www.thamesvalleychamber.co.uk

Wolverhampton
www.wton-chamber.co.uk

York & North Yorkshire
www.york.chamber.co.uk

Foreign

American
www.uschamber.org

Association of European Chambers of
Commerce
www.eurochambre.be

Austrian
www.wk.or.at

Dutch
www.nbcc.demon.co.uk

European
www.eurochambres.be

chemicals

AGA Group
www.aga.com

BOC
www.boc.com

British Biotech
www.britbio.co.uk

British Salt
www.british-salt.co.uk

Burmah Castrol
www.mcci.co.uk

Celltech Chiroscience
www.celltechgroup.com

ECC International
www.ecci.co.uk

Fisher Scientific UK
www.fisher.co.uk

Imperial Chemical Industries
www.ici.com

Johnson Matthey
www.matthey.com

Laporte
www.inspec.co.u

MacDermid
www.macdermid.co.uk

Merck
www.merck-ltd.co.uk

Scott Bader
www.scottbader.com

Ultra Group
www.ultragroup.co.uk

Unilever
www.unilever.com

couriers

Amtrak
www.amtrak.co.uk

Arrow Express
www.arrow-express.co.uk

Business Post
www.business-post.com

City Link
www.city-link.co.uk

Crossflight
www.crossflight.co.uk

DHL
www.dhl.co.uk

Federal Express
www.fedex.com

Five Ways Express
www.5ways.mcmail.com

International Association of Air Travel
Couriers
www.aircourier.co.uk

Lynx
www.lynx.co.uk

Mercury
www.mercurycourier.com

Moves
www.moves.co.uk

Parcel Force
www.parcelforce.co.uk

Post Office
www.uk-po.co.uk

Royal Mail
www.royalmail.co.uk

Sprint
www.sprintexpress.co.uk

TNT
www.tnt.co.uk

UPS
www.ups.com

World Courier
www.worldcourier.com

electrical & tecnological

Cookson Group
www.cooksongroup.co.uk

Danka Business Systems
www.danka.com

Eidos
www.eidos.com

Invensys
www.invensys.com

Logica
www.logica.com

Lynx Group
www.lynx-group.co.uk

Misys
www.misys.co.uk

Parity Group
www.parity.net/index.htm

Psion
www.psion.com

QXL.com
www.qxl.com

Sage
www.sage.com

Scoot.com
www.scoot.com

Sema Group
www.slb.com/Hub/Docs/SchlumbergerSema/

Smiths Industries
www.smiths-industries.com

energy

AgipPetroli
www.agippetroli.com

BP Amoco
www.bpamoco.com

British-Borneo Oil & Gas
www.hemscott.co.uk

Burmah Castrol
www.burmah-castrol.com

Chevron
www.chevron.com

Conoco
www.conoco.com

Enterprise Oil
www.entoil.com

Exxon (Esso)
www.exxon.com

Gulf
www.gulfoil.com

Lasmo
www.lasmo.com

Mobil
www.mobil.co.uk

Premier Oil
www.premier-oil.com

Shell Transport & Trading Company
www.shell.com

Texaco
www.texaco.co.uk

Total
www.total.com

Xerox
www.xerox.com

engineering

Arup
www.arup.com

Babcock International
www.babcock.co.uk

Rolls Royce
www.rolls-royce.com

Shipbuilders & Shiprepairers Association
www.ssa.org.uk

finance
Foreign

ABN AMRO, Netherlands
www.abnamro.nl

ABSA Bank, South Africa
www.allied.co.za

Agricultural Bank of China
www.abocn.com

Allied Bank, South Africa
www.allied.co.za

American National Bank
www.accessanb.com

American Savings Bank
www.asbhawaii.com

Arab Bank
www.arabbank.com

Asian Development Bank
www.adb.org

Australia & New Zealand Banking Group
www.anz.com

Banca Commerciale Italiana
www.bci.it

Banca d'Italia
www.bancaditalia.it

Banco Central Do Brasil
www.bcb.gov.br

Banco de España
www.bde.es

Banco de Portugal
www.bportugal.pt

Bangkok Bank, Thailand
www.bbl.co.th

Bank Austria
www.bankaustria.com

Bank of America
www.bankamerica.com

Bank of Baroda
www.bankofbaroda.com

Bank of Canada
www.bank-banque-canada.ca

Bank of China
www.bank-of-china.com

Bank of Cyprus
www.bankofcyprus.com

Bank of Estonia
www.ee/epbe/en

Bank of Finland
www.bof.fi

Bank of Greece
www.bankofgreece.gr

Bank of Hawaii
www.boh.com

Bank of India
www.webindia.com/boi

Bank of Ireland
www.bankofireland.ie

Bank of Israel
www.bankisrael.gov.il

Bank of Japan
www.boj.or.jp/en

Bank of Kuwait & the Middle East
www.bkme.com

Bank of Latvia
www.bank.lv

Bank of Lebanon
www.bdl.gov.lb

Bank of Lithuania
www.lbank.lt

Bank of Mexico
www.banxico.org.mx

Bank of Montreal
www.bmo.com

Bank of Moscow
www.mmbank.ru

Bank of Mozambique
www.bancomoc.mz

Bank of New York
www.bankofny.com

Bank of Papua New Guinea
www.datec.com.pg

Bank of Portugal
www.bportugal.bt

Bank of Russia
www.cbr.ru

Bank of Slovenia
www.bsi.si

Bank of Thailand
www.bot.or.th

Bank of Tokyo
www.btm.co.jp

Bank of Wales
www.bankofwales.co.uk

Bank of Zambia
www.boz.zm

Bankers Trust, New York
www.bankerstrust.com

Bankgesellschaft Berlin
www.bankgesellschaft.de

Banque Centrale du Luxembourg
www.bcl.lu

Banque de France
www.banque-france.fr

Banque Nationale de Belgique
www.bnb.be

Banque Nationale de Paris
www.bnp.fr

Bermuda Commercial Bank
www.bermuda-bcb.com

Bermuda Monetary Authority
www.bma.bm

Bulgarian National Bank
www.bnb.bg

Canada Trust
www.canadatrust.com

Central Bank of Armenia
www.cba.am

Central Bank of Barbados
www.centralbank.org.bb

Central Bank of Bosnia
www.cbbh.gov.ba

Central Bank of Chile
www.bcentral.cl

Central Bank of China
www.cbc.gov.tw

Central Bank of Cyprus
www.centralbank.gov.cy

Central Bank of Iceland
www.sedlabanki.is

Central Bank of India
www.centralbankofindia.co.in

Central Bank of Ireland
www.centralbank.ie

Central Bank of Jordan
www.cbj.gov.jo

Central Bank of Kenya
www.centralbank.go.ke

Central Bank of Malta
www.centralbankmalta.com

Central Bank of Switzerland
www.centralbank.sz

Central Bank of the Netherlands Antilles
www.centralbank.an

Central Bank of the Republic of Indonesia
www.bi.go.id

Central Bank of the Republic of Turkey
www.tcmb.gov.tr

Central Bank of the Russian Federation
www.cbr.ru

Central Bank of Trinidad & Tobago
www.central-bank.org.tt

Central Bank of Uruguay
www.bcu.gub.uy

Central Reserve Bank of El Salvador
www.bcr.gob.sv

Chase Manhattan
www.chase.com

Citibank
www.citibank.com

Commonwealth Bank of Australia
www.commbank.com.au

Credit Agricole, France
www.credit-agricole.fr

Creditanstalt
www.creditanstalt.co.at

Czech National Bank
www.cnb.cz/en

Danmarks Nationalbank
www.nationalbanken.dk/uk

De Nederlandsche Bank
www.dnb.nl

Deutsche Bank
www.deutsche-bank.com

Deutsche Bundesbank
www.bundesbank.de

Dresdner Kleinwort Benson
www.dresdnerkb.com

Eastern Caribbean Bank
www.eccb-centralbank.org

European Central Bank
www.ecb.int

Federal Reserve Bank, San Francisco
www.frbsf.org

Federal Reserve System (USA)
www.bog.frb.fed.us

Fidelity Federal Savings Bank
www.fidfed.com

First Chicago
www.bankone.com

ForeningsSparbanken (Swedbank)
www.foreningssparbanken.se

Fuji Bank, Japan
www.fujibank.co.jp/eng

Grindlays Private Banking
www.pb.grindlays.com

Gulf International Bank
www.gibonline.com

ING Bank, Netherlands
www.ingbank.nl

Jordan National Bank
www.ahli.com

JP Morgan
www.jpmorgan.com

Muslim Commercial Bank, Pakistan
www.mcb.com.pk

National Australia Bank
www.national.com.au

National Bank of Bahrain
www.nbbonline.com

National Bank of Moldova
www.bnm.org

National Bank of New Zealand
www.nbnz.co.nz

National Bank of the Republic of
Macedonia
www.nmrm.gov.mk

National Commercial Bank, Saudi Arabia
www.alahli.com

Oesterreichische Nationalbank (Austria)
www.oenb.co.at/oenb

Ottoman Bank, Turkey
www.ottomanbank.com.tr/english

Philippine National Bank
www.philnabank.com

Punjab National Bank, India
www.pnbindia.com

Rabobank, Netherland
www.rabobank.nl

Reserve Bank of Australia
www.rba.gov.au

Reserve Bank of India
www.rbi.org.in

Reserve Bank of New Zealand
www.rbnz.govt.nz

Reykjavík Savings Bank, Iceland
www.spron.is

Rindal Sparebank, Norway
www.rindalsbanken.no

Schweizerische Nationalbank (Switzerland)
www.snb.ch

Scotiabank
www.scotiabank.com

Standard Chartered Bank
www.standardchartered.com

State Bank of India
www.sbi.co.in

Sumitomo Bank
www.sumitomocorp.co.jp

Suomen Pankki (Finland)
www.bof.fi

Sveriges Riksbank (Sweden)
www.riksbank.se

Swiss National Bank
www.snb.ch

Unibank, Denmark
www.unibank.dk

Union Bank of Switzerland
www.ubs.com

Wells Fargo
www.wellsfargo.com

World Bank
www.worldbank.org

UK

3i Group
www.3igroup.com

Abbey National
www.abbeynational.plc.uk

Agricultural Credit Bureau
www.lltps.co.uk/ACB

Alliance & Leicester
www.alliance-leicester.co.uk

Arab Banking Corporation
www.arabbanking.com

Bank of England
www.bankofengland.co.uk

Bank of Scotland
www.bankofscotland.co.uk

Banking Liaison Group
www.bankingliaison.co.uk

British Venture Capital Association
www.bvca.co.uk

Charterhouse Bank
www.charterhouse.co.uk

Citibank
www.citibank.co.uk

Close Brothers Group
www.cbcf.com

Coinco International
www.coinco.co.uk

Halifax
www.halifax.co.uk

Lloyds TSB Group
www.lloydstsbgroup.co.uk

National Westminster Bank
www.natwest.co.uk

Northern Rock
www.northernrock.co.uk

Perpetual
www.invescoperpetual.co.uk

Provident Financial
www.providentfinancial.com

Royal Bank of Scotland
www.royalbankscot.co.uk

Salomon Smith Barney
www.sbil.co.uk

Schroders
www.schroders.com

Standard Chartered
www.standardchartered.com

UBS
www.ubs.co.uk/privatebanking

Woolwich
www.woolwich.co.uk

food, beverage & tobacco

Allied Domecq
www.allieddomecqplc.com

Associated British Foods
www.abf.co.uk

Baxters
www.baxters.co.uk

Ben & Jerry's
www.benjerry.co.uk

Bendicks
www.bendicks.co.uk

Bensons
www.bensons-crisps.co.uk

Bird's Eye
www.birdseye.com

Booker
www.booker-plc.com

Boost
www.boost.co.uk

Brannigans
www.brannigans.co.uk

British Sugar
www.britishsugar.co.uk

Brooke Bond
www.brookebond.co.uk

Buitoni
www.buitoni.co.uk

Cadbury
www.cadbury.co.uk

Cadbury Schweppes
www.cadburyschweppes.com

Cadburys Crème Egg
www.cremeegg.co.uk

Campbells
www.campbellsoup.com

Chewits
www.chewits.com

Chiltern Hills
www.chilternhills.com

Clipper Teas
www.clipper-teas.com

Crunchie
www.crunchie.co.uk

Cuervo
www.cuervo.com

Dairy Crest
www.dairycrest.co.uk

Dan Ts Inferno
www.dants.com

Danone
www.danone.com

Delice De France
www.delicedefrance.co.uk

Diageo
www.diageo.com

Dickinson & Morris Pork Pies
www.porkpie.co.uk

Discos
www.discos.co.uk

Dr Pepper
www.drpepper.com

Evian
www.evian.com

Express Dairies
www.express-dairies.co.uk

Fishermans Friend
www.fishermansfriend.co.uk

Frisps
www.frisps.co.uk

Frosties
www.frosties.co.uk

Fyffes
www.fyffes.com

Gallaher
www.gallaher-group.com

Geest
www.geest.com

Gerbers
www.gerbergoods.demon.co.uk

Ginsters
www.ginsters.co.uk

Grant & Cutler
www.grantandcutler.com

Green & Black
www.greenandblacks.com

Haagen Dazs
www.haagen-dazs.com

Haribo
www.haribo.com

Hazlewood Foods
www.hazlewoodfoods.com

Heinz
www.heinz.co.uk

Highland Distillers
www.grouse.com

Homepride
www.homepride.co.uk

Hula Hoops
www.hoopymchula.co.uk

I Can't Believe its Not Butter
www.tasteyoulove.com

Imperial Tobacco
www.imperial-tobacco.com

Irn Bru
www.irn-bru.co.uk

Jaffa Cakes
www.jaffacakes.co.uk

Jelly Belly
www.jellybelly.com

Jersey Royals
www.jerseyroyals.co.uk

Jolly Rancher
www.jolly-rancher.com

Kelloggs
www.kelloggs.co.uk

Kenko
www.kenkocoffee.co.uk

Kinder Surprise
www.kindersurprise.co.uk

Kit Kat
www.kitkat.co.uk

Klix
www.klix.com

KP Nuts
www.kpnuts.com

Kraft Foods
www.kraftfoods.com

Laughing Cow
www.thelaughingcow.co.uk

Lucozade
www.lucozade.co.uk

Mars
www.mars.com

McCain
www.mccain.com

McCoys
www.mccoys.co.uk

Milk
www.milk.co.uk

Muller
www.muller.co.uk

Natco Spices
www.natco-foods.co.uk

Nesquick
www.nesquick.co.uk

Northern Foods
www.northern-foods.co.uk

Nutra Sweet
www.nutrasweet.co.uk

Peperami
www.peperami.com

Pepsi
www.pepsi.co.uk

Perrier
www.perrier.com

Pillsbury
www.pillsbury.com

Poppets
www.poppets.com

Primebake
www.primebake.co.uk

Quaker Oats
www.quakeroats.com

Quorn
www.quorn.com

Red Bull
www.redbull.co.uk

Rodda's Clotted Cream
www.clottedcream.com

Rowntrees
www.rowntrees.co.uk

Ryvita
www.ryvita.co.uk

Sara Lee
www.saraleebakery.com

Schweppes
www.schweppes.com

Scottish & Newcastle
www.scottish-newcastle.com

Sharwoods
www.sharwoods.com

Silver Spoon
www.silverspoon.co.uk

Slush Puppy
www.slushpuppy.co.uk

Snickers
www.snickers.com

St Ivel
www.st-ivel.co.uk

Sunny Delight
www.sunnyd.com

Sweet Factory
www.sweet-factory.com

Sweet 'N' Low
www.sweetnlow.com

Tango
www.tango.co.uk

Tate & Lyle
www.tate-lyle.co.uk

Tizer
www.tizer.co.uk

Tropicana
www.tropicana.com

Twinings
www.twinings.com/ukeire

Twix
www.twix.com

Uncle Ben's
www.unclebens.com

Unigate
www.unigate.plc.uk

Unilever
www.unilever.com

United Biscuits
www.unitedbiscuits.co.uk

United Distillers & Vintners
www.diageo.com

Van den Bergh
www.vdbfoods.co.uk

Veuve-clicquot Champagne
www.veuve-clicquot.fr/home_flash_gb.html

Virgin Cola
www.virgincola.co.uk

Volvic
www.volvic.co.uk

Walkers
www.walkers.co.uk

Weetabix
www.weetabix.co.uk

Whittards
www.whittard.com

Whole Earth
www.earthfoods.co.uk

Wotsits
www.wotsits.co.uk

Wrigleys
www.wrigley.com

Yakult
www.yakult.co.uk

Yazoo
www.yazoo.co.uk

Yogz
www.yogz.com

Yoplait
www.yoplait.co.uk

ftse 100 companies

3i Group
www.3igroup.com

Abbey National
www.abbeynational.co.uk

Alliance & Leicester
www.alliance-leicester.co.uk

Alliance Unichem
www.alliance-unichem.com

Allied Domecq
www.allieddomecqplc.com

Amersham
www.amersham.co.uk

Amvescap
www.amvescap.com

Anglo American
www.angloamerican.co.uk

Associated British Foods
www.abfoods.com

AstraZeneca
www.astrazeneca.com

Aviva
www.aviva.com

BAA
www.baa.co.uk

Bae Systems
www.baesystems.com

Barclays
www.barclays.co.uk

BG Group
www.bg-group.com

BHP Billiton
www.bhp.com

BOC
www.boc.com

Boots
www.boots-plc.com

BP Amoco
www.bpamoco.com

Bradford & Bingley
www.bbg.co.uk

Brambles
www.brambles.com

British Airways
www.british-airways.com

British American Tobacco
www.bat.com

British Land
www.britishland.co.uk

British Telecom
www.bt.com

BSkyB
www.sky.co.uk

Bunzl
www.bunzl.com

Cable & Wireless
www.cwplc.com

Cadbury Schweppes
www.cadburyschweppes.com

Canary Wharf
www.canarywharf.com

Capita
www.capita.co.uk

Centrica
www.centrica.co.uk

Compass
www.compass-group.com

Corus
www.corusgroup.com

Daily Mail & General Trust
www.dmgt.co.uk

Diageo
www.diageo.com

Dixons
www.dixons-group-plc.co.uk

EMI
www.emigroup.com

Exel
www.exel.co.uk

F&C Management
www.fandc.co.uk

Friends Provident
www.friendsprovident.co.uk

Gallaher
www.gallaher-group.com

GKN
www.gknplc.com

GlaxoSmithKline
www.gsk.com

Granada
www.granada.co.uk

GUS
www.gusplc.com

Hanson
www.hansonplc.com

Hays
www.hays.co.uk

HBOS
www.hbosplc.com

Hilton
www.hilton.co.uk

HSBC
www.hsbcgroup.com

ICI
www.ici.com

Imperial Tobacco
www.imperial-tobacco.com

Invensys
www.invensys.com

Johnson Matthey
www.matthey.com

Kingfisher
www.kingfisher.co.uk

Land Securities
www.landsecurities.co.uk

Lattice
www.lattice-group.com

Legal & General
www.landg.com

Lloyds TSB
www.lloydstsb.co.uk

Man Group
www.mangroupplc.com

Marks & Spencer
www.marks-and-spencer.co.uk

Misys
www.misys.co.uk

mm02
www.mmo2.com

National Grid
www.nationalgrid.com

Next
www.next.co.uk

Northern Rock
www.northernrock.co.uk

Old Mutual
www.oldmutual.com

Orange
www.uk.orange.net

P & O
www.p-and-o.com

Pearson
www.pearson.com

Prudential
www.prudentialcorporation.com

Railtrack
www.railtrack.co.uk

Read Elsevier
www.reedelsevier.com

Reckitt Benckiser
www.reckitt.com

Rentokil Initial
www.rentokil-initial.com

Reuters
www.reuters.com

REXAM
www.rexam.com

Rio Tinto
www.riotinto.com

Rolls Royce
www.rolls-royce.com

Royal & Sun Alliance
www.royalsunalliance.co.uk

Royal Bank of Scotland
www.royalbankscot.co.uk

SAB Miller
www.sab.co.za

Safeway
www.safeway.co.uk

Sage Group
www.sage.com

Sainsburys
www.j-sainsbury.co.uk

Schroders
www.schroders.co.uk

Scottish & Newcastle
www.scottish-newcatle.com

Scottish & Southern Energy
www.scottish-southern.co.uk

Scottish Power
www.scottishpower.plc.uk

Severn Trent
www.severn-trent.com

Shell
www.shell.com

Shire Pharmaceutical
www.shiregroup.com

Six Continents
www.sixcontinents.com

Smith & Nephew
www.smith-nephew.com

Smiths Group
www.smiths-group.com

Standard Chartered
www.standard.com

Tesco
www.tesco.com

Unilever
www.unilever.com

United Utilities
www.unitedutilities.com

Vodafone
www.vodafone.co.uk

William Morrison
www.morrisons.plc.uk

Wolseley
www.wolseley.com

Woolwich
www.woolwich.co.uk

WPP
www.wpp.com

Xstrata
www.xstrata.com

insurance

Heath Group
www.heathgroup.com

Hiscox
www.hiscox.com

Jardine Lloyd Thompson
www.jltgroup.com

Legal & General
www.legal-and-general.co.uk

Lloyd's of London
www.lloydsoflondon.co.uk

Norwich Union
www.norwich-union.com

Prudential
www.prudential.co.uk

Royal & Sun Alliance
www.royalsunalliance.com

Standard Life Assurance Company
www.standardlife.com

Sun Life & Provincial Holdings
www.axa.co.uk

Unionamerica Holdings
www.unionamerica.com

Willis
www.willis.com

leisure

Airtours
www.airtours.com

Camelot Group
www.camelotplc.com

Compass Group
www.compass-group.com

Esporta
www.esporta.co.uk

First Choice Holidays
www.firstchoiceholidaysplc.com

Granada Group
www.granada.co.uk

Hilton Group
www.hiltongroup.com

J D Wetherspoon
www.jdwetherspoon.co.uk

Manchester United
www.manutd.co.uk

PizzaExpress
www.pizzaexpress.co.uk

Rank
www.rank.com

Scottish & Newcastle
www.scottish-newcastle.com

Thistle Hotels
www.thistlehotels.com

Thomas Cook Group
www.thomascook.co.uk

Thomson Travel Group
www.thomson-holidays.com

Whitbread
www.whitbread.co.uk

magazines & websites

Accountancy
www.accountancymag.co.uk

Accountancy Age
www.accountancyage.co.uk

Banker
www.thebanker.com

Business Week
www.businessweek.com

Campaign
www.campaignlive.com

Channel 4 Entrepreneurs
www.channel4.com/realdeal

Economist
www.economist.co.uk

Euromoney
www.euromoneydirectory.com

European Business Forum
www.europeanbusinessforum.com

Forbes
www.forbes.com

Harvard Business Review
www.hbsp.harvard.edu/groups/hbr

Investment Week
www.invweek.co.uk

Law Society Gazette
www.lawgazette.co.uk

Lloyd's List
www.llplimited.com

Marketing
www.marketing.haynet.com

Media Week
www.mediaweek.co.uk

Retail Week
www.retailing.co.uk

Reuters Money Network
www.moneynet.com

The Bookseller
www.thebookseller.com

Yahoo Finance
http://uk.finance.yahoo.com

manufacturing

Anti-Counterfeiting Group
www.a-cg.com

Arjo Wiggins Appleton
www.paperpoint.co.uk

Avon Rubber
www.avonrubber.co.uk

Britax International
www.britax.com

Coats Viyella
www.coats-viyella.com

Courtaulds
www.courtaulds.com

First Technology
www.firsttech.co.uk

FKI
www.fki.co.uk

GKN
www.gknplc.com

Laird
www.laird-plc.com

Morgan Crucible
www.morgancrucible.com

Pilkington
www.pilkington.com

Reckitt Benckiser
www.reckitt.com

Tomkins
www.tomkins.co.uk

TT
www.ttelectronics.com

Weir
www.weir.co.uk

materials &
construction

AAF Industries
www.aaf.co.uk

Barratt Developments
www.ukpg.co.uk/barratt

Bellway
www.bellway.co.uk

Berkeley Group
www.berkeleygroup.com

Blue Circle
www.bluecircle.co.uk

Bovis Construction
www.bovis.com

Bryant Group
www.bryant.co.uk

Caradon
www.caradon.com

Costain
www.costain.com

George Wimpey
www.wimpey.co.uk

Hanson
www.hansonplc.com

John Laing
www.john-laing.com

Persimmon
www.persimmon.plc.uk

Readymix
www.readymix.com

Rockwool
www.hardrock.co.uk

Shanks
www.shanks.co.uk

Tarmac
www.tarmac.co.uk

Taylor Woodrow
www.taywood.co.uk

Travis Perkins
www.travisperkins.co.uk

Vibroplant
www.vibroplant.com

media

British Sky Broadcasting
www.sky.co.uk

Capital Radio
www.capitalradio.plc.uk

Carat
www.carat.com

Carlton Communications
www.carltonplc.co.uk

Daily Mail & General Trust
www.dmgt.co.uk

Flextech
www.telewest.co.uk/flextech

Johnston Press
www.johnstonpress.co.uk

Newsquest
www.newsquest.co.uk

Reed Elsevier
www.reed-elsevier.com

Reuters
www.reuters.com

Scottish Media Group
www.scottishmedia.com

United News & Media
www.unm.com

Virgin
www.virgin.com

metals & mining

Anglo American
www.angloamerican.co.uk

Bodycote International
www.bodycote.com

Corus Group
www.corusgroup.com

Johnson Matthey
www.matthey.com

Metal Bulletin
www.metalbulletin.plc.uk

Rio Tinto
www.riotinto.com

office supplies & services

Conqueror
www.conqueror.com

Cucumberman
www.cucumberman.com

Filofax
www.filofax.com

Ikon
www.ikon.com

Kall Kwik
www.kallkwik.co.uk

Kyocera
www.kyocera.co.uk

NCR
www.ncr.com

Office World
www.officeworld.co.uk

Pilot Pens
www.pilotpen.co.uk

Pitney Bowes
www.pitneybowes.com/uk

Prontaprint
www.prontaprint.co.uk

Regus
www.regus.com

Ricoh
www.ricoh.com

Ryman
www.ryman.co.uk

Spicers
www.spicernet.com

Tibbett & Britten
www.tibbet-britten.com

Viking
www.viking-direct.co.uk

Wordflow
www.wordflow.co.uk

paper & packaging

Abbey Corrugated
www.abbeycorrugated.co.uk

Bunzl
www.bunzl.com

David S Smith
www.davidssmith.com

Rexam
www.rexam.co.uk

Tetrapak
www.tetrapak.com

pharmaceutical

3M
www.3m.com

Abbott
www.abbott.com

Allergan
www.allergan.com

Amersham International
www.amersham.co.uk

Asta Medica
www.astamedica.com

AstraZeneca
www.astrazeneca.com

Aventis
www.aventis.com

BASF
www.basf.com

Bayer
www.bayer.com

Bristol Myers Squibb
www.bms.com

Dura
www.durapharm.com

Eli Lilly
www.lilly.com

Fischer
www.dr-fischer.com

GlaxoSmithKline
www.gsk.com

Hoechst
www.hoechst.com

Johnson & Johnson
www.jnj.com

Medeva
www.medeva.co.uk

Merck
www.merck.com

Monsanto
www.monsanto.com

Novartis
www.novartis.com

Novo Nordisk
www.novo.dk

Nycomed Amersham
www.amersham.co.uk

Organon
www.organon.com

Pfizer
www.pfizer.com

Roche
www.roche.com

Schering-Plough
www.sch-plough.com

Searle
www.monsanto.com

Shire Pharmaceuticals Group
www.shire.com

Solvay
www.solvay.com

Takeda
www.takedapharm.com

UniChem
www.unichem.co.uk

Warner-Lambert
www.warner-lambert.com

printing & publishing

Blackwell
www.blackwellpublishers.co.uk

Bloomsbury
www.bloomsbury.com

Butterworth Heinemann
www.bh.com

Butterworths
www.butterworths.co.uk

Cambridge University Press
www.cup.cam.ac.uk

DC Thomson
www.dcthomson.co.uk

Dorling Kindersley
www.dk.com

Earthscan
www.earthscan.co.uk

Eastern Counties Newspapers
www.ecn.co.uk

Express Newspapers
www.expressnewspapers.co.uk

Fire & Water
www.fireandwater.com

Ginn
www.ginn.co.uk

Harper Collins
www.harpercollins.co.uk

Heinemann
www.heinemann.co.uk

HMSO
www.hmso.gov.uk

Hodder & Stoughton
www.hodder.co.uk

Janus Publishing
www.januspublishing.co.uk

Kogan Page
www.kogan-page.co.uk

Lion Publishing
www.lion-publishing.co.uk

Macmillan
www.macmillan.co.uk

McGraw-Hill
www.mcgraw-hill.co.uk

Miller Freeman
www.mfplc.co.uk

Minerva Press
www.minerva-press.co.uk

News International
www.newscorp.com

Orbit
www.orbitbooks.co.uk

Osborne Books
www.osbornebooks.co.uk

Oxford University Press
www.oup.co.uk

Paragon
www.paragon.co.uk

Pearson
www.pearson.co.uk

Penguin
www.penguin.co.uk

Puffin
www.puffin.co.uk

Random House
www.randomhouse.co.uk

Readers Digest
www.readersdigest.co.uk

Reed
www.reedbusiness.com

Rough Guides
www.roughguides.com

Simon & Schuster
www.simonsays.com

St. Ives
www.st-ives.co.uk

Sweet & Maxwell
www.smlawpub.co.uk

Taylor Francis Group
www.tandf.co.uk

Thames & Hudson
www.thameshudson.co.uk

Thomson
www.thomson.com

Thorsons
www.thorsons.com

Time Warner
www.timeinc.com

Trinity Mirror
www.trinity.plc.uk

Usborne Publishing
www.usborne.com

Wace Group
www.sevenww.co.uk

Western Newspapers
www.westpress.co.uk

Wiley
www.wiley.com

private investigators

Association of British Investigators
www.uklegal.com/abi

Carratu
www.carratu.com

Institute of Professional Investigators
www.ipi.org.uk

International Federation of Associations of
Private Investigators
www.i-k-d.com

Nationwide
www.nig.co.uk

professions

Accountants

Arthur Andersen
www.arthurandersen.com

Baker Tilly
www.bakertilly.co.uk

BDO Stoy Hayward
www.bdo.co.uk

Blick Rothenberg
www.blickrothenberg.com

Deloitte & Touche
www.deloitte.co.uk

Ernst & Young
www.ey.com

Fraser Williams
www.fraser-williams.com

Grant Thornton
www.grant-thornton.co.uk

Hacker Young
www.hackeryoung.co.uk

Haines Watts
www.hwca.com

Hamlyns
www.hamlyns.co.uk

Hays Allan
www.haysallan.com

Horwath Clark Whitehill
www.horwathcw.com

Hughes Allen
www.hughes-allen.co.uk

Kidsons Impey
www.kidsons.co.uk

KPMG
www.kpmg.co.uk

Levy Gee
www.levygee.co.uk

Mazars Neville Russell
www.mazars-nr.co.uk

Moores Rowland
www.moores-rowland.co.uk

Pannell Kerr Forster
www.pkf.com

PricewaterhouseCoopers
www.pwcglobal.com

Robson Rhodes
www.robsonrhodes.com

Solicitors

Addleshaw Booth & Co
www.addleshaw-booth.co.uk

Allen & Overy
www.allenovery.com

Amery-Parkes
www.ameryparkes.co.uk

Amhurst Brown Colombotti
www.abc-solicitors.com

Arnander Irvine & Zietman
www.aiz-law.com

Arnold & Porter
www.arnoldporter.com

Ashurst Morris Crisp
www.ashurst.com

Baker & McKenzie
www.bakerinfo.com

Barlow Lyde & Gilbert
www.blg.co.uk

Beachcroft Stanleys
www.beachcroft.co.uk

Beachcroft Wansbroughs
www.beachcroft.co.uk

Berryman & Co
www.berryman.co.uk

Berwin Leighton
www.berwinleighton.com

Bevan Ashford
www.bevanashford.co.uk

Bird & Bird
www.twobirds.com

Blake Lapthorne
www.blakelapthorne.co.uk

Bristows
www.bristows.com

Brodies
www.brodies.co.uk

Burges Salmon
www.burges-salmon.co.uk

Capsticks
www.capsticks.com

Carter Hodge
www.carterhodge.co.uk

Clegg & Co
www.clegglaw.com

Clifford Chance
www.cliffordchance.com

Clintons
www.clintons.co.uk

Clyde & Co
www.clydeco.com

CMS Cameron McKenna
www.law-now.com

Collyer Bristow
www.collyer-bristow.co.uk

Coudert Brothers
www.coudert.com

Cripps Harries Hall
www.crippslaw.com

Crutes
www.crutes.co.uk

Davenport Lyons
www.davenportlyons.com

Davies Arnold Cooper
www.dac.co.uk

Denton Wilde Sapte
www.dentonwildesapte.com

Dibb Lupton Alsop
www.dibbluptonalsop.co.uk

DJ Freeman
www.djfreeman.co.uk

Druces & Atlee
www.druces.com

Dundas & Wilson
www.arthuranderson.com

E Edwards Son & Noice
www.eesn.mcmail.com

Elborne Mitchell
www.elbornes.com

Eversheds
www.eversheds.com

Family Law Consortium
www.tflc.co.uk

Farleys
www.farleys.co.uk

Farrer & Co
www.farrer.co.uk

Fennemores
www.fennemores.com

Fenwick Elliot
www.fenwickelliott.co.uk

Field Fisher Waterhouse
www.ffwlaw.com

Finers
www.finers.co.uk

Fisher Meredith
www.fismer.co.uk

Fox Williams
www.foxwilliams.co.uk

Freshfields
www.freshfields.com

Gamlins
www.gamlins.co.uk

Glaisyers
www.glaisyers.com

Glasners
www.glasners.co.uk

Glenisters
www.glenisters.com

Glovers
www.glovers.co.uk

Gosschalks
www.gosschalks.co.uk

Gouldens
www.gouldens.com

Grindeys
www.grindeys.co.uk

Halliwell Landau
www.halliwells.co.uk

Hamlins
www.hamlins.co.uk

Hammond Suddards
www.hammondsuddards.co.uk

Harbottle & Lewis
www.harbottle.co.uk

Hawkins Russell Jones
www.hrjlaw.co.uk

Hempsons
www.hempsons.co.uk

Henmans
www.henmans.co.uk

Herbert Smith
www.herbertsmith.com

Hill Taylor Dickinson
www.htd.co.uk

Hobson Audley Hopkins & Wood
www.hobsonaudley.co.uk

Hodge Jones & Allen
www.hodge-jones-allen.co.uk

Howard Kennedy
www.hk.hiway.co.uk

Irwin Mitchell
www.irwinmitchell.co.uk

Jeffrey Green Russell
www.jgrweb.com

Julian Holy
www.julianholy.co.uk

Kennedys
www.kennedys-law.com

Kidd Rapinet
www.kiddrapinet.co.uk

Kingsley Napley
www.kingsleynapley.co.uk

Landau & Cohen
www.landaucohen.co.uk

Lawrence Graham
www.lawgram.com

Lawrence Jones
www.lawrencejones.co.uk

Lee & Pembertons
www.leepem.co.uk

Leigh, Day & Co
www.leighday.co.uk

Lewis Silkin
www.lewissilkin.com

Linklaters
www.linklaters.com

Lovells
www.lovells.com

MacFarlanes
www.macfarlanes.com

Maclay Murray & Spens
www.maclaymurrayspens.co.uk

Manches & Co
www.manches.com

Mason Bond
www.masonbond.co.uk

Masons
www.masons.com

McGrigor Donald
www.mcgrigors.com

Memery Crystal
www.memery-crystal.co.u

Merriman White
www.merrimanwhite.co.uk

Minter Ellison
www.minters.com.au

Mishcon de Reya
www.mishcon.co.uk

Nabarro Nathanson
www.nabarro.com

Nicholson Graham Jones
www.ngj.co.uk

Norton Rose
www.nortonrose.com

Official Solicitor to the Supreme Court
www.offsol.demon.co.uk

Olswang
www.olswang.co.uk

Osborne Clarke
www.osborne-clarke.co.uk

Paisner & Co
www.paisner.co.uk

Pannone & Partners
www.pannone.com

Pattinson & Brewer
www.pattinsonbrewer.co.uk

Penningtons
www.penningtons.co.uk

Peter Carter-Ruck & Partners
www.carter-ruck.com

Peters & Peters
www.petersandpeters.co.uk

Pinsent Curtis biddle
www.pinsent-curtis.co.uk

Pritchard Englefield
www.pritchardenglefield.co.uk

Radcliffes
www.radcliffes.co.uk

Reid Minty
www.reidminty.co.uk

Reynolds Porter Chamberlain
www.rpc.co.uk

Richards Butler
www.richardsbutler.com

Rooks Rider
www.rooksrider.co.uk

Rowe & Mawe
www.roweandmawe.co.uk

Russell Jones & Walker
www.rjw.co.uk

Sharpe Pritchard
www.sharpepritchard.co.uk

Shepherd & Wedderburn
www.shepwedd.co.uk

Shook Hardy & Bacon
www.shb.com

Shoosmiths & Harrison
www.shoosmiths.co.uk

Simkins Partnership
www.simkins.com

Simmons & Simmons
www.simmons-simmons.com

SJ Berwin & Co
www.sjberwin.com

Slaughter & May
www.slaughterandmay.com

Speechly Bircham
www.speechlybircham.co.uk

Stephen Innocent
www.stephensinnocent.com

Stephens & Scown
www.stephens-scown.co.uk

Stephenson Harwood
www.stephensonharwood.com

Tarlo Lyons
www.tarlo-lyons.com

Taylor Joynson Garrett
www.tjg.co.uk

Theodore Goddard
www.theogoddard.com

Thompsons
www.thompsons.law.co.uk

Thomson Snell & Passmore
www.ts-p.co.uk

Titmuss Sainer Dechert
www.dechert.com

Travers Smith Braithwaite
www.traverssmith.co.uk

Trowers & Hamlin
www.trowers.com

Turbervilles with Nelson Cuff
www.turbervilles.co.uk

Warner Cranston
www.warner-cranston.com

Watson Farley Williams
www.wfw.com

Wedlake Bell
www.wedlakebell.co.uk

White & Case
www.whitecase.com

Willoughby & Partners
www.iprights.com

Winward Fearon
www.winwardfearon.co.uk

Withers
www.withers.co.uk

Wragge & Co
www.wragge.com

real estate

Canary Wharf Group
www.canarywharf.com

Great Portland Estates
www.gpe.co.uk

Land Securities
www.landsecurities.co.uk

Slough Estates
www.sloughestates.com

recruitment

Agencies

Adecco
www.adecco.co.uk

Blue Arrow
www.bluearrow.co.uk

Brook Street
www.brookstreet.co.uk

Hays
www.hays-ap.com

Manpower
www.manpower.co.uk

Michael Page
www.michaelpage.com

Pareto Law
www.paretolaw.co.uk

RCR International
www.rcri.co.uk

Reed
www.reed.co.uk

Select Appointments
www.selectgroup.com

Talisman
www.talismanretail.co.uk

Job Listings

BBC
www.bbc.co.uk/jobs

Big Blue Dog
www.bigbluedog.com

Go Job
www.gojobsite.co.uk

Guardian
www.jobsunlimited.co.uk

Job Hunter
www.jobhunter.co.uk

Jobs Unlimited
www.jobsunlimited.co.uk

Jobs.co.uk
www.jobs.co.uk

Merchant Navy Recruitment
www.merchantnavy.com

Milkround Online
www.milkround.com

Monster
www.monster.co.uk

New Scientist Jobs
www.newscientistjobs.com

Prospects
www.prospects.ac.uk

Royal Air Force Recruitment
www.raf.mod.uk

Royal Navy Recruitment
www.royal-navy.mod.uk

StepStone
www.stepstone.co.uk

Summer Jobs
www.summerjobs.com

Top Jobs
www.topjobs.net

Total Jobs
www.totaljobs.com

Work Thing
www.workthing.com

Yahoo! Classifieds
http://uk.careers.yahoo.com

retail

Arcadia
www.arcadiagroup.co.uk

ASDA
www.asda.co.uk

Body Shop
www.the-body-shop.com

Boots
www.boots-plc.com

Debenhams
www.debenhams.co.uk

Dixons
www.dixons-group-plc.co.uk

Great Universal Stores
www.gusplc.co.uk

House of Fraser
www.hofbi.co.uk

Iceland
www.iceland.co.uk

J Sainsbury
www.j-sainsbury.co.uk

JJB Sports
www.jjb.co.uk

John Lewis Partnership
www.john-lewis-partnership.co.uk

Kingfisher
www.kingfisher.co.uk

Marks & Spencer
www.marksandspencer.com

MFI Homeworks
www.mfi.co.uk

Next
www.next.co.uk

Safeway
www.safeway.co.uk

Selfridges
www.selfridges.co.uk

Somerfield
www.somerfield.co.uk

Tesco
www.tesco.com

WH Smith
www.whsmith.co.uk

Wm. Morrison Supermarkets
www.morrisons.plc.uk

Wolsey
www.wolsey.com

services

Accenture (Andersen Consulting)
www.accenture.com

Association of Exhibition Organisers
www.aeo.org

Avis Europe
www.avis-europe.com

British Franchise Association
www.franchise.org.uk

British Security Association
www.bsia.co.uk

Capita Group
www.capitagroup.co.uk

Chartered Institute of Marketing
www.cim.co.uk

Chartered Institute of Purchasing & Supply
www.cips.org

Christie's International
www.christies.com

Chubb
www.chubbplc.com

Confederation of British Industry
www.cbi.org.uk

De La Rue
www.delarue.com

Federation of Small Business
www.fsb.org.uk

Hays
www.hays-plc.com

Insitute of Export
www.export.org.uk

Kidde plc
www.kidde.com

Photo-Me International
www.photo-me.co.uk

Rentokil Initial
www.rentokil-initial.com

Tempus Group
www.tempusgroup.co.uk

shipping & shipbuilding

BP Marine
www.bpmarine.com

Fairplay
www.fairplay.co.uk

Geest Line
www.geestline.co.uk

Harland & Wolff Holdings PLC
www.harland-wolff.com

Harrison Logistics
www.harrisonlogistics.co.uk

Institute of Chartered Shipbrokers
www.ics.org.uk

Maersk Company
www.maersk.co.uk

Medway Ports
www.medwayports.com

Norman Shipping Group
www.norman.co.uk

Port of Kawasaki
www.city.kawasaki.jp/english

Port of Antwerp
www.portofantwerp.be

Port of Bordeaux
www.bordeaux-port.fr

Port of Larne
www.portoflarne.co.uk

Port of Liverpool
www.portofliverpool.co.uk

Port of London
www.portoflondon.co.uk

Port of Marseilles
www.marseillesportservices.com

Port of Montreal
www.port-montreal.com

Port of Oostende
www.portofoostende.be

Port of Osaka
www.optc.or.jp

Port of Quebec
www.portquebec.ca

Port of Reykjavik
www.rvk.is/hofnin

Port of Zeebrugge
www.zeebruggeport.be

standards

Qualifications & Curriculum Authority
www.qca.org.uk

Qualifications for Industry
www.qfi.co.uk

stock & commodity exchanges & financial listings

America
www.amex.com

Amsterdam
www.aex.nl

Australia
www.asx.com.au

Baltic Exchange
www.balticexchange.co.uk

Berlin
www.berlinerboerse.de

Bermuda
www.bsx.com

Brussels
www.stockexchange.be

Bucharest
www.bvb.ro

Cayman
www.csx.com.ky

Chicago
www.chicagostockex.com

Dow Jones
www.dowjones.com

EASDAQ
www.easdaq.be

Frankfurt
www.exchange.de

Helsinki
www.hse.fi

Hong Kong
www.sehk.com.hk

International Petroleum Exchange (IPE)
www.ipe.uk.com

Johannesburg
www.jse.co.za

LIFFE
www.liffe.com

Lisbon
www.bvl.pt

London
www.londonstockex.co.uk

London Clearing House
www.lch.co.uk

London Metal Exchange
www.lme.co.uk

Madrid
www.bolsamadrid.es

Montreal
www.me.org

NASDAQ
www.nasdaq.com

New York
www.nyse.com

Paris
www.bourse-de-paris.fr

Stockholm
www.xsse.se

Switzerland
www.swx.ch

Taiwan
www.tse.com.tw

Tokyo
www.tse.or.jp

Toronto
www.tse.com

Vancouver
www.vse.ca

Warsaw
www.gpw.com.pl

telecommunications

British Telecommunications
www.bt.com

Cable & Wireless
www.cw.com

COLT Telecom Group
www.colt-telecom.com

Energis
www.energis.co.uk

Freeserve
www.freeserve.net

Marconi
www.marconi.com

Orange
www.orange.co.uk

Telewest Communications
www.telewest.co.uk

Vodafone
www.vodafone.co.uk

transport

ARRIVA
www.arriva.co.uk

Associated British Ports
www.abports.co.uk

BAA
www.baa.co.uk

British Airways
www.british-airways.com

Chamber of Shipping
www.british-shipping.org

Eurotunnel
www.eurotunnel.co.uk

Exel
www.nfc.co.uk

FirstGroup
www.firstgroup.com

Go-Ahead
www.go-ahead.com

Lloyds Register
www.lr.org

National Express
www.gobycoach.com

Port of Liverpool
www.merseydocks.co.uk

Railtrack
www.railtrack.co.uk

Road Haulage Association
www.rha.net

Sea Containers
www.seacontainers.com

Stagecoach Holdings
www.stagecoachholdings.com

us corporations

Amerada Hess
www.hess.com

American Electric Power
www.aep.com

American Express
www.americanexpress.com

American Home Products
www.ahp.com

American Standard
www.americanstandard.com

Amoco
www.bpamoco.com

Apple Computer
www.apple.com

AT&T
www.att.com

BankAmerica Corp.
www.bankamerica.com

Barnes & Noble
www.barnesandnoble.com

Bell Atlantic
www.bell-atl.com

Black & Decker
www.blackanddecker.com

Boeing
www.boeing.com

CBS
www.cbs.com

Cendant
www.cendant.com

Chase Manhattan Corp.
www.chase.com

Chevron
www.chevron.com

Chubb
www.chubb.com

Coca-Cola
www.coca-cola.com

Colgate-Palmolive
www.colgate.com

Computer Associates
www.compusa.com

Continental Airlines
www.flycontinental.com

Delta Airlines
www.delta-air.com

Dow Chemical
www.dow.com

Du Pont
www.dupont.com

Eastman Kodak
www.kodak.com

Electronic Data Systems
www.eds.com

Eli Lilly
www.lilly.com

Exxon
www.exxon.com

Federal Express
www.fedex.com

Ford Motor
www2.ford.com

General Electric
www.ge.com

General Mills
www.generalmills.com

General Motors
www.gm.com

Goodyear
www.goodyear.com

Hershey Foods
www.hersheys.com

Hewlett-Packard
www.hewlett-packard.com

Hilton Hotels
www.hilton.com

Honeywell
www.honeywell.com

Intel
www.intel.com

J.C. Penney
www.jcpenney.com

Johnson & Johnson
www.jnj.com

JP Morgan
www.jpmorgan.com

Kellogg
www.kelloggs.com

Kimberly-Clark
www.kimberly-clark.com

Lockheed Martin
www.lmco.com

Manpower
www.manpower.com

McDonald's
www.mcdonalds.com

McGraw-Hill
www.mcgraw-hill.com

Merck
www.merck.com

Merrill Lynch
www.ml.com

Microsoft
www.microsoft.com

Monsanto
www.monsanto.com

Morgan Stanley Dean Witter Discover
www.deanwitterdiscover.com

NCR
www.ncr.com

Nickelodeon
www.nick.com

Occidental Petroleum
www.oxy.com

Paramount Pictures
www.paramount.com

PepsiCo
www.pepsico.com

Pfizer
www.pfizer.com

Pharmacia & Upjohn
www.pharmacia.se

Philip Morris
www.pmdocs.com

Proctor & Gamble
www.pg.com

Quaker Oats
www.quakeroats.com

Reader's Digest Association
www.readersdigest.com

RJR Nabisco Holdings
www.rjrnabisco.com

Rockwell International
www.rockwell.com

Sara Lee
www.saralee.com

Schering-Plough
www.sch-plough.com

Sears Roebuck
www.sears.com

Texas Instruments
www.ti.com

Time Warner
www.pathfinder.com/corp

Union Carbide
www.unioncarbide.com

Union Pacific
www.up.com

Unisys
www.unisys.com

United Airlines
www.ual.com

United Parcel Service
www.ups.com

United Technologies
www.utc.com

Viacom
www.viacom.com

Wal-Mart
www.wal-mart.com

Walt Disney
www.disney.go.com

Warner-Lambert
www.warner-lambert.com

Whirlpool
www.whirlpool.com

Xerox
www.xerox.com

utilities

Amerada
www.amerada.co.uk

Anglian Water
www.anglianwater.co.uk

BG
www.bg-group.com

Bournemouth & West Hampshire Water
www.bwhwater.co.uk

Bristol Water
www.bristolwater.co.uk

British Energy
www.british-energy.com

British Nuclear Fuels
www.bnfl.co.uk

Centrica
www.centrica.co.uk

East of Scotland Water
www.esw.co.uk

Eastern Energy
www.easternenergy.co.uk

Essex & Suffolk Water
www.eswater.co.uk

Innogy
www.innogy.com

International Power
www.internationalpowerplc.com

Kelda
www.keldagroup.com

London Electricity
www.london-electricity.co.uk

MEB
www.meb.co.uk

Mid-Kent Water
www.midkentwater.co.uk

National Grid
www.nationalgrid.com

National Power
www.national-power.com

North of Scotland Water Authority
www.noswa.co.uk

North Surrey Water
www.north-surrey-water.co.uk

North West Water
www.nww.co.uk

Northern Ireland Electricity
www.nie.co.uk

Northumbrian Water Limited
www.nwl.co.uk

Pennon Group
www.pennon-group.co.uk

Portsmouth Water
www.portsmouthwater.co.uk

PowerGen
www.pgen.com

Scottish & Southern Energy
www.scottish-southern.co.uk

Scottish Hydro-Electric
www.hydro.co.uk

Scottish Nuclear
www.snl.co.uk

Scottish Power
www.scottishpower.plc.uk

Severn Trent
www.severn-trent.com

South West Water
www.swwater.co.uk

Southern Water
www.southernwater.co.uk

Sutton & East Surrey Water
www.waterplc.com

SWALEC
www.swalec.com

Thames Water
www.thames-water.com

TXU Energy
www.txuenergi.co.uk

United Utilities
www.unitedutilities.com

Viridian Group
www.viridiangroup.co.uk

Wessex Water
www.wessexwater.plc.uk

Yorkshire Water Services
www.yorkshirewater.com

bullying

Antibully
www.antibully.org.uk

Bullying
www.bullying.co.uk

Don't Suffer in Silence
www.dontsufferinsilence.com

cartoon characters

Asterix
www.asterix.tm.fr

Batman
www.batman.com

Bugs Bunny
www.cartoonnetwork.com/BUGS

Captain America
www.winghead.org

Casper
www.u-net.com/casper

Daffy Duck
www.cartoonnetwork.com/DAFFY

Danger Mouse
www.dangermouse.org

Dick Tracy
www.comicspage.com/dicktracy

Dilbert
www.unitedmedia.com/comics/dilbert

Doonsbury
www.doonesbury.com

Dumbo
http://disney.go.com/disney-videos/animated-films/dumbo

Felix the Cat
www.felixthecat.com

Flintstones
www.cartoonnetwork.com/flintsones

Fred Basset
www.comicspage.com/fred

Garfield
www.garfield.com

Hagar the Horrible
www.kingfeatures.com/comics/hagar

Inspector Gadget
www.inspector-gadget.net

Marmaduke
www.unitedmedia.com/comics/marmaduke

Noggin The Nog
www.nogginthenog.co.uk

Pokemon
www.pokemon.com

Popeye
www.popeyethesailor.com

Scooby Doo
www.scoobydoo.com

Simpsons
www.thesimpsons.com

Teenage Mutant Ninja Turtles
www.ninjaturtles.com

X-men
www.x-men.com

clubs & activities

Boys' Brigade
www.boys-brigade.org.uk

Crusaders
www.crusaders.org.uk

Duke of Edinburgh Award
www.theaward.org

Girl Guides
www.guides.org.uk

National Rounders Association
www.nra-rounders.co.uk

Ocean Youth Trust
www.oyc.org.uk

Pony Club
www.pony-club.org.uk

Roald Dahl Club
www.roalddahlclub.com

ScoutNet
www.scoutnet.org.uk

Scouts
www.scoutbase.org.uk

Sea Cadets
www.sea-cadets.org

Tumbletots
www.tumbletots.com

computer games

Ash Design
www.ashdesign.com

Blues News
www.bluesnews.com

Cheat Station
www.cheatstation.com

Compter Games Websites
www.computergameswebsites.co.uk

Console Domain
www.consoledomain.com

Electronics Boutique
www.eb.uk.com

Evomouse
www.evomouse.com

Free Fun Games
www.freefungames.com

Freeloader
www.freeloader.com

Game Retail
www.game-retail.co.uk

Games Paradise
www.gamesparadise.com

Games Street
www.gamesstreet.infront.co.uk

Nintendo
www.nintendo.com

Nintendo Game Cube
www.nintendogamecube.com

Play Palace
www.playpalace.co.uk

PlayStation
www.playstation.com

Sega
www.sega.com

Sega Dreamcast
www.dreamcast-europe.com

Software First Online
www.softwarefirst.com

Software Zone
www.softwarezone.co.uk

Xbox
www.xbox.com

days out

Adventure Island
www.adventureisland.co.uk

Alton Towers
www.alton-towers.co.uk

American Adventure Theme Park
www.adventureworld.co.uk

Babbacombe Model Village
www.babbacombemodelvillage.co.uk

Bekonscot Model Village
www.bekonscot.org.uk

Bingham's Park Farm
www.binghams.co.uk

Blackgang Chine
www.blackgangchine.com

Blackpool Pleasure Beach
www.bpbltd.com

Blackpool Tower
www.theblackpooltower.co.uk

Brighton Palace Pier
www.brightonpier.co.uk

Camelot Theme Park
www.camelotthemepark.co.uk

Cedarpoint
www.cedarpoint.com

Chessington World of Adventure
www.chessington.co.uk

Crealy Park
www.crealy.co.uk

Dome
www.dome2000.co.uk

Drayton Manor
www.draytonmanor.co.uk

Eureka!
www.eureka.org.uk

Fantasy Island
www.fantasyisland.co.uk

Flambards Village
www.flambards.co.uk

Football World
www.football-world.co.uk

Great Yarmouth Pleasure Beach
www.pleasure-beach.co.uk

Harbour Park
www.harbourpark.com

Heron's Brook
www.herons-brook.co.uk

Kidsnet
www.kidsnet.co.uk

Kidstravel
www.kidstravel.co.uk

Lands End
www.landsend-landmark.co.uk

Legoland
www.legoland.co.uk

Lightwater Valley
www.lightwatervalley.co.uk

Lowther Leisure & Wildlife Park
www.lowtherpark.co.uk

Oakwood Park
www.oakwood-leisure.com

Plan It For Kids
www.planit4kids.com

Pleasure Island
www.pleasure-island.co.uk

Pleasureland
www.pleasureland.uk.com

Rheged Discovery Centre
www.rheged.com

Robin Hill
www.robin-hill.com

Secret Bunker St Andrews
www.secretbunker.co.uk

Southend on Sea Pier
www.swine.co.uk

Thorpe Park
www.thorpepark.co.uk

Wicksteed Park
www.wicksteedpark.co.uk

film & television

4Learning
www.4learning.co.uk

Animal Zone
www.bbc.co.uk/animalzone

Art Attack
www.artattack.co.uk

Barney
www.barneyonline.com

Batman & Robin
www.batman-robin.com

Bill Nye the Science Guy
www.billnye.com

Blue Peter
www.bbc.co.uk/bluepeter

Bob the Builder
www.bobthebuilder.org

Bug's Life
www.pixar.com/featurefilms/abl/index.html

Cartoon Network
www.cartoon-network.co.uk

CBBC
www.bbc.co.uk/cbbc

Channel 4 Schools
www.4learning.co.uk

CITV
www.citv.co.uk

Clangers
www.clangers.co.uk

Diggit
www.diggit.co.uk

Discovery Channel
www.discovery.com

Disney Channel
www.disneychannel.co.uk

Fairy Tale
www.fairytalemovie.com

Fox Kids
www.foxkids.co.uk

Garfield
www.garfield.com

Hyperlinks
www.bbc.co.uk/hyperlinks

Munsters
www.munsters.com

Muppets
www.muppets.com

Muppets from Space
www.muppetsfromspace.com

Newsround
www.bbc.co.uk/newsround

Nickelodeon
www.nicktv.co.uk

Pelswick
www.channel4.com/plus/pelswick

Pokemon the First Movie
www.pokemonthemovie.com

Popeye
www.kingfeatures.com/comics/popeye

Postman Pat
www.postmanpat.org.uk

Power Rangers
www.powerrangersonline.com

Rugrats
www.cooltoons.com/shows/rugrats

Rupert Bear
www.ee.ed.ac.uk

Sabrina the Teenage Witch
www.paramount.com/television/sabrina

Sesame Street
www.sesamestreet.com

Simpsons
www.thesimpsons.com

Star Trek
www.startrek.com

Star Wars
www.starwars.com

Tarzan
www.tarzan.co.uk

Teddy Bears
www.theteddybears.com

Teletubbies
www.teletubbies.com

The Saturday Show
www.bbc.co.uk/cbbc/saturdayshow

Thunderbirds
www.thunderbirdsonline.com

Top of the Pops
www.totp.beeb.com

Tweenies
www.bbc.co.uk/education/tweenies

Universal Studios
www.universalstudios.com

Wallace & Gromit
www.aardman.com

Warner Bros
www.kids.warnerbros.com

Xena Warrior Princess
www.mca.com/tv/xena

games & toys

Airfix Models
www.airfix.com

Barbie
www.barbie.com

Beanie Babies
www.ty.com

Brio
www.brio.co.uk

Corgi
www.corgi.co.uk

Crayola
www.crayola.com

Dawson & Son
www.dawson-and-son.com

Fisher Price
www.fisher-price.com

Fuzzy Felt
www.fuzzyfelt.com

Hasbro
www.hasbro.com

Hasbro Interactive
www.hasbro-interactive.com

Hornby
www.hornby.co.uk

Knex
www.knex.co.uk

Lego
www.lego.com

Little Tikes
www.littletikes.com

Matchbox
www.matchboxtoys.com

Mattel
www.mattel.com

Meccano
www.meccano.fr

Monopoly
www.monopoly.com

Mr Potato Head
www.mrpotatohead.com

Panini
www.panini.co.uk

Plan Creations
www.plantoys.com

Playmobil
www.playmobil.de

Pokemon
www.pokemon.com

Quadro
www.quadro-toys.co.uk

Scalextric
www.scalextric.co.uk

Scrabble
www.scrabble.com

Tomy
www.tomy.co.uk

Trivial Pursuits
www.trivialpursuit.com

Young Embroiderers
www.hiraeth.com/ytg

homework & revision

A-levels
www.a-levels.co.uk

Algebra Online
www.algebra-online.com

Bitesize Revision
www.bbc.co.uk/education/revision

BJ Pinchbeck Homework Helper
www.bjpinchbeck.com

Coursework Help
www.courseworkhelp.co.uk

Discovery School
www.discoveryschool.com

Freeserve
www.frewwserve.com/learning

Freeserve Revision
www.freeserve.net/education/examrevision

GCSE Answers
www.gcse.com

GCSE Bitesize Revision
www.bbc.co.uk/education/gcsebitesize

Homework Elephant
www.homeworkelephant.co.uk

Homework Help
www.homeworkhelp.com

Homework High
www.homeworkhigh.com

Learn Free
www.learnfree.co.uk

Learnthings
www.learn.co.uk

LineOne Learning
www.lineone.net/learning

Maximus
www.minimus-etc.co.uk

S-Cool
www.s-cool.co.uk

Thunk.Com
www.thunk.com

Topmarks
www.topmarks.co.uk

Topmarks Education
www.topmarkseducation.com

magazines, books & authors

Anne Fine
www.annefine.co.uk

Beano
www.beano.co.uk

Beatrix Potter
www.peterrabbit.co.uk

Bright Sparks (Junior Mensa Magazine)
www.mensa.org.uk/mensa/junior/magazine.html

British Arthur Ransome Society
www.arthur-ransome.org

Children's Book Council
www.cbcbooks.org

DC Comics
www.dccomics.com

Dorling Kindersley
www.dk.com

Dr Seuss
www.seussville.com

Enid Blyton
www.blyton.com

Eric Carle
www.eric-carle.com

Flash Gordon
www.kingfeatures.com/comics/fgordon

Girl Talk
www.girltalkmag.com

Girl's World
www.agirlsworld.com

Goosebumps
www.scholastic.com/goosebumps

Hagar the Horrible
www.kingfeatures.com/comics/hagar

HarperCollin's Childrens Books
www.harperchildrens.com

Harry Potter
www.harrypotter.com

Judy Blume
www.judyblume.com

Marvel Comics
www.marvelcomics.com

Miffy
www.miffy.org

National Geographic for Kids
www.nationalgeographic.com/kids

Paddington Bear
www.paddingtonbear.co.uk

Right Start
www.rightstartmagazine.co.uk

Roald Dahl
www.roalddahl.org

Snoopy
www.snoopy.com

Thomas the Tank Engine
www.thomasthetankengine.com

Tintin
www.tintin.be

Watership Down
www.watershipdown.net

Willie Wonka
www.wonka.com

Winnie the Pooh
www.winniethepooh.co.uk

theatre

Mersey Young Peoples Theatre
www.mypt.uk.com

National Association of Youth Theatre
www.nayt.org.uk

Polka Children's Theatre
www.polkatheatre.com

Puppeteers Company
www.puppco.demon.co.uk

QuickSilver
www.quicksilvertheatre.org

websites

Alfy
www.alfy.co.uk

Animal Ark
www.animalark.co.uk

AOL UK Kid's Channel
www.aol.co.uk/channels/kids

Ask Jeeves for Kids
www.ajkids.com

Beanie Babies Official Club
www.beaniebabyofficialclub.com

Bonus.com
www.bonus.com

Brain Teaser
www.brain-teaser.com

Carnegie Museum - Discovery Room
www.clpgh.org/cmnh/discovery

ChildLine
www.childline.org.uk

Compuserve Kids
www.compuserve.com/gateway/kids

Disney Interactive
www.disney.co.uk/disneyinteractive

EcoKids
www.bytesize.com/ecokids

Enchanted Learning
www.enchantedlearning.com

Galaxy Kids
www.galaxykids.co.uk

Gridclub (DfES)
www.gridclub.com

Hoobs
www.4learning.co.uk/hoobs

How Stuff Works
www.howstuffworks.com

Kids' Almanac
www.kids.infoplease.com

Kids' Crosswords
www.kidcrosswords.com

Kids' Jokes
www.kidsjokes.com

Kidscape
www.kidscape.org.uk

Lifebytes
www.lifebytes.gov.uk

Microsoft Kids
www.microsoft.com/kids

MindBodySoul
www.mindbodysoul.gov.uk

Numbercrew
www.numbercrew.com

Pooh Corner
www.pooh-corner.com

Pupil Line
www.pupiline.net

RSPCA Kid's Stuff
www.rspca.org.uk/content/kids_stuff.html

Science Year
www.scienceyear.com

The Junction
www.thej.co.uk

Warner Bros Kid's Page
www.kids.warnerbros.com

Yahoo! Games
www.games.yahoo.com

Yahooligans!
www.yahooligans.com

agriculture

Royal Agricultural College
www.royagcol.ac.uk

Scottish Agricultural College
www.sac.ac.uk

apprenticeship

Modern Apprenticeship
www.realworkrealpay.info

art & architecture

Architectural Association School of
Architecture
www.arch-assoc.org.uk

Courtauld Institute
www.courtauld.ac.uk

Glasgow School of Art
www.gsa.ac.uk

Hull School of Architecture
www.humber.ac.uk/arc

Institute of Contemporary Art
www.ica.org.uk

London College of Printing
www.linst.ac.uk/lcp

National Society for Education in Art &
Design
www.nsead.org

National Training Organisation for Arts &
Entertainment (Metier)
www.metier.org.uk

Royal College of Art
www.rca.ac.uk

Ruskin School of Drawing & Fine Art
www.ruskin-sch.ox.ac.uk

Slade
www.ucl.ac.uk/slade

Surrey Institute of Art & Design
www.surrart.ac.uk

ballet, drama & music

Arts Educational London Schools
www.artsed.co.uk

Associated Board of the Royal Schools of
Music
www.abrsm.ac.uk

Birmingham School of Speech & Drama
www.bssd.ac.uk

Bristol Old Vic Theatre School
www.oldvic.ac.uk

Brit School
www.brit.croydon.sch.uk

Central School of Speech & Drama
www.cssd.ac.uk

Cygnet Training Theatre (Exeter)
www.drama.ac.uk/cygnet.html

De Montfort University
www.dmu.ac.uk

Drama Centre London
http://dcl.drama.ac.uk

East 15 Acting School
http://east15.ac.uk

Elmhurst School for Dance & Performing
Arts
www.elmhurstdance.co.uk

English National Ballet School
www.en-ballet.co.uk/school

Guildhall School of Music & Drama
www.gsmd.ac.uk

John Moore's University
www.livjm.ac.uk

Lee Strasberg
www.strasberg.com

Liverpool Institute for Performing Arts
www.lipa.ac.uk

London Academy of Music & Dramatic Art
(LAMDA)
www.lamda.org.uk

London Contemporary Dance School
www.theplace.org.uk

London International Film School
www.lifs.org.uk

Manchester Metropolitan University,
School of Theatre
www.artdes.mmu.ac.uk

Mountview Theatre School
www.mountview.ac.uk

Music Education Council
www.mec.org.uk

National Council for Drama Training
www.ncdt.co.uk

National Film & Television School
www.nftsfilm-tv.ac.uk

North of England College of Dance
www.zebra.co.uk/necd

Northern School of Contemporary Dance
www.nscd.ac.uk

Oxford School of Drama
http://oxford.drama.ac.uk

Queen Margaret College, School of Drama
(Edinburgh)
www.drama.ac.uk/queenm.html

Rambert School
www.brunel.ac.uk/faculty/arts/rambert

Rose Bruford College of Speech & Drama
www.bruford.ac.uk

Royal Academy of Dramatic Art (RADA)
www.rada.org

Royal Academy of Music
www.ram.ac.uk

Royal Ballet School
www.royal-ballet-school.org.uk

Royal College of Music
www.rcm.ac.uk

Royal Northern College
www.rncm.ac.uk

Royal Scottish Academy of Music & Drama
www.rsamd.ac.uk

Trinity College of Music
www.tcm.ac.uk

University of Surrey
www.surrey.ac.uk/Dance

Webber Douglas Academy of Dramatic Art
www.drama.ac.uk/webberd.html

Welsh College of Music & Drama
www.wcmd.ac.uk

business & law

Aberdeen Business School
www.abs.ac.uk

Australian College of Law
www.lawcol.org.uk

BPP Law School
www.bpp.com

College of Law
www.lawcol.org.uk

London Business School
www.lbs.lon.ac.uk

Manchester Business School
www.mbs.ac.uk

careers guidance

Prospects
www.prospects.co.uk

UK Coursefinder
www.ukcoursefinder.com

catering

Gordon Ramsay Scholar Award
www.ramsayscholar.com

colleges of further education

Amersham & Wycombe College
www.amersham.ac.uk

Ayr College
www.ayrcoll.ac.uk

Brockenhurst College
www.brock.ac.uk

Havering College
www.havering-college.ac.uk

Ruskin College
www.ruskin.ac.uk

South East Essex College
www.se-essex-college.ac.uk

Stanmore College
www.stanmore.ac.uk

West Suffolk College
www.westsuffolk.ac.uk

complementary health

Academy of Curative Hypnotherapists
www.ach.co.uk

British College of Naturopathy & Osteopathy
www.bcno.org.uk

British School of Homeopathy
www.homeopathy.co.uk

College of Integrated Chinese Medicine
www.cicm.org.uk

London College of Clinical Hypnosis
www.lcch.co.uk

London College of Traditional Acupuncture & Oriental Medicine
www.lcta.com

Royal College of Speech & Language Therapists
www.rcslt.org

educational organisations

General

Association of Recognised English Language Schools
www.arels.org.uk

Book Trust
www.booktrust.org.uk

Civil Service College
www.open.gov.uk/college/cschome.htm

Community Education Development Centre
www.cedc.org.uk

Countryside Foundation for Education
www.countrysidefoundation.org.uk

Dyslexia Institute
www.dyslexia-inst.org.uk

National Institute of Adult Continuing Education
www.niace.org.uk

National Literacy Trust
www.literacytrust.org.uk

On Course
www.oncourse.co.uk

Qualifications & Curriculum Authority
www.qca.org.uk

Scottish Book Trust
www.scottishbooktrust.com

Scottish Council For Research In Education
www.scre.ac.uk

Scottish Qualifications Authority
www.sqa.org.uk

Governing Bodies

British Association for Open Learning
www.baol.co.uk

British Educational Communications & Technology Agency (BECTA)
www.becta.org.uk

Central Council for Education & Training in Social Work
www.ccetsw.org.uk

City & Guilds Institute
www.city-and-guilds.co.uk

Higher Education Funding Council for England
www.hefce.ac.uk

Higher Education Funding Council for Scotland
www.shefc.ac.uk

Higher Education Funding Council for Wales
www.niss.ac.uk/education/hefcw

National Council for Drama Training
www.ncdt.co.uk

National Council for the Training of Journalists
www.nctj.com

Royal Institution of Great Britain
www.ri.ac.uk

Scottish Council for Educational Technology
www.scet.org.uk

Teacher Training Agency
www.teach-tta.gov.uk

Training & Enterprise Councils
www.tec.co.uk

UK Council for Graduate Education
www.warwick.ac.uk/ukcge

health & sex education

Channel 4 Sex Education
www.channel4.com/sex

Sex Education Forum
www.ncb.org.uk/sexed.htm

Teenage Pregnancy Unit
www.teenagepregnancyunit.gov.uk

Wired for Health
www.wiredforhealth.gov.uk

higher education

The Guardian
www.guardian.co.uk/clearing

The Independent
www.advancement.independent.co.uk/higher

UCAS
www.ucas.ac.uk

World of Study
www.worldofstudy.com

ict

RM
www.rm.com

magazines & websites

@School
www.atschool.co.uk

BBC Education
www.bbc.co.uk/education

BT Teaching Awards
www.teachingawards.com

Education Show
www.education-net.co.uk

Floodlight
www.floodlight.co.uk

Gabbitas
www.gabbitas.com

Good Schools Guide
www.goodschoolsguide.co.uk

Guide to UK Boarding Schools
www.boarding-schools.com

Incorporated Association of Preparatory Schools
www.iaps.org.uk

Independent Schools Directory
www.indschools.co.uk

Independent Schools Information Service
www.isis.org.uk

Learn
www.learn.co.uk

National Curriculum
www.nc.uk.net

National Grid for Learning
www.ngfl.gov.uk

Nelson Books
www.nelson.co.uk

On Course
www.oncourse.co.uk

Special Educational Needs
www.dfes.gov.uk/sen

Student Magazine
www.StudentMagazine.com

Times Educational Supplement
www.tes.co.uk

Times Higher Educational Supplement
www.thesis.co.uk

Times Literary Supplement
www.the-tls.co.uk

medical & dental

Eastman Dental Institute
www.eastman.ucl.ac.uk

Glasgow Caledonian University
www.gcal.ac.uk

Glasgow Dental School
www.gla.ac.uk/Acad/Dental

Imperial College of Science, Technology & Medicine
www.ic.ac.uk

King's College School of Medicine & Dentistry
www.smd.kcl.ac.uk

Liverpool School of Tropical Medicine
www.liv.ac.uk/lstm

London School of Hygiene & Tropical Medicine
www.lshtm.ac.uk

London School of Medicine
www.mds.qmw.ac.uk

Royal College of Paediatrics & Child Health
www.rcpch.ac.uk

Royal College of Physicians
www.rcplondon.ac.uk

Royal College of Psychiatrists
www.rcpsych.ac.uk

Royal Free & University College Medical

School
www.rfc.ucl.ac.uk

St Bartholomew's & The Royal London School of Medicine & Dentistry
www.mds.qmw.ac.uk

St George's Hospital Medical School
www.sghms.ac.uk

United Medical & Dental Schools of King's, Guy's & St Thomas' Hospitals
www.umds.ac.uk

University of Aberdeen
www.bms.abdn.ac.uk

University of Birmingham School of Medicine
www.medweb.bham.ac.uk

University of Hull
www.hull.ac.uk/Hull/health_ps

University of Nottingham
www.nottingham.ac.uk/schools-index.html

University of Southampton
www.medschool.soton.ac.uk

University of Wales, Cardiff
www.uwcm.ac.uk

postgraduate & research

Greenwich Maritime Institute
www.nri.org/GMI

Nuffield Trust
www.nuffieldtrust.org.uk

Royal Academy of Engineers
www.raeng.org.uk

Royal Institute of International Affairs
www.riia.org

Society of Antiquaries
www.sal.org.uk

Tenovus
www.tenovus.org.uk

pre-school

Montessori Foundation
www.montessori.org

Norland Nanny School
www.norland.co.uk

Sure Start
www.surestart.gov.uk

reading & literacy

Federation of Children's Book Groups
www.fcbg.mcmail.com

Reading is Fundamental
www.rif.org.uk

Sainsbury's Bookstart
www.booktrust.org.uk

World Book Day
www.worldbookday.com

World Dyslexia Network Foundation
www.ukonline.co.uk/wdnf

schools

Independent

American Community Schools
www.acs-england.co.uk

American School in London
www.asl.org

Gabbitas Guide to Independent Schools
www.gabbitas.net

Incorporated Association of Preparatory Schools
www.iaps.org.uk

Independent Schools Directory
www.indschools.co.uk

Independent Schools in the UK
www.ipta.co.uk

Independent Schools Information Service
www.isis.org.uk

Public

Ampleforth
www.ampleforth.org.uk

Benenden
www.benenden.kent.sch.uk

Cheltenham College
www.cheltcoll.gloucs.sch.uk

Dulwich College
www.dulwich.org.uk

Eton College
www.etoncollege.com

Gordonstoun
www.gordonstoun.org.uk

King's
www.ksw.org.uk

Manchester Grammar
www.mgs.org

Millfield
www.millfield.somerset.sch.uk

Oundle
www.oundleschool.org.uk

Roedean
www.roedean.co.uk

Rugby
www.rugby-school.co.uk

Shrewsbury
www.shrewsbury.org.uk

St Paul's
www.stpauls.co.uk

Stowe
www.stowe.co.uk

Uppingham
www.uppingham.co.uk

Westminster
www.westminster.org.uk

Winchester College
www.wincoll.ac.uk

Wrekin College
www.wrekin-college.salop.sch.uk

sport

United States Sports Academy
www.sport.ussa.edu

students

BUNAC
www.bunac.org.uk

Camp America
www.campamerica.co.uk

London Student Newspaper
www.londonstudent.org.uk

National Union of Students
www.nusonline.co.uk

Student Radio Association
www.studentradio.org.uk

Student UK
www.studentuk.com

StudentZone
www.studentzone.org.uk

University & Colleges Admissions Service
www.ucas.ac.uk

teacher training

Teacher Training Agency
www.canteach.gov.uk

tuition & part-time learning

Cyberitalian
www.cyberitalian.com

Floodlight
www.floodlight.co.uk

German for Travellers
www.germanfortravellers.com

Institut Francais
www.ambafrance.org.uk

Japanese Tutor
www.japanese-online.com

Kumon Maths
www.kumon.co.uk

Learn Direct
www.learndirect.co.uk

Lifelong Learning (DfES)
www.lifelonglearning.co.uk

Linguaphone
www.linguaphone.co.uk

National Literacy Trust
www.literacytrust.org.uk

National Organisation for Adult Learning
www.niace.org.uk

Oncourse
www.oncourse.co.uk

Study Spanish
www.studyspanish.com

Travlang
www.travlang.com

University of the Third Age
www.u3a.org.uk

Workers' Educational Association
www.wea.org.uk

universities

Aberdeen
www.abdn.ac.uk

Abertay Dundee
www.abertay-dundee.ac.uk

Aberystwyth
www.aber.ac.uk

American International University
www.richmond.ac.uk

Aston
www.aston.ac.uk

Bangor
www.bangor.ac.uk

Bath
www.bath.ac.uk

Birkbeck College London
www.bbk.ac.uk

Birmingham
www.birmingham.ac.uk

Bournemouth
www.bournemouth.ac.uk

Bradford
www.brad.ac.uk

Brighton
www.bton.ac.uk

Bristol
www.bris.ac.uk

Brunel
www.brunel.ac.uk

Buckinghamshire Chilterns University College
www.buckscol.ac.uk

Cambridge
www.cam.ac.uk

Canterbury Christ Church University College
www.cant.ac.uk

Cardiff
www.cf.ac.uk

Central Lancashire
www.uclan.ac.uk

City
www.city.ac.uk

Coventry
www.coventry.ac.uk

Cranfield
www.cranfield.ac.uk

De Montfort
www.dmu.ac.uk

Derby
www.derby.ac.uk

Dundee
www.dundee.ac.uk

Durham
www.dur.ac.uk

East London
www.uel.ac.uk

Edinburgh
www.ed.ac.uk

Essex
www.essex.ac.uk

Exeter
www.exeter.ac.uk

Glamorgan
www.glam.ac.uk

Glasgow
www.gla.ac.uk

Glasgow Caledonian
www.gcal.ac.uk

Goldsmiths College London
www.goldsmiths.ac.uk

Greenwich
www.greenwich.ac.uk

Guildhall London
www.lgu.ac.uk

Heriot-Watt
www.hw.ac.uk

Hertfordshire
www.herts.ac.uk

Huddersfield
www.hud.ac.uk

Hull
www.hull.ac.uk

Imperial College
www.ic.ac.uk

Keele
www.keele.ac.uk

Kent
www.ukc.ac.uk

King's College London
www.kcl.ac.uk

Kingston-upon-Thames
www.kingston.ac.uk

Lancaster
www.lancs.ac.uk

Leeds
www.leeds.ac.uk

Leeds Metropolitan
www.lmu.ac.uk

Leicester
www.leicester.ac.uk

Lincoln
www.ulh.ac.uk

Liverpool
www.liv.ac.uk

London
www.lon.ac.uk

London Business School
www.lbs.ac.uk

London Guildhall
www.lgu.ac.uk

London School of Economics
www.lse.ac.uk

Loughborough
www.lut.ac.uk

Luton
www.luton.ac.uk

Manchester
www.man.ac.uk

Manchester Metropolitan
www.mmu.ac.uk

Middlesex
www.mdx.ac.uk

Napier
www.napier.ac.uk

Newcastle
www.ncl.ac.uk

North London
www.unl.ac.uk

Northumbria
www.unn.ac.uk

Nottingham
www.nott.ac.uk

Nottingham Trent
www.ntu.ac.uk

Open University
www.open.ac.uk

Oxford
www.ox.ac.uk

Oxford Brookes
www.brookes.ac.uk

Paisley
www.paisley.ac.uk

Plymouth
www.plym.ac.uk

Portsmouth
www.port.ac.uk

Queen Mary
www.qmw.ac.uk

Queen's, Belfast
www.qub.ac.uk

Reading
www.reading.ac.uk

Robert Gordon
www.rgu.ac.uk

Royal Holloway London
www.rhbnc.ac.uk

Salford
www.salford.ac.uk

Sheffield
www.shef.ac.uk

Sheffield Hallam
www.shu.ac.uk

South Bank
www.sbu.ac.uk

Southampton
www.soton.ac.uk

St Andrews
www.st-and.ac.uk

St Mark & St John
www.marjon.ac.uk

Staffordshire
www.staffs.ac.uk

Stirling
www.stir.ac.uk

Strathclyde
www.strath.ac.uk

Sunderland
www.sunderland.ac.uk

Surrey
www.surrey.ac.uk

Sussex
www.sussex.ac.uk

Swansea
www.swan.ac.uk

Teesside
www.tees.ac.uk

Thames Valley
www.tvu.ac.uk

Ulster
www.ulst.ac.uk

University College London
www.ucl.ac.uk

Wales Institute
www.uwic.ac.uk

Warwick
www.warwick.ac.uk

West of England
www.uwe.ac.uk

Westminster
www.wmin.ac.uk

Wolverhampton
www.wlv.ac.uk

York
www.york.ac.uk

Australia

Australian National University
www.anu.edu.au

Canberra Institute of Technology
www.cit.act.edu.au

Central Queensland University
www.cqu.edu.au

Northern Territory University
www.ntu.edu.au

University of Adelaide
www.adelaide.edu.au

University of Melbourne
www.unimelb.edu.au

University of New South Wales
www.unsw.edu.au

University of Queensland
www.uq.edu.au

University of South Australia
www.unisa.edu.au

University of Southern Queensland
www.usq.edu.au

University of Sydney
www.usyd.edu.au

University of Tasmania
www.utas.edu.au

University of Western Australia
www.uwa.edu.au

Canada

University of Alberta
www.ualberta.ca

New Zealand

Auckland University of Technology
www.aut.ac.nz

University of Auckland
www.auckland.ac.nz

University of Canterbury
www.canterbury.ac.nz

University of Otago
www.otago.ac.nz

United States

Arizona State University
www.asu.edu

California State University
www.csuchico.edu

Colorado State University
www.colostate.edu

Florida State University
www.fsu.edu

Harvard University
www.harvard.edu

Indiana University
www.indiana.edu

Iowa State University
www.iastate.edu

Kansas University
www.ukans.edu

Massachusetts Institute of Technology
www.mit.edu

Michigan State University
www.msu.edu

Minnesota State University
www.msus.edu

Mississippi State University
www.msstate.edu

New York University
www.nyu.edu

North Dakota University
www.nodak.edu

Ohio State University
www.ohio-state.edu

Oklahoma State University
www.okstate.edu

Oregon State University
www.orst.edu

Pennsylvania State University
www.psu.edu

Princeton University
www.princeton.edu

San Diego State University
www.sdsu.edu

San Jose State University
www.sjsu.edu

Smithsonian Institution
www.si.edu

Stanford University
www.stanford.edu

UC Berkeley
www.berkeley.edu

UCLA
www.ucla.edu

University of Arizona
www.arizona.edu

University of Chicago
www.uchicago.edu

University of Colorado
www.colorado.edu

University of Delaware
www.udel.edu

University of Georgia
www.uga.edu

University of Idaho
www.uidaho.edu

University of Illinois
www.uiuc.edu

University of Iowa
www.uiowa.edu

University of Maryland
www.umd.edu

University of Michigan
www.umich.edu

University of Minnesota
www.umn.edu

University of Missouri-Columbia
www.missouri.edu

University of Oregon
www.uoregon.edu

University of Pennsylvania
www.upenn.edu

University of Southern California
www.usc.edu

University of Texas
www.utexas.edu

University of Utah
www.utah.edu

University of Virginia
www.virginia.edu

University of Washington
www.washington.edu

University of Wisconsin-Madison
www.wisc.edu

Washington State University
www.wsu.edu

Yale University
www.yale.edu

veterinary schools

Bristol
www.bris.ac.uk/Depts/VetSci/wel.htm

Cambridge
www.vet.cam.ac.uk

Edinburgh
www.vet.ed.ac.uk

Glasgow
www.gla.ac.uk/faculties/vet/weblinks.htm

Liverpool
www.liv.ac.uk/vets/vethome.html

Royal College of Veterinary Surgeons
(London)
www.rcvs.org.uk

Royal Veterinary College (London)
www.rvc.ac.uk

Environment

agriculture

Dalgety Arable
www.dalgety.co.uk

East of England Agricultural Society
www.eastofengland.org.uk

Farmers' Union of Wales
www.fuw.org.uk

Farmers Weekly Interactive
www.fwi.co.uk

Home Grown Cereals Authority
www.hgca.co.uk

Institute for Animal Health
www.iah.bbsrc.ac.uk

Institute of Arable Crops Research
www.res.bbsrc.ac.uk

Institute of Food Research
www.ifrn.bbsrc.ac.uk

John Innes Centre
www.uea.ac.uk/nrp/jic

Milk Marque
www.milkmarque.com

National Institute of Agricultural Botany
www.niab.com

Royal Agricultural Society
www.rase.org.uk

Royal Bath & West Society
www.bathandwest.co.uk

Royal Highland and Agricultural Society of
Scotland
www.rhass.org.uk

Royal Ulster Agricultural Society
www.ruas.co.uk

Royal Welsh Agricultural Society
www.rwas.co.uk

Soil Association
www.earthfoods.co.uk

Tenant Farmers Association
www.tenant-farmers.org.uk

Yorkshire Agricultural Society
www.yas.co.uk

architecture

Archinet
www.archinet.co.uk

Architects Journal
www.constructionplus.co.uk

Architectural Heritage
www.eup.ed.ac.uk/journals/architectural

Architectural Heritage Fund
www.ahfund.co.uk

Architectural Review
www.arplus.com

Architecture Centre, Bristol
www.arch-centre.demon.co.uk

Architecture Foundation
www.architecturefoundation.org.uk

Architecture Week
www.archweek.co.uk

Architecturelink
www.architecturelink.org.uk

Association for Environment Conscious
Building
www.aecb.net

Civic Trust
www.civictrust.org.uk

Commission for Architecture & the Built
Environment (CABE)
www.cabe.org.uk

Commonwealth Association of Architects
www.archexchange.org

Frank Lloyd Wright
www.wrightplus.com

Guild of Architectural Ironmongers (GAI)
www.martex.co.uk/gai/index.htm

International Union of Architects
www.uia-architectes.org

Pevsner Architectural Guides
www.pevsner.co.uk

RIAS, Scotland
www.rias.org.uk

RIBA Publications
www.ribabookshop.com

Royal Institute of British Architects
www.architecture.com

Society of Architectural Historians of Great
Britain
www.sahgb.org.uk

Stirling Prize
www.ribaawards.co.uk

Twentieth Century Society
www.c20society.freeserve.co.uk

World Architecture
www.world-architecture.co.uk

construction

Association of Consulting Engineers
www.acenet.co.uk

Association of Project Management
www.apm.org.uk

BEPAC
www.bepac.dmu.ac.uk

British Construction Industry Awards
www.bciawards.org.uk

Concrete Society
www.concrete.org.uk

Construction Industry Board
www.ciboard.org.uk

Construction Industry Council
www.cic.org.uk

Construction Industry Research and
Information Association
www.ciria.org.uk

Energy-Efficient Building Association
www.eeba.org

European Construction Institute
www.eci-online.org

Housing Forum
www.thehousingforum.org.uk

Institution of Civil Engineers
www.ice.org.uk

National Homebuilder Awards
www.nationalhomebuilder.com

Steel Construction Institute
www.steel-sci.org

Urban Design Alliance
www.udal.org.uk

government

Countryside Agency
www.countryside.gov.uk

Countryside Council for Wales
www.ccw.gov.uk

Department of Environment, Transport &
the Regions
www.detr.gov.uk

English Nature
www.english-nature.org.uk

Environment Agency Wales
www.environment-agency.wales.gov.uk

Environmental Body Council
www.ebco.org.uk

GRID – Global Resource Information
Database (United Nations)
www.grida.no

Ministry of Agriculture, Fisheries & Food
www.open.gov.uk/maff

National Environment Research Council
www.nerc.ac.uk

National Heritage
www.heritage.gov.uk

Natural Environment Research Council
www.nerc.ac.uk

Royal Commission on Historical
Manuscripts
www.hmc.gov.uk

Royal Commission on the Ancient &
Historical Monuments of Scotland
www.rcahms.gov.uk

Royal Commission on the Ancient &
Historical Monuments of Wales
www.rcahmw.org.uk

Scottish Environment Protection Agency
www.sepa.org.uk

Town & Country Planning Association
www.tcpa.org.uk

green issues

Action for the Environment
www.groundwork.org.uk

British Wind Energy Association
www.bwea.com

Can-Do Community Recycling
www.fraserburgh.org.uk/cando

Centre for Alternative Technology
www.cat.org.uk

Common Ground
www.commonground.org.uk

Conservation Foundation
www.conservationfoundation.co.uk

Countryside Foundation for Education
www.countrysidefoundation.org.uk

Countryside Watch
www.countrysidewatch.co.uk

Earthwatch
www.uk.earthwatch.org

Energy Saving Trust
www.est.org.uk

Friends of the Earth
www.foe.co.uk

Friends of the Earth Scotland
www.foe-scotland.org.uk

Game Conservancy Trust
www.game-conservancy.org.uk

Going for Green
www.gfg.iclnet.co.uk

Greenpeace International
www.greenpeace.org

Landlife
www.landlife.org.uk

Waste Watch
www.wastewatch.org.uk

landscape

Alliance for Historic Landscape
Preservation
www.mindspring.com/~ahlp/

Association of Gardens Trusts
www.gardenstrusts.org.uk

Association of National Park & Countryside
Voluntary Wardens
www.naturenet.net/orgs/acvw

British Land Reclamation Society
www.blrs.org

British Urban Regeneration Association
www.bura.org.uk

Field Magazine
www.thefield.co.uk

Flora Locale
www.floralocale.org

Green Corridor
www.greencorridor.co.uk

Historic Gardens Foundation
www.historicgardens.freeserve.co.uk

Landscape Design Trust
www.landscape.co.uk

Landscape Institute
www.l-i.org.uk

Learning Through landscapes
www.ltl.org.uk

Moorland Association
www.cla.org.uk/moorland

National Countryside Show
www.countrysideshow.co.uk

preservation

Antiquity Magazine
http://intarch.ac.uk/antiquity

Architectural Heritage Society of Scotland
www.ahss.org.uk

Assemblage Archaeology Journal
www.shef.ac.uk/~assem

Association for Industrial Archaeology
www.twelveheads.demon.co.uk/aia.htm

Association for the Protection of Rural
Scotland
www.aprs.org.uk

Association of Archaeological Illustrators &
Surveyors
www.aais.org.uk

Association of Local Government
Archaeological Officers
www.algao.org.uk

British Archaeology Magazine
www.britarch.ac.uk/ba/ba.html

British Trust for Conservation Volunteers
www.btcv.org.uk

Construction History Society
www.construct.rdg.ac.uk/chs

Council for British Archaeology
www.britarch.ac.uk

Current Archaeology
www.archaeology.co.uk

Ecclesiological Society
www.ecclsoc.org

English Heritage
www.english-heritage.org.uk

European Association of Archaeologists
www.e-a-a.org

Historic Chapels Trust
www.hct.org.uk

Historic Houses Association
www.historic-houses-assn.org

Institute of Field Archaeologists
www.archaeologists.net

Institution of Historic Building Conservation
www.ihbc.org.uk

Landmark Trust
www.landmarktrust.co.uk

Museum of London Archaeology Service
www.molas.org.uk

National Trust
www.nationaltrust.org.uk

National Trust for Scotland
www.nts.org.uk

Open Churches Trust
www.merseyworld.com/faith/html_file/octhead.htm

Regeneration Through Heritage
www.bitc.org.uk/rth

RESCUE (British Archaeology Trust)
www.rescue-archaeology.freeserve.co.uk

River Thames Society
www.riverthamessociety.org.uk

Royal Highland Education Trust
www.sfacet.org.uk

Royal Society for Nature Conservation
www.rsnc.org

Society for the Protection of Ancient
Buildings
www.spab.org.uk

United Kingdom Institute for Conservation
www.ukic.org.uk

Woodland Trust
www.woodland-trust.org.uk

York Archaeological Trust
www.pastforward.co.uk

rural life

Country Landowners' Association
www.cla.org.uk

NFU Countryside
www.nfucountryside.org.uk

transport

Environmental Transport Association
www.eta.co.uk

Sustrans
www.sustrans.org.uk

trees

Arboricultural Association
www.trees.org.uk

Black Country Urban Forest
www.blackcountryurbanforest.org.uk

British Land Reclamation Society
www.blrs.org

Central Forest of Scotland
www.csct.co.uk

Children's Forest
www.childrensforest.com

Coed Cymru
www.coedcymru.mid-wales.net

Dendrologist
www.treematters.freeserve.co.uk

Forest of Avon
www.forestofavon.org

Forest of Marston Vale
www.marstonvale.org

Forest of Mercia
www.forestofmercia.co.uk

Forest Research Agency
www.forestry.gov.uk

Forestry Commission
www.forestry.gov.uk

Great Western Community Forest
www.gwestcf.org.uk

Greenwood Community Forest
www.communityforest.org.uk/Greenwood

International Society of Arboriculture
www.isa-arbor.com

International Tree Foundation
www.tree-foundation.org.uk

Marches Woodland Initiative
www.mwi.org.uk

Mersey Forest
www.merseyforest.org.uk

National Arborist Association
www.natlarb.com

National Forest
www.nationalforest.org

National Urban Forestry Unit
www.nufu.org.uk

Red Rose Forest
www.redroseforest.co.uk

Royal Forestry Society
www.rfs.org.uk

Sherwood Forest
www.sherwoodforest.org.uk

Small Woods Association
www.smallwoods.org.uk

South Yorkshire Forest
www.syforest.co.uk

Tees Forest
www.teesforest.org.uk

Thames Chase
www.thameschase.org.uk

Tree Council
www.treecouncil.org.uk

Tree Register
www.tree-register.org

Trees for Life
www.treesforlife.org.uk

Watling Chase Community Forest
www.watlingchase.org.uk

Woodland Trust
www.woodland-trust.org.uk

Food & Drink

Breweries

Abbey Ales
www.abbeyales.co.uk

Amstel
www.amstel.com

Badger
www.breworld.com/badger

Bass Ale
www.bassale.com

Beamish
www.aardvark.ie/beamish

Beck's
www.becks-beer.com

Blacksheep
www.blacksheep.co.uk

Boddingtons
www.boddingtons.com

Brains
www.sabrain.co.uk

Budweiser
www.budweiser.com

Budweiser Budvar
www.budweiser.cz

Caffrey's
www.caffreys.ie

Carlsberg
www.carlsberg.co.uk

Cobra
www.cobrabeer.com

Corona
www.corona.com

Dos Equis
www.dosx.com

Duvel
www.duvel.be

Felinfoel
www.felinfoel-brewery.com

Foster's
www.fostersbeer.com

Freedom
www.freedombrew.com

Fuller's
www.fullers.co.uk

Grolsch
www.grolsch.com

Guinness
www.guinness.ie

Heineken
www.heineken.com

Holsten
www.holsten.de

HP Bulmer
www.bulmer.com

JD Wetherspoon
www.jdwetherspoon.co.uk

Kronenbourg
www.k1664.co.uk

Labatt's
www.labatt.com

Maclay Thistle
www.maclay.com

Marston's
www.breworld.com/marstons

Merrydown
www.merrydown.co.uk

Miller Lite
www.millerlite.com

Molson
www.molson.com

Morland
www.morland.co.uk

Ridleys
www.ridleys.co.uk

Rolling Rock
www.rollingrock.co.uk

Ruddles
www.ruddles.co.uk

Scrumpy Jack
www.scrumpyjack.com

Shepherd Neame
www.shepherd-neame.co.uk

Singha
www.singha.com

Strongbow
www.strongbow.com

Thwaites
www.thwaites.co.uk

Woodfordes
www.woodfordes.co.uk

Wychwood Brewery
www.wychwood.co.uk

Young's
www.youngs.co.uk

chefs

Albert Roux
www.albertroux.co.uk

Craft Guild of Chefs
www.chefpoint.co.uk

Delia Smith
www.deliaonline.com

Gary Rhodes
www.garyrhodes.com

Gordon Ramsay
www.gordonramsay.com

Jamie Oliver
www.jamieoliver.net

Keith Floyd
www.keithfloyd.co.uk

Raymond Blanc
www.manoir.co.uk

Rick Stein
www.rickstein.com

clubs & associations

British Meat
www.meatmatters.com

British Nutrition Foundation
www.nutrition.org.uk

CAMRA (Campaign for Real Ale)
www.camra.org.uk

Chocolate Society
www.chocolate.co.uk

Circle of Wine Writers
www.circleofwinewriters.org

Guild of Food Writers
www.gfw.co.uk

National Pork Producers Council
www.nppc.org

Slow Food
www.slowfood.com

Vegan Society
www.vegansociety.com

Vegetarian Society
www.vegsoc.org

famous brands

Absolut Vodka
www.absolutvodka.com

All Bran
www.all-bran.co.uk

Anchor Foods
www.anchorfoods.com

Asian Home Gourmet
www.asianhomegourmet.com

Bacardi
www.bacardi.com

Bahlsen
www.bahlsen.co.uk

Baileys
www.baileys.com

Baxters
www.baxters.co.uk

Beefeater
www.beefeater.co.uk

Ben & Jerry's
www.benjerry.co.uk

Bendicks of Mayfair
www.bendicks.co.uk

Bensons Crisps
www.bensons-crisps.co.uk

Birds Eye Walls
www.birdseye.com

Blue Dragon
www.bluedragon.co.uk

Boaters Coffee
www.boaters.co.uk

Boost
www.boost.co.uk

Brannigans
www.brannigans.co.uk

Brook Bond
www.brookebond.co.uk

Budweiser
www.budweiser.com

Buitoni
www.buitoni.co.uk

Cadbury's
www.cadbury.co.uk

Campbell's
www.campbellsoup.com

Captain Morgan Rum
www.rum.com

Celebrations
www.celebrations365.com

Chewits
www.chewits.com

Chiltern Hills
www.chilternhills.co.uk

Clipper Teas
www.clipper-teas.com

Coca Cola
www.cocacola.com

Colman's Mustard
www.mustardshop.com

Courvoisier
www.courvoisier.com

Crème Egg
www.cremeegg.co.uk

Crunchie
www.crunchie.co.uk

Cuervo
www.cuervo.com

Culpeper
www.culpeper.co.uk

Danepak
www.danepak.co.uk

Danone
www.danone.com

Del Monte
www.delmonte.com

Delifrance
www.delifrance.com

Dickinson & Morris Pork Pies
www.porkpie.co.uk

Discos
www.discos.co.uk

Douwe Egberts
www.douwe-egberts.co.uk

Dr Pepper
www.drpepper.com

Drambuie
www.drambuie.co.uk

Evian
www.evian.com

Finlandia Vodka
www.finlandia-vodka.com

Fishermans Friends
www.fishermansfriend.co.uk

Fresh Food Company
www.freshfood.co.uk

Frisps
www.frisps.co.uk

Frosties
www.frosties.co.uk

Fyffes
www.fyffes.com

Gerber Foods
www.gerberfoods.com

Ginsters
www.ginsters.co.uk

Godiva
www.godiva.com

Gourmet World
www.gourmet-world.co.uk

Grahams Port
www.grahams-port.com

Grand Marnier
www.grand-marnier.com

Haagen Dazs
www.haagen-dazs.com

Haribo
www.haribo.com

Harmonie
www.harmonie.co.uk

Harveys of Bristol
www.harveysbc.com

Heinz
www.heinz.co.uk

Homepride
www.homepride.co.uk

Horizon Foods
www.horizonfoods.com

Hula Hoops
www.hulahoops.co.uk

I Can't Believe It's Not Butter
www.tasteyoulove.com

Irn Bru
www.irn-bru.co.uk

Jelly Belly
www.jellybelly.com

Jersey Royals
www.jerseyroyals.co.uk

Jolly Rancher
www.jolly-rancher.com

Kellogg's
www.kelloggs.co.uk

Kenco
www.kencocoffee.co.uk

Kerrygold
www.kerrygold.co.uk

Kettle Chips
www.kettlechips.co.uk

Kinder Surprise
www.kindersurprise.co.uk

Kit-Kat
www.kitkat.co.uk

KP Nuts
www.kpnuts.com

Kraft
www.kraftfoods.com

Laughing Cow
www.thelaughingcow.co.uk

Lavazza
www.lavazza.com

Lift
www.lifttea.co.uk

Loch Fyne
www.loch-fyne.com

Lucozade
www.lucozade.co.uk

Mackies
www.mackies.co.uk

Malibu
www.malibu-rum.com

Marmite
www.marmite.com

Mars
www.mars.com

McCain
www.mccain.com

McCoys
www.mccoys.co.uk

Melitta
www.melitta.com

Mini Heroes
www.miniheroes.co.uk

Moet & Chandon
www.moet.com

Moy Park
www.moypark.co.uk

Muller
www.muller.co.uk

Nescafe
www.nescafe.co.uk

Nesquik
www.nesquik.co.uk

Nestle
www.nestle.co.uk

Nimble
www.nimblebread.co.uk

Nutrasweet
www.nutrasweet.com

Old Speckled Hen
www.oldspeckledhen.co.uk

Olivetum Olive Oil
www.olivetum.com

Pepsi
www.pepsi.co.uk

Pernod-Ricard
www.pernod-ricard.fr

Perrier
www.perrier.com

Pillsbury
www.pillsbury.com

Plymouth Gin
www.plymouthgin.com

Poppets
www.poppets.com

Primebake
www.primebake.co.uk

Pro Plus
www.proplus.co.uk

Quaker Oats
www.quakeroatmeal.com

Quorn
www.quorn.com

Raclette Cheese
www.raclette-suisse.ch

Rank Hovis
www.rankhovis.co.uk

Red Bull
www.redbull.co.uk

Remy Martin
www.remy.com

Ridgways
www.ridgways.co.uk

Rivella
www.rivella.co.uk

Rodda's Clotted Cream
www.clottedcream.com

Rombouts
www.rombouts.co.uk

Rowntrees
www.rowntrees.co.uk

Ryvita
www.ryvita.co.uk

Sara Lee
www.saraleebakery.com

Schwartz Herbs
www.schwartz.co.uk

Sharwood's
www.sharwoods.com

Silver Spoon
www.silverspoon.co.uk

Slush Puppy
www.slushpuppy.co.uk

Smint
www.smint.co.uk

Smirnoff
www.smirnoff.com

Snickers
www.snickers.com

Southern Comfort
www.southerncomfort.com

Spam
www.spam.com

Special K
www.specialk.co.uk

St Ivel
www.st-ivel.co.uk

Sunny Delight
www.sunnyd.co.uk

Sweet Factory
www.sweet-factory.com

Sweet'N Low
www.sweetnlow.com

Tango
www.tango.co.uk

Tate & Lyle
www.tateandlyle.com

Tetly Tea
www.tetley.com

Thorntons
www.thorntons.co.uk

Tia Maria
www.tiamaria.co.uk

Tiptree
www.tiptree.com

Tizer
www.tizer.co.uk

Tropicana
www.tropicana.com

Twinings Tea
www.twinings.co.uk

Twix
www.twix.com

Typhoo
www.typhoo.com

Uncle Ben's
www.unclebens.com

Unigate
www.unigate.plc.uk

United Biscuits
www.unitedbiscuits.co.uk

Utterly Butterly
www.utterly-butterly.co.uk

Van den Bergh Foods
www.vdbfoods.co.uk

Vichy
www.vichy.com

Virgin Cola
www.virgincola.co.uk

Walkers
www.walkers.co.uk

Weetabix
www.knex.co.uk/weetabix

Wensleydale
www.wensleydale.co.uk

Whittards of Chelsea
www.whittard.com

Whitworths
www.whitworths.co.uk

Whole Earth
www.earthfoods.co.uk

Wotsits
www.wotsits.co.uk

Wrigley's
www.wrigley.com

Yakult
www.yakult.co.uk

Yazoo
www.yazoo.co.uk

Yeo Valley
www.yeo-organic.co.uk

Yogz
www.yogz.com

Yoplait
www.yoplait.co.uk

fast food

Burger King
www.burgerking.co.uk

Deliverance
www.deliverance.co.uk

Domino's Pizza
www.dominos.co.uk

Dunkin' Donuts
www.dunkindonuts.com

KFC
www.kfc.co.uk

Little Chef
www.little-chef.co.uk

McDonald's
www.mcdonalds.co.uk

Perfect Pizza
www.perfectpizza.co.uk

Pret A Manger
www.pret.com

Roadchef
www.roadchef.com

Room Service
www.roomservice.co.uk

Starbucks
www.starbucks.com

Subway
www.subway.com

food & drink online

Betty's By Post (Harrogate)
www.bettysbypost.com

Bottoms Up
www.bottomsup.co.uk

Fortnum & Mason
www.fortnumandmason.co.uk

Harrods
www.harrods.com

Heinz Direct
www.heinz-direct.co.uk

Jane Asher Party Cakes
www.jane-asher.co.uk

Le Gourmet Francais
www.gourmet2000.co.uk

Oddbins
www.oddbins.co.uk

Organics Direct
www.organicsdirect.com

Paxton & Whitfield
www.cheesemongers.co.uk

Price Offers
www.priceoffers.co.uk

Real Meat Company
www.realmeat.co.uk

Selfridges
www.selfridges.co.uk

Threshers
www.thresherwineshop.co.uk

Vegnet
www.vegnet.co.uk

Victoria Wine
www.victoriawine.co.uk

Whittards of Chelsea
www.whittard.com

Wine Cellar
www.winecellar.co.uk

food marketing

British Cheese Board
www.britishcheese.com

British Egg Information Service
www.britegg.co.uk

British Potato Council
www.potato.org.uk

Fairtrade
www.fairtrade.org.uk

Food from Britain
www.foodfrombritain.com

National Dairy Council
www.milk.co.uk

Tea Council
www.tea.co.uk

magazines & websites

Brewer
www.breworld.com/the_brewer

British Food Journal
www.mcb.co.uk/bfj.htm

Carlton Food Network
www.cfn.co.uk

Cooking Light
www.cookinglight.com

Cook's Delight
www.cooksdelight.co.uk

International Vegetarian Union
www.ivu.org

Lancrigg Vegetarian Country House Hotel
www.lancrigg.co.uk

Oz Clarke
www.ozclarke.com

Pub Guide
www.licensee.co.uk

The Grocer
www.foodanddrink.co.uk

The Redwood Wholefood Company Ltd.
www.redwoodfoods.co.uk

V1 Vegetarian Fast Food
www.v-1.co.uk

Veg Veg
www.veganvillage.co.uk

Vegetarian Pages
www.veg.org

Vegetarian Websites
www.vegetarianwebsites.co.uk

Wine Spectator
www.winespectator.com

Wine Today
www.winetoday.com

restaurants & bars

Aquarium
www.theaquarium.co.uk

Balls Brothers
www.ballsbrothers.co.uk

Bank
www.bankrestaurant.co.uk

Belgo
www.belgo-restaurants.co.uk

Benihana
www.benihana.co.uk

Bibendum
www.bibendum.co.uk

Blue Elephant
www.blueelephant.com

Blue Print Café
www.conran-restaurants.co.uk
/restaurants/restaurants/blueprint/info.html

Brown's Restaurant
www.browns-restaurants.com

Café Rouge
www.caferouge.co.uk

Carluccios
www.carluccios.com

Chez Gerard
www.chezgerard.co.uk

Clifford Media Associates
www.dine-online.co.uk

Cuisine Net
www.cuisinenet.co.uk

Fashion Café
www.fashion-cafe.com

Fatty Arbuckle's
www.fatty-arbuckles.co.uk

Fish!
www.fishdiner.co.uk

Football Football
www.footballfootball.com

Greenhouse
www.capital-london.net/greenhouse/index.html

Hard Rock Café
www.hardrock.com

Harry Ramsden's
www.harryramsdens.co.uk

Hogsgead
www.hogshead.co.uk

J D Wetherspoon
www.jdwetherspoon.co.uk

Jazz Café
www.jazzcafe.co.uk

Leith's
www.leiths.com

Menumaster
www.menumaster.co.uk

Moshi Moshi
www.moshimoshi.co.uk

Mustards Smithfields Brasserie
www.mustards.co.uk

Nando's Chickenland UK
www.nandos.co.uk

Offshore
www.offshore.co.uk

People's Palace
www.capital-london.net/peoples-palace/index.html

Pharmacy
www.outpatients.co.uk

Pizza Express
www.pizzaexpress.co.uk

Pizza Hut
www.pizzahut.co.uk

Planet Hollywood
www.planethollywood.com

Porters
www.porters.uk.com

Rainforest Café
www.rainforestcafe.com

Red Fort
www.redfort.co.uk

Restaurant Websites
www.restaurantwebsites.co.uk

Restaurants.co.uk
www.restaurants.co.uk

Ritz
www.theritzhotel.co.uk/restaurant

Rock Garden
www.rockgarden.co.uk

Rock Garden Café
www.rockgarden.co.uk

Rules
www.rules.co.uk

Sardis
www.sardis.com

Savoy Grill
www.savoy-group.co.uk/savoy/dining/savoy_grill.html

Squaremeal
www.squaremeal.co.uk

Sticky Fingers
www.stickyfingers.co.uk

Table Sir
www.tablesir.com

Time Out
www.timeout.co.uk

Top Table
www.toptable.co.uk

UK Takeaways
www.eats.co.uk

Veeraswamy
www.veeraswamy.com

Wagamama
www.wagamama.com

Waterside Inn
www.waterside-inn.co.uk

Web Collective Plc
www.curryhouse.net

Whitbread
www.whitbread.co.uk

Wiltons
www.wiltons.co.uk

Yates Wine Lodge
www.yates-wine-lodge.com

Yo! Sushi
www.yosushi.co.uk

Youngs
www.youngs.co.uk

supermarkets

Aldi
www.aldi-stores.co.uk

Asda
www.asda.co.uk

Budgens
www.budgens.co.uk

Co-op
www.co-op.co.uk

Iceland
www.iceland.co.uk

Londis
www.londis.co.uk

Marks & Spencer
www.marksandspencer.com

Morrisons
www.morrisons.plc.uk

Safeway
www.safeway.co.uk

Sainsburys
www.jsainsbury.co.uk

Somerfield
www.somerfield.co.uk

Spar
www.spar.co.uk

Tesco
www.tesco.com

Waitrose
www.waitrose.co.uk

whisky

Adelphi Distillery
www.highlandtrail.co.uk

Ardbeg
www.ardbeg.com

Arran
www.arranwhisky.com

Bowmore
www.bowmorescotch.com

Chivas
www.chivas.com

Cragganmore
www.scotch.com

Dalwhinnie
www.scotch.com

Dew of Ben Nevis
www.bennevis.co.uk

Edradour
www.edradour.co.uk

Famous Grouse
www.famousgrouse.com

Glen Moray
www.glenmoray.com

Glen Ord
www.glenord.com

Glencoe
www.bennevis.co.uk

Glenfarclas
www.glenfarclas.co.uk

Glenfiddich
www.glenfiddich.com

Glengoyne
www.glengoynedistillery.co.uk

Glenkinchie
www.scotch.com

Glenlivet
www.glenlivet.com

Glenmorangie
www.glenmorangie.com

Glenturret
www.glenturret.com

Gordon & MacPhail
www.gordonandmacphail.com

Highland Park
www.highlandpark.co.uk

Islay
www.islaywhiskysociety.com

J & B
www.jbscotch.com

Jack Daniels
www.jackdaniels.co.uk

Jim Beam
www.jimbeam.com

Johnny Walker
www.scotch.com

Lagavulin
www.scotch.com

Laphroaig
www.laphroaig.com

Macallan
www.themacallan.com

Oban
www.scotch.com

Scotch
www.Scotchwhisky.com

Scotch Whisky Heritage Centre
www.whisky-heritage.co.uk

Seagram
www.seagram.com

Talisker
www.scotch.com

Whisky Shop
www.whiskyshop.com

wine

Beaujolais
www.beaujolais.com

Berry Bros & Rudd
www.berry-bros.co.uk

Bodegas Faustino
www.bodegasfaustino.com

Bordeaux Direct
www.bordeauxdirect.co.uk

Cloudy Bay
www.cloudybay.co.nz

Hardys
www.hardys-wines.com

International Wine Challenge
www.intwinechallenge.co.uk

Jacobs Creek
www.jacobscreek.com

Laytons
www.laytons.co.uk

Lindemans
www.lindemans.co.uk

Orgasmic Wines
www.orgasmicwines.com

Rouge & Blanc
www.rouge-blanc.com

Vinopolis
www.vinopolis.com

Virgin Wines
www.virginwines.com

Government

117

armed forces

Air Training Corps (ATC)
www.open.gov.uk/ATC

Army Records Office
www.army.mod.uk/army/contact/army_ro.htm

British Army
www.army.mod.uk

RAF Careers
www.raf-careers.com

Royal Air Force
www.raf.mod.uk

Royal Air Forces Association
www.rafa.org.uk

Royal Auxillary Air Force
www.rauxaf.mod.uk

Royal Marines
www.royal-marines.mod.uk

Royal Navy
www.royal-navy.mod.uk

Royal Navy Careers
www.royal-navy.mod.uk/careers

Territorial Army
www.army.mod.uk/army/recruit/ta

embassies

British Embassies Abroad

Australia
www.uk.emb.gov.au

Azerbaijan
www.intrans.baku.az/british

Bahrain
www.ukembassy.gov.bh

Belgium
www.british-embassy.be

Bulgaria
www.british-embassy.bg

Cameroon
http://britcam.org

Canada
www.canada.org.uk

Cyprus
www.britain.org.cy

Czech Republic
www.britain.cz

Denmark
www.britishembassy.dk

Fiji
www.ukinthepacific.bhc.org.fj

Finland
www.ukembassy.fi

France
www.ambafrance.org.uk

Germany
www.britischebotschaft.de

Greece
www.british-embassy.gr

Hong Kong
www.britishconsulate.org.hk

India
www.ukinindia.org

Indonesia
www.britain-in-indonesia.or.id

Israel
www.britemb.org.il

Italy
www.britain.it

Japan
www.uknow.or.jp

Jordan
www.britain.org.jo

Lebanon
www.britishembassy.org.lb

Mexico
www.embajadabritanica.com.mx

Netherlands
www.britishembassy.org.lb

New Zealand
www.brithighcomm.org.nz

Norway
www.britain.no

Singapore
www.britain.org.sg

South Africa
www.britain.org.za

Sweden
www.britishembassy.com

Switzerland
www.britain-in-switzerland.ch

Tunisia
www.british-emb.intl.tn

Ukraine
www.britemb-ukraine.net

United Arab Emirates
www.britain-uae.org

United Nations
www.ukun.org

USA
www.britainusa.com

Venezuela
www.britain.org.ve

Foreign Embassies & Consulates in the UK

Algerian
www.personal.u-net.com/~consalglond

American
www.usembassy.org.uk

Argentinian
www.britain.org.ar

Australian
www.australia.org.uk

Austrian
www.bmaa.gv.at/embassy/uk

Belgian
www.belgium-embassy.co.uk

Brazilian
www.brazil.org.uk

Canadian
www.canada.org.uk

Chilean
www.echileuk.demon.co.uk

Chinese
www.chinese-embassy.org.uk

Costa Rican
www.embcrlon.demon.co.uk

Czech
www.czechembassy.org.uk

Danish
www.denmark.org.uk

Egyptian
www.egypt-embassy.org.uk

Estonian
www.estonia.gov.uk

Finnish
www.finemb.org.uk

French
www.ambafrance.org.uk

German
www.german-embassy.org.uk

Indian
www.hcilondon.org

Iranian
www.iran-embassy.org.uk

Israeli
www.israel-embassy.org.uk

Italian
www.embitaly.org.uk

Jamaican
www.jhcuk.com

Japanese
www.embjapan.org.uk

Jordanian
www.jordanembassyuk.gov.jo

Luxembourg
www.luxembourg.co.uk

Mexican
www.embamex.co.uk

New Zealand
www.newzealandhc.org.uk

Norwegian
www.norway.org.uk

Peruvian
www.peruembassy-uk.com

Philippines
www.microton.net/philemb

Polish
www.poland-embassy.org.uk

Portuguese
www.portembassy.gla.ac.uk

Russian
www.britemb.msk.ru

Slovenian
www.embassy-slovenia.org.uk

South African
www.southafricahouse.com

Spanish
www.spanishembassy.org.uk

Swedish
www.swedish-embassy.org.uk

Swiss
www.swissembassy.org.uk

Tanzanian
www.tanzania-online.gov.uk

Thai
www.thaiconsul-uk.com

Turkish
www.turkishembassy-london.com

Venezuelan
www.venezlon.demon.co.uk

foreign governments

Albanian
http://president.gov.al

Andorran
www.andorra.ad/govern

Angolan
www.angola.org

Argentinian
www.senado.gov.ar

Australian
www.fed.gov.au

Australian Parliament
www.aph.gov.au

Austrian
www.parlinkom.gv.at

Bangladeshi
www.bangladeshonline.com/gob

Barbadan
www.barbados.gov.bb

Belarussian
www.president.gov.by/eng

Belgian
www.belgium.fgov.be

Bolivian
www.congreso.gov.bo

Botswanan
www.gov.bw

Brazilian
www.brasil.gov.br

Brunei
www.brunet.bn

Bulgarian
www.eto.org.uk/nat/bg

Burkina Faso
www.primature.gov.bf

Canadian
www.canada.gc.ca

Chilean
www.presidencia.cl

Chinese
www.gov.cn

Costa Rican
www.casapres.go.cr

Croatian
www.sabor.hr

Cypriot
www.pio.gov.cy

Czech
www.vlada.cz

Danish
www.folketinget.dk

Dominican
www.presidencia.gov.do

Dutch
www.parlement.nl

Egyptian
www.presidency.gov.eg

Estonian
www.vm.ee/eng

Finnish
www.om.fi

French
www.assemblee-nat.fr

Gambian
www.gambia.com

German
www.government.de

German (Parliament)
www.bundesregierung.de

Greek
www.mpa.gr

Hong Kong
www.info.gov.hk

Hungarian
www.mkogy.hu

Icelandic
www.althingi.is

Indian Government
http://alfa.nic.in

Indonesian
www.dpr.go.id

Irish
www.irlgov.ie

Israeli
www.info.gov.il

Italian
www.camera.it

Jamaica
www.cabinet.gov.jm

Japanese
www.kantei.go.jp

Jordanian
www.parliament.gov.jo/english

Kenyan
www.kenyaweb.com/government

Korean
www.assembly.go.kr

Kuwaiti
www.kna.org.kw

Latvian
www.mfa.gov.lv

Lebanese
www.lp.gov.lb/english

Liberian
www.liberiaemb.org

Liechtenstein
www.firstlink.li/regierung

Luxembourg
www.chd.lu

Malaysian
www.parlimen.gov.my

Maltese
www.gov.mt

Mauritanian
www.mauritania.mr

Mexican
www.senado.gob.mx

Mongolian
www.pmis.gov.mn

Mozambiqui
www.mozambique.mz

New Zealand
www.govt.nz

Norwegian
www.stortinget.no

Omani
www.omanet.com

Pakistani
www.pak.gov.pk/govt

Panamanian
www.presidencia.gob.pa

Peruvian
www.congreso.gob.pe

Philippino
www.gov.ph

Polish
www.poland.pl

Portuguese
www.parlamento.pt

Romanian
www.guv.ro/english

Russian
www.gov.ru

Russian (Parliament)
www.duma.ru

Senegalese
www.primature.sn

Singaporean
www.gov.sg

Slovakian
www.government.gov.sk

South African
www.polity.org.za/gnu

South Korean
www.cwd.go.kr/english

Spanish
www.la-moncloa.es

Swaziland
www.swazi.com/government

Swedish
www.royalcourt.se/eng

Swiss
www.admin.ch

Tanzanian
www.bungetz.org

Thai
www.parliament.go.th

Togan
www.republicoftogo.com

Trinidad & Tobagan
www.ttparliament.org

Tunisian
www.ministeres.tn

Turkish
www.tbmm.gov.tr

Turkish Cypriot
www.cm.gov.nc.tr

Ukranian
www.rada.kiev.ua

United Arab Emirates
www.uae.gov.ae

Uruguayan
www.parlamento.gub.uy

USA – CIA
www.cia.gov

USA – Congress
www.congress.org

USA – FBI
www.fbi.gov

USA – House of Representatives
www.house.gov

USA – Republican National Committee
www.rnc.org

USA – Senate
www.senate.gov

USA – Supreme Court
www.uscourts.gov

USA – White House
www.whitehouse.gov

Uzbekistani
www.gov.uz

Vatican
www.vatican.va

Venezuelan
www.venezuela.gov.ve

Yemenite
www.yemeninfo.gov.ye

Yugoslavian
www.gov.yu

Zambian
www.statehouse.gov.zm

international organisations

Amnesty International
www.amnesty.org

Arctic Council
www.arctic-council.org

Commonwealth
www.thecommonwealth.org

Council of Europe
www.coe.fr

European Central Bank
www.ecb.int

European Commission
www.europa.eu.int

European Court of Justice
www.curia.eu.int/en

European Investment Bank
www.eib.org

European Monetary Union
www.europeanmovement.ie/emu.htm

European Parliament
www.europarl.eu.int

European Trade Union Confederation
www.etuc.org

European Union
www.europa.eu.int

G8
www.g7.utoronto.ca

Institute of World Politics
www.iwp.edu

International Albert Schweitzer Foundation
www.schweitzer.org

International Atomic Agency
www.icao.int

International Crisis Group
www.intl-crisis-group.org

International Maritime Organisation
www.imo.org

International Monetary Fund
www.imf.org

International Red Cross
www.icrc.org

NATO
www.nato.int

Organisation for Economic Co-operation &
Development (OECD)
www.oecd.org

Organisation of Petroleum Exporting
Countries (OPEC)
www.opec.org

Smithsonian Institution
www.si.edu

UNESCO
www.unesco.org

UNICEF (United Nations Children's Fund)
www.unicef.org

United Nations
www.un.org

World Bank
www.worldbank.org

World Health Organisation
www.who.int

World Meteorological Organisation
www.wmo.ch

World Trade Organisation
www.wto.org

law

Advisory, Conciliation & Arbitration Service
www.acas.org.uk

Bar Council
www.barcouncil.org.uk

Civil Justice Council
www.open.gov.uk/civjustice

Court Service of England & Wales
www.courtservice.gov.uk

Criminal Cases Review Commission
www.ccrc.gov.uk

Criminal Justice System
www.criminal-justice-system.gov.uk

Crown Prosecution Service
www.cps.gov.uk

Employment Appeal Tribunal
www.employmentappeals.gov.uk

European Court of Human Rights
www.echr.coe.int

European Court of Justice
http://curia.eu.int/en/index.htm

HM Land Registry
www.landreg.com

International Court of Justice
www.icj-cij.org

Law Society of England & Wales
www.lawsoc.org.uk

Law Society of Scotland
www.lawscot.org.uk

Legal Aid
www.legal-aid.gov.uk

Lord Chancellor's Department
www.open.gov.uk/lcd

Magistrates' Association
www.magistrates-association.org.uk

Official Solicitor's Department
www.offsol.demon.co.uk

Scottish Courts Service
www.scotcourts.gov.uk

Serious Fraud Office
www.sfo.gov.uk

Society for Computers & Law
www.scl.org

Youth Justice Board
www.youth-justice-board.gov.uk

legal institutions abroad

Argentina
www.pjn.gov.ar/corte/corte.htm

Australia
www.fedcourt.gov.au

Austria
www.ris.bka.gv.at

Brazil
www.stf.gov.br

Canada
www.scc-csc.gc.ca

Finland
www.kko.fi

France
www.courdecassation.fr

Germany
www.kanzlei.de

Iceland
www.haestirettur.is

India
www.supremecourtofindia.com

Indonesia
www.mari.go.id

Ireland
www.courts.ie

Israel
www.court.gov.il

Japan
www.courts.go.jp

Malaysia
www.mahkamah.gov.my

Mexico
www.supremecourt.nm.org

Netherlands
www.rechtspraak.nl

New Zealand
www.courts.govt.nz

Pakistan
www.supremecourt.gov.pk

Peru
www.pj.gob.pe

Poland
www.sn.pl

Portugal
www.cidadevirtual.pt/stj

Singapore
www.supcourt.gov.sg

South Africa
www.law.wits.ac.za

Sweden
www.notisum.se/rnp/domar/hd.htm

Switzerland
www.bger.ch

Thailand
www.judiciary.go.th

USA
www.uscourts.gov

Uganda
www.judicature.go.ug/supreme.html

monarchy

European

Belgium
http://belgium.fgov.be/monarchie/en_index.htm

Liechtenstein
www.news.li/fam/fam.htm

Monaco
www.monaco.mc/monaco

Netherlands
www.koninklijkhuis.nl

Sweden
www.royalcourt.se/eng/index.html

Yugoslavia
www.royalfamily.org

General

Crown Estate
www.crownestate.co.uk

Golden Jubilee
www.goldenjubilee.gov.uk

Middle & Far East

Brunei
www.bruneisultan.com

Jordan
www.kinghussein.gov.jo/rfamily_left.html

Morocco
www.mincom.gov.ma

Thailand
www.escati.com/king_of_thailand.htm

Royal Family

Diana, Princess of Wales (Obituary)
www.royal.gov.uk/start.htm

HM Queen Elizabeth
www.royal.gov.uk/family/hmqueen

HM Queen Elizabeth, Queen Mother
www.royal.gov.uk/family/mother

HRH Duke of York
www.royal.gov.uk/family/york

HRH Earl of Wessex
www.royal.gov.uk/family/edward

HRH Prince of Wales
www.princeofwales.gov.uk

HRH Prince Philip, Duke of Edinburgh
www.royal.gov.uk/family/philip

HRH Princess Alexandra
www.royal.gov.uk/family/alex.htm

HRH Princess Margaret
www.royal.gov.uk/family/margaret.htm

HRH Princess Royal
www.royal.gov.uk/family/royal

TRH Duke & Duchess of Kent
www.royal.gov.uk/family/kent1.htm

TRH Princess Alice, Duchess of Gloucester
& the Duke & Duchess of Gloucester
www.royal.gov.uk/family/gloucs.htm

Royal Palaces

Balmoral
www.royal.gov.uk/palaces/balmoral.htm

Buckingham Palace
www.royal.gov.uk/palaces/bp.htm

Frogmore House
www.royal.gov.uk/palaces/frogmore.htm

Holyroodhouse
www.royal.gov.uk/palaces/holyrood.htm

Kensington Palace
www.royal.gov.uk/palaces/kengsingt.htm

Sandringham House
www.royal.gov.uk/palaces/sandring.htm

St James's Palace
www.royal.gov.uk/palaces/stjamess

Windsor Castle
www.royal.gov.uk/palaces/windsor.htm

overseas territories & crown dependencies

Falklands Islands Government
www.falklands.gov.fk

Isle of Man Government
www.gov.im

political parties

British

Communist Party
www.cpgb.org.uk

Conservative Party
www.conservatives.com

Democratic Unionist Party, Northern
Ireland
www.dup.org.uk

Green Party, England & Wales
www.greenparty.org.uk

Green Party, Scotland
www.scottishgreens.org.uk

Green Party, Wales
www.walesgreenparty.org.uk

Labour Party
www.labour.org.uk

Liberal Democratic Party
www.libdems.org.uk

Natural Law Party
www.natural-law-party.org.uk

Plaid Cymru, Wales
www.plaidcymru.org

Progrssive Unionist Party
www.pup-ni.org.uk

Scottish Liberal Democratic Party
www.scotlibdems.org.uk

Scottish Nationalist Party
www.snp.org.uk

Sinn Fein, Northern Ireland
www.sinnfein.ie

Social & Democratic Labour Party,
Northern Ireland
www.sdlp.ie

Socialist Party
www.socialistparty.org.uk

Ulster Democratic Party
www.dup.org.uk

Ulster Unionist Party
www.uup.org

Foreign

African National Congress, South Africa
www.anc.org.za

Christian Democratic Party
www.cda.nl

Christian Democratic Party, Netherlands
www.cda.nl

Communist Party, USA
www.hartford-hwp.com/cp-usa

Democratic Party, Australia
www.democrats.org.au

Democratic Party, USA
www.democrats.org

International Socialist Organisation
www.internationalsocialist.org

Labour Party, Australia
www.alp.org.au

Labour Party, New Zealand
www.labour.org.nz

Labour Party, Norway
www.dna.no

Liberal Democratic Party, Japan
www.jimin.or.jp/jimin/english

Liberal Party, Australia
www.liberal.org.au

Liberal Party, Canada
www.liberal.ca

National Party, New Zealand
www.national.org.nz

Nationalist Party, Vietnam
www.vietquoc.com

People's Party, Pakistan
www.ppp.org.pk

Reform Party
www.reformparty.org

Republican Movement, Australia
www.republic.org.au

Republican Party, Ireland
www.fiannafail.ie

Republican Party, USA
www.rnc.org

Social Democratic Party, Germany
www.spd.de/english

United Democratic Front, Nigeria
www.udfn.com

post offices

Consignia
www.consignia.com

Guernsey
www.guernseypost.com

Ireland
www.anpost.ie

Isle of Man
www.gov.im/postoffice

Jersey
www.jerseypost.com

Post Office
www.postoffice.co.uk

Post Office Counters
www.postoffice-counters.co.uk

Royal Mail
www.royalmail.co.uk

research councils

Biotechnology & Biological Sciences
www.bbsrc.ac.uk

Council for the Central Laboratory
www.cclrc.ac.uk

Economic & Social
www.esrc.ac.uk

Engineering & Physical Sciences
www.epsrc.ac.uk

Medical
www.mrc.ac.uk

Natural Environment
www.nerc.ac.uk

Particle Physics & Astronomy
www.pparc.ac.uk

uk government

Government agencies

Advisory, Conciliation & Arbitration Service
www.acas.org.uk

Air Accident Investigation Branch
www.open.gov.uk/aaib

Arts Council
www.artscouncil.org.uk

Audit Commission
www.audit-commission.gov.uk

Benefits Agency
www.dss.gov.uk/ba

British Council
www.britcoun.org

British Railways Board
www.brb.gov.uk

British Trade International
www.brittrade.com

British Waterways
www.british-waterways.org

Central Computer & Telecommunications
Agency (CCTA)
www.ccta.gov.uk

Central Office of Information
www.coi.gov.uk

Centre for Policy Studies
www.cps.org.uk

Charity Commission
www.charity-commission.gov.uk

Child Support Agency
www.dss.gov.uk/csa

Citizens' Charter
www.open.gov.uk/charter

Commission for Architecture & the Built
Environment (CABE)
www.cabe.org.uk

Commission for Racial Equality
www.cre.gov.uk

Commonwealth War Graves Commission
www.cwgc.org

Communicable Disease Surveillance
Centre
www.open.gov.uk/cdsc

Companies House
www.companieshouse.gov.uk

Contributions Agency
www.dss.gov.uk/ca

Crafts Council
www.craftscouncil.org.uk

Crown Prosecution Service (CPS)
www.cps.gov.uk

Data Protection Register
www.dpr.gov.uk

Design Council
www.design-council.org.uk

Driver & Vehicle Licensing Agency (DVLA)
www.open.gov.uk/dvla

Driving Standards Agency (DSA)
www.dsa.gov.uk

Employment Service
www.employmentservice.gov.uk

Equal Opportunities Commission
www.eoc.org.uk

Equality Commission for Northern Ireland
www.equalityni.org

Forestry Commission of Great Britain
www.forestry.gov.uk

Government Communications
Headquarters (GCHQ)
www.gchq.gov.uk

Government Information Service
www.open.gov.uk

Health & Safety Executive
www.hse.gov.uk

Highways Agency
www.highways.gov.uk

HM Customs & Excise
www.hmce.gov.uk

HM Land Registry
www.landreg.gov.uk

HM Prison Service
www.open.gov.uk/prison/prisonhm

HM Stationery Office
www.hmso.gov.uk

HM Treasury Euro Site
www.euro.gov.uk

Housing Corporation
www.housingcorp.gov.uk

Inland Revenue
www.inlandrevenue.gov.uk

Insolvency Service
www.insolvency.gov.uk

Institute for Fiscal Studies
www.ifs.org.uk

Law Commission
www.open.gov.uk/lawcomm

Local Government Association
www.lga.gov.uk

Medical Devices Agency
www.medical-devices.gov.uk

Medicines Control Agency
www.open.gov.uk/mca

MI5
www.mi5.gov.uk

Museums & Galleries Commission
www.cornucopia.org.uk

National Association of Citizens Advice
Bureaux
www.nacab.org.uk

National Audit Office
www.nao.gov.uk

National Criminal Intelligence Service
www.ncis.co.uk

National Grid for Learning
www.ngfl.gov.uk

National Health Service
www.nhs.uk

National Institute for Social Work
www.nisw.org.uk

National Playing Fields Association
www.npfa.co.uk

National Rivers Authority
www.highway57.co.uk

New Deal
www.newdeal.gov.uk

Occupational Pensions Regulatory
Authority
www.opra.gov.uk

Office of Technology
www.dti.gov.uk/ost

Official Publications
www.ukop.co.uk

Ordnance Survey
www.ordsvy.gov.uk

Parliamentary Monitoring & Information
Service
www.pamis.gov.uk

Passport Agency
www.ukpa.gov.uk

Planning Inspectorate
www.open.gov.uk/pi/pihome

Port of London Authority
www.portoflondon.co.uk

Post Office
www.postoffice.co.uk

Public Record Office
www.pro.gov.uk

Regional Arts Boards of England
www.arts.org.uk

Royal Mint
www.royalmint.com

Stationery Office
www.tsonline.co.uk

Teacher Training Agency
www.teach-tta.gov.uk

Trade UK
www.tradeuk.com

Trading Standards Central
www.tradingstandards.gov.uk

Traffic Committee for London
www.tcfl.gov.uk

Transport for London
www.transportforlondon.gov.uk

United Kingdom Hydrographic Office
www.hydro.gov.uk

Vehicle Inspectorate
www.via.gov.uk

Wales Information Society
www.wis.org.uk

Women's National Commission
www.thewnc.org.uk

Government Departments

Cabinet Office
www.cabinet-office.gov.uk

Crown Estates
www.crownestate.co.uk

Culture, Media & Sport
www.culture.gov.uk

Department of Education for Northern
Ireland
www.deni.gov.uk

Department of the Environment for
Northern Ireland
www.doeni.gov.uk

Education & Skills
www.dfes.gov.uk

Environment, Transport & the Regions
www.detr.gov.uk

Foreign & Commonwealth Office
www.fco.gov.uk

Health
www.doh.gov.uk

HM Treasury
www.hm-treasury.gov.uk

Home Office
www.homeoffice.gov.uk

International Development
www.dfid.gov.uk

Lord Chancellor's Department
www.open.gov.uk/lcd

Ministry of Agriculture, Fisheries & Food
www.open.gov.uk/maff

Ministry of Defence
www.mod.uk

National Heritage
www.heritage.gov.uk

Northern Ireland Office
www.nio.gov.uk

Social Security
www.dss.gov.uk

Trade & Industry
www.dti.gov.uk

Local Government

Aberdeen
www.aberdeencity.gov.uk

Aberdeenshire
www.aberdeenshire.gov.uk

Adur
www.adur.co.uk

Alnwick
www.alnwick.gov.uk

Amber Valley
www.ambervalley.gov.uk

Anglesey
www.anglesey.gov.uk

Angus
www.angus.gov.uk

Antrim
www.antrim.gov.uk

Ards
www.ards-council.gov.uk

Argyll & Bute
www.argyll-bute.gov.uk

Armagh
www.armagh.gov.uk

Arun
www.arun.gov.uk

Ashfield
www.ashfield.gov.uk

Ashford
www.ashford.gov.uk

Aylesbury
www.aylesburyvaledc.gov.uk

Babergh
www.babergh-south-suffolk.gov.uk

Ballymoney
www.ballymoney.gov.uk

Banbridge
www.banbridge.com

Banbury
www.banburytown.co.uk

Barking & Dagenham
www.barking-dagenham.gov.uk

Barnet
www.barnet.gov.uk

Barnsley
www.barnsley.gov.uk

Barrow-in-Furness
www.barrowbc.gov.uk

Basildon
www.basildon.gov.uk

Basingstoke
www.basingstoke.gov.uk

Bassetlaw
www.bassetlaw.gov.uk

Bath
www.bathnes.gov.uk

Bedford
www.bedford.gov.uk

Bedfordshire
www.bcclgis.gov.uk

Belfast
www.belfastcity.gov.uk

Berwick-upon-Tweed
www.berwick-upon-tweed.gov.uk

Bexley
www.bexley.gov.uk

Birmingham
www.birmingham.gov.uk

Blaby
www.blaby.gov.uk

Blackburn
www.blackburn.gov.uk

Blackpool
www.blackpool.gov.uk

Blyth Valley
www.blythvalley.gov.uk

Bolsover
www.bolsover.gov.uk

Bolton
www.bolton.gov.uk

Boston
www.boston.gov.uk

Bournemouth
www.bournemouth.gov.uk

Bracknell Forest
www.bracknell-forest.gov.uk

Bradford
www.bradford.gov.uk

Braintree
www.braintree.gov.uk

Breckland
www.breckland.gov.uk

Brent
www.brent.gov.uk

Brentwood
www.brentwood-council.gov.uk

Bridgend
www.bridgend.gov.uk

Brighton & Hove
www.brighton-hove.gov.uk

Bristol
www.bristol-city.gov.uk

Broadland
www.broadland.gov.uk

Bromley
www.bromley.gov.uk

Bromsgrove
www.bromsgrove.gov.uk

Broxbourne
www.broxbourne.gov.uk

Broxtowe
www.broxtowe.gov.uk

Buckinghamshire
www.buckscc.gov.uk

Burnley
www.burnley.gov.uk

Bury
www.bury.gov.uk

Caerphilly
www.caerphilly.gov.uk

Calderdale
www.calderdale.gov.uk

Cambridge
www.cambridge.gov.uk

Cambridgeshire
www.camcnty.gov.uk

Camden
www.camden.gov.uk

Cannock
www.cannockchasedc.gov.uk

Canterbury
www.canterbury.gov.uk

Caradon
www.caradon.gov.uk

Cardiff
www.cardiff.gov.uk

Carlisle
www.carlisle-city.gov.uk

Carmarthenshire
www.carmarthenshire.gov.uk

Carrick
www.carrick.gov.uk

Carrickfergus
www.carrickfergus.org

Castle Morpeth
www.castlemorpeth.gov.uk

Castlereagh
www.castlereagh.gov.uk

Ceredigion
www.ceredigion.gov.uk

Chard
www.chard.gov.uk

Charnwood
www.charnwoodbc.gov.uk

Chelmsford
www.chelmsfordbc.gov.uk

Cheltenham
www.cheltenham.gov.uk

Cherwell
www.cherwell-dc.gov.uk

Cheshire
www.cheshire.gov.uk

Chester
www.chestercc.gov.uk

Chester le Street
www.chester-le-street.gov.uk

Chesterfield
www.chesterfieldbc.gov.uk

Chichester
www.chichester.gov.uk

Chiltern
www.chiltern.gov.uk

Christchurch
www.christchurch.gov.uk

Colchester
www.colchester.gov.uk

Coleraine
www.colerainebc.gov.uk

Congleton
www.congleton.gov.uk

Conwy
www.conwy.gov.uk

Cookstown
www.cookstown.gov.uk

Copeland
www.copelandbc.gov.uk

Cornwall
www.cornwall.gov.uk

Corporation of London
www.cityoflondon.gov.uk

Cotswold
www.cotswold.gov.uk

Coventry
www.coventry.gov.uk

Craigavon
www.craigavon.gov.uk

Craven
www.cravendc.demon.co.uk

Crawley
www.crawley.gov.uk

Crewe & Nantwich
www.crewe-nantwich.gov.uk

Croydon
www.croydon.gov.uk

Cumbria
www.cumbria.gov.uk

Dacorum
www.dacorum.gov.uk

Darlington
www.darlington.gov.uk

Daventry
www.daventrydc.gov.uk

Denbighshire
www.denbighshire.gov.uk

Derby
www.derby.gov.uk

Derbyshire
www.derbyshire.gov.uk

Derbyshire Dales
www.derbyshiredales.gov.uk

Derry
www.derrycity.gov.uk

Derwentside
www.derwentside.gov.uk

Devizes
www.devizes-tc.gov.uk

Devon
www.devon-cc.gov.uk

Doncaster
www.doncaster.gov.uk

Dorset
www.dorset-cc.gov.uk

Dover
www.dover.gov.uk

Down
www.downdc.gov.uk

Dudley
www.dudley.gov.uk

Dumfries & Galloway
www.dumgal.gov.uk

Dunbarton
www.west-dunbarton.gov.uk

Dundee
www.dundeecity.gov.uk

Dungannon
www.dungannonrugby.co.uk

Durham (City)
www.durhamcity.gov.uk

Durham (County)
www.durham.gov.uk

Ealing
www.ealing.gov.uk

Easington
www.easington.gov.uk

East Ayrshire
www.east-ayrshire.gov.uk

East Devon
www.east-devon.gov.uk

East Dorset
www.eastdorset.gov.uk

East Dunbartonshire
www.e-dunbarton.org.uk

East Grinstead
www.egnet.co.uk/egtc

East Hampshire
www.easthants.gov.uk

East Hertfordshire
www.eastherts.gov.uk

East Lindsey
www.e-lindsey.gov.uk

East Lothian
www.eastlothian.gov.uk

East Northamptonshire
www.east-northamptonshire.gov.uk

East Renfrewshire
www.eastrenfrewshire.gov.uk

East Riding
www.east-riding-of-yorkshire.gov.uk

East Sussex
www.eastsussexcc.gov.uk

Eastbourne
www.eastbourne.gov.uk

Eastleigh
www.eastleigh.gov.uk

Eden
www.eden.gov.uk

Edinburgh
www.edinburgh.gov.uk

Elmbridge
www.elmbridge.gov.uk

Enfield
www.enfield.gov.uk

Epping Forest
www.eppingforestdc.gov.uk

Epsom
www.epsom-ewell.gov.uk

Erewash
www.erewash.gov.uk

Essex
www.essexcc.gov.uk

Exeter
www.exeter.gov.uk

Falkirk
www.falkirk.gov.uk

Fareham
www.fareham.gov.uk

Felixstowe
www.felixstowe.gov.uk

Fenland
www.fenland.gov.uk

Fermanagh
www.fermanagh.gov.uk

Fife
www.fife.gov.uk

Flintshire
www.flintshire.gov.uk

Forest Heath
www.forest-heath.gov.uk

Forest of Dean
www.fdean.gov.uk

Fylde
www.fylde.gov.uk

Gateshead
www.gateshead.gov.uk

Gedling
www.gedling.gov.uk

Glasgow
www.glasgow.gov.uk

Gloucester
www.glos-city.gov.uk

Gloucestershire
www.gloscc.gov.uk

Godalming
www.godalming-tc.gov.uk

Gosport
www.gosport.gov.uk

Gravesham
www.gravesham.gov.uk

Great Yarmouth
www.great-yarmouth.gov.uk

Greater London Assembly & Mayor of
London
www.london.gov.uk

Greenwich
www.greenwich.gov.uk

Guildford
www.guildford.gov.uk

Gwynedd
www.gwynedd.gov.uk

Hackney
www.hackney.gov.uk

Halton
www.halton-borough.gov.uk

Hambleton
www.hambleton.gov.uk

Hammersmith & Fulham
www.lbhf.gov.uk

Hampshire
www.hants.gov.uk

Harborough
www.harborough.gov.uk

Haringey
www.haringey.gov.uk

Harlow
www.harlow.gov.uk

Harrogate
www.harrogate.gov.uk

Harrow
www.harrow.gov.uk

Hart
www.hart.gov.uk

Hartlepool
www.hartlepool.gov.uk

Hastings
www.hastings.gov.uk

Havant
www.havant.gov.uk

Havering
www.havering.gov.uk

Herefordshire
www.herefordshire.gov.uk

Hertfordshire
www.hertsdirect.org

Hertsmere
www.hertsmere.gov.uk

High Peak
www.highpeak.gov.uk

Highland
www.highland.gov.uk

Hillingdon
www.hillingdon.gov.uk

Horsham
www.horsham.gov.uk

Hounslow
www.hounslow.gov.uk

Huntingdonshire
www.huntsdc.gov.uk

Hyndburn
www.hyndburnbc.gov.uk

Ipswich
www.ipswich.gov.uk

Isle of Wight
www.isleofwight.gov.uk

Islington
www.islington.gov.uk

Jersey
www.jersey.gov.uk

Kennet
www.kennet.gov.uk

Kensington & Chelsea
www.rbkc.gov.uk

Kent
www.kent.gov.uk

Kerrier
www.kerrier.gov.uk

Kettering
www.kettering.gov.uk

Kings Lynn & West Norfolk
www.west-norfolk.gov.uk

Kingston-upon-Hull
www.hullcc.gov.uk

Kingston-upon-Thames
www.kingston.gov.uk

Kirklees
www.kirkleesmc.gov.uk

Knowsley
www.knowsley.gov.uk

Lambeth
www.lambeth.gov.uk

Lancashire
www.lancashire.gov.uk

Lancaster
www.lancaster.gov.uk

Larne
www.larne.com

Leeds
www.leeds.gov.uk

Leicester
www.leicester.gov.uk

Leicestershire
www.leics.gov.uk

Lewes
www.lewes.gov.uk

Lewisham
www.lewisham.gov.uk

Lichfield
www.lichfield.gov.uk

Lincoln
www.lincoln-info.org.uk

Lincolnshire
www.lincolnshire.gov.uk

Lisburn
www.lisburn.gov.uk

Liverpool
www.liverpool.gov.uk

Londonderry
www.derrycity.gov.uk

Luton
www.luton.gov.uk

Macclesfield
www.macclesfield.gov.uk

Maidstone
www.digitalmaidstone.co.uk

Maldon
www.maldon.gov.uk

Manchester
www.manchester.gov.uk

Mansfield
www.mansfield.gov.uk

Medway
www.medway.gov.uk

Melton
www.melton.gov.uk

Mendip
www.mendip.gov.uk

Merthyr Tydfil
www.merthyr.gov.uk

Merton
www.merton.gov.uk

Mid Bedfordshire
www.midbeds.gov.uk

Mid Devon
www.middevon.gov.uk

Middlesbrough
www.middlesbrough.gov.uk

Midlothian
www.midlothian.gov.uk

Mid-Sussex
www.midsussex.gov.uk

Milton Keynes
www.miltonkeynes.gov.uk

Mole Valley
www.mole-valley.gov.uk

Monmouthshire
www.monmouthshire.gov.uk

Moray
www.moray.gov.uk

Moyle
www.moyle-council.org

Neath Port Talbot
www.neath-porttalbot.gov.uk

New Forest
www.nfdc.gov.uk

Newark
www.newark.gov.uk

Newcastle-under-Lyme
www.newcastle-staffs.gov.uk

Newcastle-upon-Tyne
www.newcastle.gov.uk

Newham
www.newham.gov.uk

Newport
www.newport.gov.uk

Newton Abbot
www.newtonabbot-tc.gov.uk

Norfolk
www.norfolk.gov.uk

North Ayrshire
www.north-ayrshire.gov.uk

North Cornwall
www.ncdc.gov.uk

North Devon
www.northdevon.gov.uk

North Dorset
www.north-dorset.gov.uk

North Down
www.north-down.gov.uk

North East Derbyshire
www.ne-derbyshire.gov.uk

North East Lincolnshire
www.lgce.gov.uk

North Hertfordshire
www.nhdc.gov.uk

North Kesteven
www.n-kesteven.gov.uk

North Lanarkshire
www.northlan.gov.uk

North Lincolnshire
www.northlincs.gov.uk

North Norfolk
www.north-norfolk.gov.uk

North Shropshire
www.nshropshire.gov.uk

North Somerset
www.n-somerset.gov.uk

North Tyneside
www.northtyneside.gov.uk

North Warwickshire
www.warwickshire.gov.uk

North West Leicestershire
www.nwleicsdc.gov.uk

North Wiltshire
www.northwilts.gov.uk

North Yorkshire
www.northyorks.gov.uk

Northampton
www.northampton.gov.uk

Northamptonshire
www.northamptonshire.gov.uk

Northumberland
www.northumberland.gov.uk

Norwich
www.norwich.gov.uk

Nottingham
www.nottinghamcity.gov.uk

Nottinghamshire
www.nottscc.gov.uk

Oadby
www.oadby-wigston.gov.uk

Oldham
www.oldham.gov.uk

Oxford
www.oxford.gov.uk

Oxfordshire
www.oxfordshire.gov.uk

Pembrokeshire
www.pembrokeshire.gov.uk

Pendle
www.pendle.gov.uk

Penwith
www.penwith.gov.uk

Perth & Kinross
www.pkc.gov.uk

Peterborough
www.peterborough.gov.uk

Plymouth
www.plymouth.gov.uk

Poole
www.poole.gov.uk

Portsmouth
www.portsmouthcc.gov.uk

Powys
www.powys.gov.uk

Preston
www.preston.gov.uk

Reading
www.reading.gov.uk

Redbridge
www.redbridge.gov.uk

Redcar & Cleveland
www.redcar-cleveland.gov.uk

Redditch
www.redditchbc.gov.uk

Reigate & Banstead
www.reigate-banstead.gov.uk

Renfrewshire
www.renfrewshire.gov.uk

Rhondda-Cynon-Taff
www.rhondda-cynon-taff.gov.uk

Ribble Valley
www.ribblevalley.gov.uk

Richmond
www.richmond.gov.uk

Richmondshire
www.richmondshire.gov.uk

Rochdale
www.rochdale.gov.uk

Rochford
www.rochford.gov.uk

Rother
www.rother.gov.uk

Rotherham
www.rotherham.gov.uk

Runnymede
www.runnymede.gov.uk

Rushcliffe
www.rushcliffe.gov.uk

Rutland
www.rutland.gov.uk

Ryedale
www.ryedale.gov.uk

Salford
www.salford.gov.uk

Salisbury
www.salisbury.gov.uk

Sandwell
www.sandwellmbc.broadnet.co.uk

Scarborough
www.scarborough.gov.uk

Scottish Borders
www.scotborders.gov.uk

Sedgefield
www.sedgefield.gov.uk

Sefton
www.sefton.gov.uk

Selby
www.selby.gov.uk

Sevenoaks
www.sevenoaks.gov.uk

Sheffield
www.sheffield.gov.uk

Shepway
www.shepway.gov.uk

Shetland Islands
www.shetland.gov.uk

Shrewsbury & Atcham
www.shrewsbury-atcham.gov.uk

Shropshire
www.shropshire-cc.gov.uk

Slough
www.slough.gov.uk

Solihull
www.solihull.gov.uk

Somerset
www.somerset.gov.uk

South Ayrshire
www.south-ayrshire.gov.uk

South Bedfordshire
www.southbeds.gov.uk

South Buckinghamshire
www.southbucks.gov.uk

South Cambridgeshire
www.scambs.gov.uk

South Gloucestershire
www.southglos.gov.uk

South Hams
www.south-hams-dc.gov.uk

South Kesteven
www.skdc.com

South Lanarkshire
www.southlanarkshire.gov.uk

South Norfolk
www.south-norfolk.gov.uk

South Oxfordshire
www.southoxon.gov.uk

South Ribble
www.south-ribblebc.gov.uk

South Shropshire
www.southshropshire.gov.uk

South Somerset
www.southsomerset.gov.uk

South Staffordshire
www.sstaffs.gov.uk

South Tyneside
www.s-tyneside-mbc.gov.uk

Southampton
www.southampton.gov.uk

Southend-on-Sea
www.southend.gov.uk

Southwark
www.southwark.gov.uk

Spelthorne
www.spelthorne.gov.uk

St Albans
www.stalbans.gov.uk

St Edmundsbury
www.stedmundsbury.gov.uk

St Helens
www.sthelens.gov.uk

Stafford
www.staffordbc.gov.uk

Staffordshire
www.staffordshire.gov.uk

Stevenage
www.stevenage.gov.uk

Stockport
www.stockportmbc.gov.uk

Stockton-on-Tees
www.stockton-bc.gov.uk

Stoke-on-Trent
www.stoke.gov.uk

Strabane
www.strabanedc.org.uk

Stroud
www.stroud.gov.uk

Suffolk
www.suffolkcc.gov.uk

Sunderland
www.sunderland.gov.uk

Surrey
www.surreycc.gov.uk

Surrey Heath
www.surreyheath.gov.uk

Sutton
www.sutton.gov.uk

Swale
www.swale.gov.uk

Swansea
www.swansea.gov.uk

Swindon
www.swindon.gov.uk

Tameside
www.tameside.gov.uk

Tamworth
www.tamworth.gov.uk

Tandridge
www.tandridgedc.gov.uk

Taunton Deane
www.tauntondeane.gov.uk

Teesdale
www.teesdale.gov.uk

Teignbridge
www.teignbridge.gov.uk

Telford & Wrekin
www.telford.gov.uk

Tendring
www.tendringdc.gov.uk

Test Valley
www.testvalley.gov.uk

Thanet
www.thanet.gov.uk

Three Rivers
www.3rivers.gov.uk

Thurrock
www.thurrock.gov.uk

Tonbridge & Malling
www.tmbc.gov.uk

Torbay
www.torbay.gov.uk

Torfaen
www.torfaen.gov.uk

Torridge
www.torridge.gov.uk

Tower Hamlets
www.towerhamlets.gov.uk

Trafford
www.trafford.gov.uk

Tunbridge Wells
www.tunbridgewells.gov.uk

Tynedale
www.tynedale.gov.uk

Uttlesford
www.uttlesford.gov.uk

Vale of Glamorgan
www.valeofglamorgan.gov.uk

Vale Royal
www.valeroyal.gov.uk

Wakefield
www.wakefield.gov.uk

Walsall
www.walsall.gov.uk

Waltham Forest
www.lbwf.gov.uk

Wandsworth
www.wandsworth.gov.uk

Wansbeck
www.wansbeck.gov.uk

Warrington
www.warrington.gov.uk

Warwickshire
www.warwickshire.gov.uk

Watford
www.watford.gov.uk

Waveney
www.waveney.gov.uk

Waverley
www.waverley.gov.uk

Wealden
www.wealden.gov.uk

Wear Valley
www.wearvalley.gov.uk

Wellingborough
www.wellingborough.gov.uk

Welwyn Hatfield
www.welhat.gov.uk

West Berkshire
www.westberks.gov.uk

West Devon
www.wdbc.gov.uk

West Dorset
www.westdorset-dc.gov.uk

West Dunbartonshire
www.west-dunbarton.gov.uk

West Oxfordshire
www.westoxon.gov.uk

West Sussex
www.westsussex.gov.uk

West Wiltshire
www.west-wiltshire-dc.gov.uk

Western Isles
www.w-isles.gov.uk

Westminster
www.westminster.gov.uk

Weymouth & Portland
www.weymouth.gov.uk

Wigan
www.wiganmbc.gov.uk

Wiltshire
www.wiltshire.gov.uk

Winchester
www.winchester.gov.uk

Windsor & Maidenhead
www.rbwm.gov.uk

Wirral
www.wirral.gov.uk

Woking
www.woking.gov.uk

Wokingham
www.wokingham.gov.uk

Wolverhampton
www.wolverhampton.gov.uk

Worcester
www.cityofworcester.gov.uk

Worcestershire
www.worcestershire.gov.uk

Worthing
www.worthing.gov.uk

Wrexham
www.wrexham.gov.uk

Wychavon
www.wychavon.gov.uk

Wycombe
www.wycombe.gov.uk

Wyre
www.wyrebc.gov.uk

Wyre Forest
www.wyreforestdc.gov.uk

York
www.york.gov.uk

Parliament

General Election
www.election.co.uk

House of Commons
www.parliament.uk/commons/hsecom.htm

House of Lords
www.parliament.uk/about_lords/about_lords.cfm

Isle of Man
www.tynwald.isle-of-man.org.im

Northern Ireland Assembly
www.ni-assembly.gov.uk

Parliament
www.parliament.uk

Scottish Parliament
www.scotland.gov.uk

States of Jersey
www.jersey.gov.uk

Welsh Assembly
www.wales.gov.uk

ancillary services

Anthony Nolan Bone Marrow Trust
www.anthonynolan.com

British Blood Transfusion Service
www.bbts.org.uk

British Organ Donor Society
www.argonet.co.uk/body

British Safety Council
www.britishsafetycouncil.co.uk

British Toxicology Society
www.bts.org

Health Education Authority
www.hea.org.uk

Health Education Board of Scotland
www.hebs.scot.nhs.uk

Institute of Food Science & Technology
www.ifst.org

Medical Advisory Services for Travellers Abroad (MASTA)
www.masta.org

National Blood Service
www.bloodnet.nbs.nhs.uk

Nursing Homes Registry
www.nursinghomes.co.uk

Royal Institute of Public Health & Hygiene
www.riphh.org.uk

Scottish National Blood Transfusion Service
www.show.scot.nhs.uk/snbts

Welsh Blood Transfusion Service
www.welsh-blood.org.uk

animal health

National Office of Animal Health
www.noah.co.uk

Veterinary Medicines Directorate
www.open.gov.uk/vmd

complementary

Academy of Curative Hypnotherapists
www.ach.co.uk

Alexander Technique
www.ati.com

Bach Flower Essences
www.nelsonbach.com/bachessences

British Homeopathic Association
www.trusthomeopathy.org

British Homoeopathic Library
www.hom-inform.org

British School of Homeopathy
www.homoeopathy.co.uk

College of Integrated Chinese Medicine
www.cicm.org.uk

Foundation for Traditional Chinese Medicine
www.ftcm.org.uk

Homeopathic Medical Association
www.homoeopathy.org

Homeopathy Today
www.homeopathstoday.com

National Institute of Ayurvedic Medicine
www.niam.com

Osteopathic Information Service
www.osteopathy.org.uk

Register of Chinese Herbal Medicine
www.rchm.co.uk

Trepanation Trust
www.trepanation.com

dentistry

Adentec & UK Smiles
www.uksmiles.co.uk

BriteSmile UK
www.britesmile.co.uk

British Dental Association
www.bda-dentistry.org.uk

British Dental Health Foundation
www.dentalhealth.org.uk

British Dental Journal
www.bdj.co.uk

Confederation of Dental Employers
www.derweb.co.uk/code

Davis Schottlander & Davis
www.schottlander.co.uk

Denplan
www.denplan.co.uk

Dental Anxiety & Phobia Association
www.healthyteeth.com

Dentistry Websites
www.dentistrywebsites.co.uk

Dentsure Ltd
www.dentsure.co.uk

General Dental Council
www.gdc-uk.org

Kent Express
www.kentexpress.co.uk

National Dentists Directory
www.nationaldirectories.net

National Radiological Protection Board
www.nrpb.org.uk

Ortho-Care (UK) Ltd
www.orthocare.co.uk

PE Robinsons
www.dentalcare.free-online.co.uk

The Amsel & Wilkins Dental Partnership
www.dentalheaven.co.uk

The Dental Directory
www.dental-directory.co.uk

government agencies

Institute of Health Service Management
www.ihm.org.uk

Medical Devices Agency
www.medical-devices.gov.uk

Medicines Control Agency
www.open.gov.uk/mca

NHS Confederation
www.nhsconfed.org

health authorities

Avon
www.avonhealth.org.uk

Barking & Havering
www.bhha.org.uk

Birmingham
www.birminghamhealth.org.uk

Bradford
www.bradford-ha.nhs.uk

Buckinghamshire
www.buckshealth.com

Cambridge & Huntingdon
www.cambs-ha.nhs.uk

Cornwall & Isles of Scilly
www.cornwallhealth.org.uk

Croydon
www.croydon.nhs.uk

Doncaster
www.donhlth.demon.co.uk

Dorset
www.dorset.swest.nhs.uk

Ealing, Hammersmith & Hounslow
www.ehh-ha.nthames.nhs.uk

East Kent
www.ekent-ha.sthames.nhs.uk

East London & The City
www.elcha.co.uk

East Surrey
www.surreyweb.org.uk/esha

East Sussex, Brighton & Hove
www.esbhhealth.ndirect.co.uk

Enfield & Haringey
www.enhar-ha.org.uk

Gloucestershire
www.glos-health.org.uk

Grampian
www.show.scot.nhs.uk/ghb

Gwent
www.gwent-ha.wales.nhs.uk

Hillingdon
www.hhcu.demon.co.uk

Isle of Wight
www.iwha.swest.nhs.uk

Kingston & Richmond
www.krha.demon.co.uk

Lambeth, Southwark & Lewisham
www.lslha.nhs.uk

Leeds
www.leedshealth.org.uk

Leicestershire
www.leicester-ha.trent.nhs.uk

Liverpool
www.liverpool-ha.org.uk

Lothian
www.lothianhealth.scot.nhs.uk

Manchester
www.manchesterhealth.co.uk

Morecambe Bay
www.morecmbe-ha.nwest.nhs.uk

North & Mid Hampshire
www.hants.gov.uk/nmhha

North Cumbria
www.ncumbria.demon.co.uk

North Essex
www.ne-ha.nthames.nhs.uk

North Wales
www.nwales-ha.wales.nhs.uk

North West Lancashire
www.nwlha.fsnet.co.uk

North Yorkshire
www.nyha.org.uk

Northamptonshire
www.northants-ha.anglox.nhs.uk

Portsmouth & South East Hampshire
www.iowpseha.hants.org.uk

Redbridge & Waltham Forest
www.rwf-ha.nthames.nhs.uk

Shropshire
www.shropshireha.wmids.nhs.uk

South & West Devon
www.sw-devon-ha.swest.nhs.uk

South Cheshire
www.scheshire-ha.nwest.nhs.uk

South Essex
www.nthames-health.tpmde.ac.uk

South Humber
www.southhumberha.org.uk

Southampton & South West Hampshire
www.sswhha.org.uk

St. Helens & Knowsley
www.warrington-health.co.uk

Wakefield
www.wakefieldhealth.nhs.uk

Warwickshire
www.warwick-ha.wmids.nhs.uk

West Hertfordshire
www.wherts-ha.nthames.nhs.uk

West Surrey
www.surreyweb.org.uk/wsha

West Sussex
www.westsussexhealth.org.uk

Worcestershire
www.phwhc.demon.co.uk

hospitals, clinics & nhs trusts

Complementary

Hale Clinic
www.haleclinic.com

NHS

Aberdeen Royal Infirmary
www.abdn-royal.com

Addenbrooke's
www.addenbrookes.org.uk

Alder Hey Children's
www.alderhey.org.uk

Belfast Royal Hospitals
www.royalhospitals.ac.uk

Blackpool Victoria
www.blackpool-victoria.nhs.uk

Bolton Hospice
www.boltonhospice.org

City Hospital, Birmingham
www.cityhospital.org.uk

Dartford & Gravesham
www.general-hospital.co.uk

Elizabeth Garrett Anderson
www.uclh.org/services/ega/index.shtml

Great Ormond Street
www.ich.ucl.ac.uk

Heatherwood & Wexham Park Hospitals
www.hwph-tr.fsnet.co.uk

Hope University
www.hop.man.ac.uk

Hospital for Tropical Diseases
www.uclh.org/htd

Leicester Royal Infirmary
www.nhsetrent.gov.uk/trent/trusts/glenhnt.ht

Lifespan Healthcare
www.lifespan.org.uk

Middlesbrough General
www.southtees.northy.nhs.uk

Middlesex
www.uclh.org/about/middx.shtml

Moorfields
www.moorfields.org.uk

National Hospital for Neurology & Neurosurgery
www.uclh.org/about/nhnn.shtml

North Riding Infirmary
www.southtees.northy.nhs.uk

North Staffs Acute Psychiatric Unit
www.general-hospital.co.uk

Poole
www.poolehos.org

Queen Victoria, East Grinstead
www.queenvic.demon.co.uk

Royal Bournemouth
www.rbh.org.uk

Royal Brompton
www.rbh.nthames.nhs.uk

Royal Buckinghamshire
www.royalbucks.co.uk

Royal Infirmary of Edinburgh
www.show.scot.nhs.uk/rie

Royal Marsden
www.royalmarsden.org

Royal United Hospital Bath
www.ruh-bath.swest.nhs.uk

South Cleveland
www.southtees.northy.nhs.uk

Southampton University Hospitals
www.suht.nhs.uk

Southern General, Glasgow
www.general-hospital.co.uk

St Andrews Group
www.stah.org

Swindon
www.general-hospital.co.uk

UCL Hospitals
www.uclh.org

University College
www.ucl.ac.uk

University Hospital of Wales
www.cardiffandvale.wales.nhs.uk

Private

Betty Ford Center
www.bettyfordcenter.org

BMI Healthcare
www.bmihealth.co.uk

Bristol Cancer Help Centre
www.bristolcancerhelp.org

BUPA
www.bupa.co.uk

Cromwell
www.cromwell-hospital.co.uk

London Clinic
www.lonclin.co.uk

London Radiosurgical Centre
www.radiosurgery.co.uk

Marie Stopes Health Clinics
www.mariestopes.org.uk

Mayo Clinic
www.mayoclinic.com

Nuffield
www.nuffieldhospitals.org.uk

Partnerships in Care
www.partnershipsincare.co.uk

PPP Healthcare
www.ppphealthcare.co.uk

PPP/Columbia
www.columbiahealthcare.co.uk

Priory
www.priory-hospital.co.uk.

St Martin's Healthcare
www.stmartins-healthcare.co.uk

Surgicare
www.surgicare.co.uk

journals, magazines & websites

Association for Post Natal Illness
www.apni.org

BBC Online
www.bbc.co.uk/health/womens

Breakthrough Breast Cancer
www.breakthrough.org.uk

Breast Cancer Care
www.breastcancercare.org.uk

British Journal of General Practice
www.rcgp.org.uk/rcgp/journal/index.asp

British Journal of Healthcare Management
www.bjhcm.com

British Journal of Nursing
www.britishjournalofnursing.com

British Medical Journal
www.bmj.com

British Nursing News
www.nurse-nurses-nursing.com/bnno.html

European Institute of Women's Health
www.eurohealth.ie

Family Planning Association
www.fpa.org.uk

Health Centre
www.healthcentre.org.uk

Health Service Journal
www.hsj.co.uk

Hospital Doctor
www.health-news.co.uk

Journal of Community Nursing
www.jcn.co.uk

Journal of Neonatal Nursing
www.bizjet.com/jnn

Journal of Public Health Medicine
www.oup.co.uk/pubmed

Journal of the British Acupuncture Council
www.acupuncture.org.uk/ejom

Lancet
www.thelancet.com

Marie Stopes International
www.mariestopes.org.uk

Medic Direct
www.medicdirect.co.uk

Medisearch
www.medisearch.co.uk

National Association of Premenstrual Syndrome
www.pms.org.uk

Net Doctor
www.netdoctor.co.uk

NHS Digest
www.nhsdigest.org

NHS Direct
www.nhsdirect.nhs.uk

Nursing Standard
www.nursing-standard.co.uk

Nursing Times
www.nursingtimes.net

Portfolio of British Nursing
www.british-nursing.com

Positive Health
www.positivehealth.com

Practice Nursing
www.practicenursing.com

Reuters Health Information
www.reutershealth.com

The London Woman's Clinic
www.lwclinic.co.uk

The Miscarriage Association
www.the-ma.org.uk

Woman's Health Information
www.womens-health.co.uk

Woman's Nutritional Advisory Service
www.wnas.org.uk

Women's Health Websites
www.womenshealthwebsites.co.uk

medicine & surgery

British Fertility Society
www.britishfertilitysociety.org.uk

British Geriatrics Society
www.bgs.org.uk

Centre for Medicines Research
www.cmr.org

Institute of Child Health
www.ich.bpmf.ac.uk

Medical Research Council
www.mrc.ac.uk

National Sports Medicine Institute
www.nsmi.org.uk

NHS Primary Care Group Alliance
www.nhsalliance.org

Royal Society of Medicine
www.roysocmed.ac.uk

nursing & midwifery

Active Birth Centre
www.activebirthcentre.com

Association for Improvements in Maternity Services
www.aims.org.uk

Association of Radical Midwives
www.radmid.demon.co.uk

British Nursing Agencies
www.nursing-list.com

Florence Nightingale Foundation
www.florence-nightingale-foundation.org.uk

Foundation of Nursing Studies
www.fons.org

NHS Nursing
www.doh.gov.uk/nursing.htm

pharmacy

Association of the British Pharmaceutical Industry
www.abpi.org.uk

British Pharmacopoeia
www.pharmacopoeia.org.uk

European Agency for the Evaluation of Medicinal products
www.eudra.org

Medicines Control Agency
www.open.gov.uk/mca/mcahome.htm

National Pharmaceutical Association
http://npa.co.uk

Pharmaceutical Journal
www.pharmj.com

Royal Pharmaceutical Society of Great Britain
www.rpsgb.org.uk

United Kingdom Medicines Information Pharmacists Group
www.druginfozone.org

psychiatry & psychology

Institute of Mental Health
www.imhl.com

Institute of Psychiatry
www.iop.kcl.ac.uk

Institute of Psychotherapy & Social Studies
www.ipss.dircon.co.uk

Manchester Institute of Psychotherapy
www.mcpt.co.uk

United Kingdom Council for Psychotherapy
www.psychotherapy.org.uk

research

AIDS Education & Research Trust
www.avert.org

Canadian Neuro-Optic Research Institute
www.cnri.edu

RAFT Institute
www.raft.ac.uk

Society for the Study of Fertility
www.ssf.org.uk

Tenovus
www.tenovus.org.uk

vision

Medical

CIBAVision
www.cibavision.co.uk

College of Optometrists
www.college-optometrists.org

Opticians

20/20 Opticians
www.20-20.co.uk

Boots Opticians
www.bootsopticians.co.uk

David Clulow
www.davidclulow.com

Dolland & Aitchison
www.danda.co.uk

Eye Clinic
www.eye-clinic.co.uk

Optika
www.davidclulow.com

Specsavers
www.specsavers.com

Vision Express
www.visionexpress.co.uk

Zeiss Direct
www.zeiss-direct.co.uk

Help!

ambulance services •

breakdown services •

charities & helplines •

consumer problems •

fire & rescue services •

funeral services •

police •

pressure groups •

watchdogs & ombudsmen •

147

advice online

Channel 4 Health Advice
www.channel4.com/illness

Channel 4 Stress Advice Service
www.channel4.com/stress

ambulance services

Avon
www.avonambulance.org.uk

Berkshire
www.rbat.com

County Air Ambulance
www.ambulance.co.uk

Essex
www.essexambhq.demon.co.uk

Lancashire
www.lancashireambulance.com

London
www.lond-amb.sthames.nhs.uk

Northern Ireland
www.niamb.co.uk

St John's Ambulance Brigade
www.london.sja.org.uk

Sussex
www.sussamb.co.uk

breakdown services

AA
www.theaa.co.uk

Green Flag
www.greenflag.co.uk

RAC
www.rac.co.uk

charities & helplines

Animals

Animal Aid
www.animalaid.org.uk

Animal Health Trust
www.aht.org.uk

Animal Rescue
www.animalrescue.org.uk

AnimalKind
www.netcomuk.co.uk/~jcox

Battersea Dogs Home
www.dogshome.org

Blue Cross
www.thebluecross.org.uk

Brigitte Bardot Foundation
www.fondationbrigittebardot.fr/uk

British Horse Society
www.bhs.org.uk

Care for the Wild International
www.careforthewild.org.uk

Cat Care Society
www.catcaresociety.org

Cats Protection League
www.cats.org.uk

Dian Fossey Gorilla Fund
www.gorillas.org

Donkey Sanctuary
www.thedonkeysanctuary.org.uk

International Animal Rescue
www.iar.org.uk

International Fund for Animal Welfare
www.ifaw.org

International League for the Protection of Horses
www.ilph.org

National Anti-Vivisection Society
www.navs.org

National Canine Defence League
www.ncdl.org.uk

National Pet Week
www.nationalpetweek.org.uk

National Welfare Trust
www.nawt.org.uk

PDSA
www.pdsa.org.uk

People for the Ethical Treatment of Animals
www.peta.org

Royal Society for the Prevention of Cruelty to Animals (RSPCA)
www.rspca.org.uk

Royal Society for the Protection of Birds (RSPB)
www.rspb.org.uk

Save the Rhino
www.savetherhino.co.uk

VIVA
www.viva.org.uk

World Society for the Protection of Animals
www.wspa.org.uk

Children

Action on Child Exploitation
www.ache.org.uk

Adoption Information Line
www.adoption.org.uk

Association for Families who have Adopted from Abroad
www.afaa.mcmail.com

Barnado's
www.barnardos.org.uk

British Agencies for Adoption & Fostering
www.baaf.org.uk

Child Accident Prevention Trust
www.capt.org.uk

Childline
www.childline.org.uk

Children in Need
www.bbc.co.uk/cin

Children With AIDS
www.cwac.org

Children's Legal Centre
www2.essex.ac.uk/clc

Children's Society
www.the-childrens-society.org.uk

Contact a Family
www.cafamily.org.uk

Country Holidays for Inner City Kids
www.chicks.org.uk

Families Need Fathers
www.fnf.org.uk

First Cheque 2000
www.firstcheque2000.org.uk

Fostering Information Line
www.fostering.org.uk

Gingerbread
www.gingerbread.org.uk

Kidscape
www.kidscape.org.uk

Missing Kids
www.missingkids.co.uk

National Society for the Prevention of
Cruelty to Children (NSPCC)
www.nspcc.org.uk

NCH
www.nch.org

NCH Action for Children
www.nchafc.org.uk

PACT
www.pactcharity.co.uk

Save the Children
www.savethechildren.org.uk

SPARKS (Sport Aiding Medical Research
for Kids)
www.sparks.org.uk

Variety Club of Great Britain
www.varietyclub.org.uk

Community

Action for Victims of Medical Accidents
www.avma.org.uk

Addaction
www.addaction.org.uk

Age Concern
www.ace.org.uk

British Association for Counselling
www.counselling.co.uk

Business in the Community
www.bitc.org.uk

Centrepoint
www.centrepoint.org.uk

Church Action on Poverty
www.church-poverty.org.uk

Citizens Advice Bureau
www.adviceguide.org.uk

Comic Relief
www.comicrelief.org.uk

Crisis
www.crisis.org.uk

Diana Memorial Fund
www.theworkcontinues.org

Drugscope
www.drugscope.org.uk

English-Speaking Union
www.esu.org

Free2give
www.free2give.co.uk

Gamblers Anonymous
www.gamblersanonymous.org.uk

Give As You Earn
www.giveasyouearn.org

Help the Aged
www.helptheaged.org.uk

Leonard Cheshire Foundation
www.lcf.org.uk

Neighbourhood Watch
www.neighbourhoodwatch.net

Nuffield Trust
www.nuffieldtrust.org.uk

Prince's Trust
www.princes-trust.org.uk

RAF Benevolent Fund
www.raf-benfund.org.uk

Relate
www.relate.org.uk

Rotary International
www.rotary.org

Royal Air Forces Association
www.rafa.org.uk

Royal National Institute for Deaf People
(RNID)
www.rnid.org.uk

Royal National Institute for the Blind (RNIB)
www.rnib.org.uk

Royal National Lifeboat Institution (RNLI)
www.rnli.org.uk

Royal Society for the Prevention of
Accidents (ROSPA)
www.rospa.co.uk

Salvation Army
www.salvationarmy.org.uk

Samaritans
www.samaritans.org.uk

Shelter
www.shelter.org.uk

UK Firework Safety
www.fireworksafety.co.uk

UK National Workplace Bullying Advice
Line
www.successunlimited.co.uk

Unison
www.unison.org.uk

VSO
www.vso.org.uk

Women's Aid
www.womensaid.org.uk

Education

Book Trust
www.booktrust.org.uk

British Association for Open Learning
www.baol.co.uk

British Dyslexia Association
www.bda-dyslexia.org.uk

Careers Services National Association
www.careers-uk.com

Raleigh International
www.raleigh.org.uk

Scottish Book Trust
www.scottishbooktrust.com

Health

Ability
www.ability.org.uk

Action against Breast Cancer
www.aabc.org.uk

Action for Cancer Trust
www.actionforcancertrust.com

Action for ME
www.afme.org.uk

Action for Tinnitus Research
www.tinnitus-research.org

Action on Pre-eclampsia
www.apec.org.uk

Alcohol Concern
www.alcoholconcern.org.uk

Alcoholics Anonymous
www.alcoholics-anonymous.org

Alzheimer's Association
www.alz.org

Alzheimer's Disease Society
www.alzheimers.org.uk

Anorexia & Bulimia Care
www.anorexiabulimiacare.co.uk

Anthony Nolan Bone Marrow Trust
www.anthonynolan.com

Arachnoiditis Trust
www.merseyworld.com/arach

Arthritis Care
www.arthritiscare.org.uk

Association for International Cancer
Research
www.aicr.org.uk

Association for Post-Natal Illness
www.apni.org

Association for Spina Bifida &
Hydrocephalus
www.asbah.demon.co.uk

Bliss
www.bliss.org.uk

Bob Champion Cancer Trust
www.bobchampion.org.uk

Breast Cancer Campaign
www.bcc-uk.org

Breast Cancer Care
www.breastcancercare.org.uk

Breast Clinic
www.thebreastclinic.com

British Acoustic Neuroma Association
www.ukan.co.uk/bana

British Cardiac Society
www.cardiac.org.uk

British Deaf Association
www.bda.org.uk

British Diabetic Association
www.diabetes.org.uk

British Epilepsy Association
www.epilepsy.org.uk

British Heart Foundation
www.bhf.org.uk

British Lung Foundation
www.lunguk.org.uk

Cancer Bacup
www.cancerbacup.org.uk

Cancer Research Fund
www.crc.org.uk

Centre for Recovery from Drug & Alcohol
Abuse
www.recovery.org.uk

Council for Disabled Children
www.ncb.org.uk/cdc.htm

Crusaid
www.crusaid.org.uk

Cystic Fibrosis Trust
www.cftrust.org.uk

Depression Alliance
www.gn.apc.org/da

Diabetes Insight
www.diabetic.org.uk

Disability Now
www.disabilitynow.org.uk

Disabled Living Foundation
www.atlas.co.uk/dlf

Down's Syndrome Association
www.dsa-uk.com

Ectopic Pregnancy Trust
www.ectopic.org.uk

Enuresis Resource & Information Centre
www.eric.org.uk

Epilepsy Research Foundation
www.erf.org.uk

Glaucoma Research Foundation
www.glaucoma.org

Haemophilia Society
www.haemophilia.org.uk

Institute for the Study of Drug Dependency
www.isdd.co.uk

Jewish Deaf Association
www.jda.dircon.co.uk

King's Fund
www.kingsfund.org.uk

Leukaemia Research Fund
www.leukaemia-research.org.uk

Macmillan Relief
www.macmillan.org.uk

Marie Curie Cancer Care
www.mariecurie.org.uk

Mencap
www.mencap.org.uk

Meningitis Research Foundation
www.meningitis.org.uk

Mind
www.mind.org.uk

Miscarriage Association
www.the-ma.org.uk

Multiple Births Foundation
www.multiplebirths.org.uk

Multiple Sclerosis Society
www.mssociety.org.uk

Muscular Dystrophy Campaign
www.muscular-dystrophy.org

NACC
www.nacc.org.uk

National AIDS Trust
www.nat.org.uk

National Association for Premenstrual Syndrome
www.pms.org.uk

National Asthma Campaign
www.asthma.org.uk

National Autistic Society
www.oneworld.org/autism_uk

National Back Pain Association
www.backpain.org

National Deaf Children's Society
www.ndcs.org.uk

National Endometriosis Society
www.endo.org.uk

National Fertility Association
www.issue.co.uk

National Kidney Research Fund
www.nkrf.org.uk

National Meningitis Trust
www.meningitis-trust.org.uk

National Osteoporosis Society
www.nos.org.uk

Northern Ireland Chest, Heart & Stroke Association
www.nichsa.com

Nuffield Trust
www.nuffieldtrust.org

Paralinks
www.paralinks.net

Parkinson's Disease Society
www.parkinsons.org.uk

Primary Immunodeficiency Association
www.pia.org.uk

Prostate Cancer
www.prostate-cancer.org.uk

Reach
www.reach.org.uk

Roy Castle Lung Cancer Foundation
www.roycastle.org

Scope
www.scope.org.uk

SIDS – Foundation
www.sids.org.uk

Stillbirth & Neonatal Death Society
www.uk-sands.org

Stroke Association
www.stroke.org.uk

Terence Higgins Trust
www.tht.org.uk

World Federation of Haemophilia
www.wfh.org

Third World

Action Aid
www.oneworld.org/actionaid

Amnesty International
www.amnesty.org

Care International
www.care.org

Christian Aid
www.christian-aid.org.uk

Oxfam
www.oxfam.org.uk

Red Cross
www.redcross.org.uk

Sight Savers
www.sightsavers.org

consumer problems

British Standards Institute
www.bsi-global.com

British Weights & Measures Association
www.footrule.org

Consumer Gateway (DTI)
www.consumer.gov.uk

Consumers in Europe Group
www.nfcg.org.uk/ConsNews/cn189p00.htm

European Agency of Information on
Consumer Affairs
www.euro-conso.org

Local Authorities Co-ordinating Body on
Food & Trading Standards
www.lacots.org.uk

National Association of Citizens Advice
Bureaux
www.nacab.org.uk

South East Trading Standards
www.setsa.org.uk

Trading Standards Office
www.tradingstandards.gov.uk

Watchdog
www.bbc.co.uk/watchdog

fire & rescue services

British Fire Service
www.fire.org.uk

Cheshire Fire Brigade
www.cheshirefire.co.uk

Cleveland Fire Brigade
www.clevelandfire.gov.uk

Coastguard Agency
www.mcga.gov.uk

Gosport & Fareham Inshore Rescue
Service
www.hants.gov.uk/gafirs

International Rescue Corps
www.ps2.com/irc

London Fire & Civil Defence Authority
www.london-fire.gov.uk

London Fire Brigade
www.london-fire.gov.uk

Maritime & Coastguard Agency
www.mcagency.org.uk

Mountain Rescue
www.mra.org

Royal Naval Lifeboat Institution
www.rnli.org.uk

Tyne & Wear Metropolitan Fire Brigade
www.twfire.org

West Sussex Fire Brigade
www.wsfb.co.uk

funeral services

British Institute of Embalmers
www.bioe.co.uk

British Institute of Funeral Directors
www.bifd.org.uk

Co-operative Funeral Services
www.funeral-services.co.uk

Funeral Ombudsman
www.funeralombudsman.org.uk

Funeral Services Journal
www.fsj.co.uk

Funeral Standards Council
www.funeral-standards-council.co.uk

National Association of Funeral Directors
www.nafd.org.uk

National Association of Memorial Masons
www.namm.org.uk

National Association of Pre-paid Funeral
Plans
www.napfp.org.uk

National Society of Allied & Independent
Funeral Directors
www.saif.org.uk

police
Constabularies

Avon & Somerset
www.avonandsomerset.police.uk

Bedfordshire
www.bedfordshire.police.uk

British Transport Police
www.btp.police.uk

Cheshire
www.cheshire.police.uk

City of London
www.cityoflondon.police.uk

Cleveland
www.cleveland.police.uk

Derbyshire
www.derbyshire.police.uk

Devon & Cornwall
www.devon-cornwall.police.uk

Durham
www.durham.police.uk

Dyfed & Powys
www.dyfed-powys.police.uk

Essex
www.essex.police.uk

Gloucestershire
www.gloucestershire.police.uk

Greater Manchester
www.gmp.police.uk

Hampshire
www.hampshire.police.uk

Hertfordshire
www.herts.police.uk

Humberside
www.humberside.police.uk

Lancashire
www.lancashire.police.uk

Leicestershire
www.leics.police.uk

Lincolnshire
www.lincs.police.uk

Merseyside
www.merseyside.police.uk

Metropolitan Police
www.met.police.uk

North Wales
www.north-wales.police.uk

Northamptonshire
www.norpol.com

Northumbria
www.northumbria.police.uk

Royal Ulster Constabulary
www.nics.gov.uk/ruc

Scotland
www.scottish.police.uk

South Wales
www.south-wales.police.uk

South Yorkshire
www.southyorks.police.uk

Staffordshire
www.staffordshire.police.uk

Suffolk
www.suffolk.police.uk

Surrey
www.surrey.police.uk

Sussex
www.sussex.police.uk

Thames Valley
www.thamesvalley.police.uk

West Mercia
www.westmercia.police.uk

West Midlands
www.west-midlands.police.uk

West Yorkshire
www.westyorkshire.police.uk

Wiltshire
www.wiltshire.police.uk

Organisation

Europol
www.europol.eu.int

Interpol
www.interpol.com

National Crime Squad
www.nationalcrimesquad.police.uk

Recruitment
www.policecouldyou.co.uk

UK National Criminal Intelligence Service
www.ncis.co.uk

pressure groups

Adam Smith Institute
www.adamsmith.org.uk

Amnesty International
www.amnesty.org.uk

ASH
www.ash.org.uk

Association of British Counties
www.abcounties.co.uk

Association of British Drivers
www.abd.org.uk

Bruges Group
www.eurocritic.demon.co.uk

Campaign Against Censorship of the Internet in Britain
www.liberty.org.uk/cacib

Campaign for an English Parliament
www.englishpm.demon.co.uk

Campaign for Dark Skies
www.dark-skies.freeserve.co.uk

Campaign for Freedom of Information
www.cfoi.org.uk

Campaign for Nuclear Disarmament (CND)
www.cnduk.org

Campaign for Press & Broadcasting
Freedom
www.architechs.com/CPBF

Campaign for Safe E-Commerce
Legislation
www.stand.org.uk

Campaign for Shooting
www.foresight-cfs.org.uk

Charter 88
www.charter88.org.uk

Country Landowners Association
www.cla.org.uk

Crimestoppers
www.crimestoppers-uk.org

Democracy Movement
www.democracy-movement.org.uk

Electoral Reform Society
www.electoral-reform.org.uk

Fabian Society
www.fabian-society.org.uk

Fairtrade
www.fairtrade.org.uk

Fireworks Safety Campaign
www.fireworksafety.co.uk

Free Britain
www.freebritain.co.uk

Friends of the Earth
www.foe.co.uk

Going for Green
www.gfg.iclnet.co.uk

Greenpeace International
www.greenpeace.org

League Against Cruel Sports
www.league.uk.com

Liberty (National Council for Civil Liberties)
www.liberty-human-rights.org.uk

London Cycling Campaign
www.lcc.org.uk

National Pure Water Association
www.npwa.freeserve.co.uk

Portman Group
www.portman-group.org.uk

Privacy International
www.privacyinternational.org

Searchlight
www.s-light.demon.co.uk

Silent Majority

www.silentmajority.co.uk

UK Independence Party
www.independenceuk.org.uk

Vegetarian Society
www.vegsoc.org

Voluntary Euthanasia Society
www.ves.org.uk

watchdogs & ombudsmen

Adjudicator's Office
www.open.gov.uk/adjoff/index.htm

Adult Learning Inspectorate
www.ali.gov.uk

Advertising Standards Authority
www.asa.org.uk

Banking Ombudsman
www.financial-ombudsman.org.uk

Broadcasting Standards Commission
www.bsc.org.uk

Chartered Institute of Environmental Health
www.cieh.org.uk

Data Protection Registrar
www.dataprotection.gov.uk

Drinking Water Inspectorate
www.dwi.detr.gov.uk

Estate Agents Ombudsman
www.oea.co.uk

Funeral Ombudsman
www.funeralombudsman.org.uk

Health Service Ombudsman
www.ombudsman.org.uk

Independent Complaints Reviewer to HM
Land Registry
www.icrev.demon.co.uk/icrbook.htm

Independent Television Commission
www.itc.org.uk

Insurance Ombudsman Bureau
www.theiob.org.uk

Internet Watch Foundation
www.iwf.org.uk

Local Government Ombudsman
www.open.gov.uk/lgo

Northern Ireland Ombudsman
www.ni-ombudsman.org.uk

OFFER (Electricity)
www.open.gov.uk/offer

Office for the Supervision of Solicitors
www.lawsociety.org.uk

Office of Fair Trading
www.oft.gov.uk

OFGAS (Gas)
www.ofgas.gov.uk

OFSTED (Teaching)
www.open.gov.uk/ofsted

OFTEL (Telecommunications)
www.oftel.org

OFWAT (Water)
www.open.gov.uk/ofwat

Parliamentary Ombudsman
www.ombudsman.org.uk

Press Complaints Commission
www.pcc.org.uk

Radio Authority
www.radioauthority.org.uk

Rail Users' Consultative Committees
www.rail-reg.gov.uk/rucc

Scottish Legal Services Ombudsman
www.slso.org.uk

arts & crafts

Bead Society of Great Britain
www.beadsociety.freeserve.co.uk

Calligraphy & Lettering Arts Society
www.clas.co.uk

Ceramics Monthly
www.ceramicsmonthly.org

Classic Stitch
www.classicstitch.co.uk

Colour Craft Needlework
www.colour-craft.com

County Needlecraft
www.countyneedlecraft.com

Craft UK
www.craft-fair.co.uk

Crochet Design
www.crochet.co.uk

Daler Rowney
www.daler-rowney.com

Embroiderers' Guild
www.embroiderersguild.org.uk

Glass Art Society
www.glassart.org

Guild of Silk Painters
www.silkpainters-guild.co.uk

Husqvarna
www.husqvarnastudio.co.uk

Knitting Now
www.knittingnow.com

Knitting Today
www.knittingtoday.com

Lace Guild
www.laceguild.demon.co.uk

Lace Magazine
www.lacemagazine.com

Marquetry Society
www.marquetry.org

Quick & Easy Cross Stitch
www.futurenet.com/futureonline/magazines

Quilters' Guild of the British Isles
www.quiltersguild.org.uk

Quilting Directory
www.quiltingdirectory.co.uk

Rowan
www.rowanyarns.co.uk

Royal School of Needlework
www.royal-needlework.co.uk

Singer
www.singerco.com

Society of Scribes & Illuminators
www.calligraphy.org

Stoll UK
www.stolluk.co.uk

UK Cross Stitch Club
www.crossstitch.org

UK Stained Glass News
www.stainedglassnews.co.uk

Vogue Knitting
www.vogueknitting.com

astrology

Association of Professional Astrologers
www.professionalastrologers.org

Astrological Association of Great Britain
www.astrologer.com/aanet

British Astrological & Psychic Society
www.bapsoc.co.uk

Centre for Psychological Astrology
www.cpalondon.com

Jonathan Cainer
www.cainer.com

Metalog Directory of Astrologers
www.astrologer.com/metalog

Russell Grant
www.russellgrant.com

ballooning

Adventure Balloons
www.adventureballons.co.uk

British Association of Balloon Operators
www.babo.org.uk

British Balloon & Airship Club
www.bbac.org

Virgin Challenger
www.challenger.virgin.net

birds

African Bird Club
www.africanbirdclub.org

Association of Field Ornithologists
www.afonet.org

Birds of Britain
www.birdsofbritain.co.uk

Birdwatch Magazine
www.birdwatch.co.uk

British Falconers Club
www.britishfalconersclub.co.uk

British Homing World
www.pigeonracing.com

British Ornithologists' Union
www.bou.org.uk

British Trust for Ornithology
www.birdcare.com

Budgerigar Society
www.budgerigarsociety.com

Budgerigar World
www.tuxford.dabsol.co.uk

Falconry UK
www.falconryuk.co.uk

Game Conservancy Trust
www.game-conservancy.org.uk

National Birds of Prey Centre
www.nbpc.co.uk

National Flying Club
www.nationalflyingclub.co.uk

Oriental Bird Club
www.orientalbirdclub.org

Parrot Society UK
www.theparrotsocietyuk.org

Racing Pigeon Magazine
www.racingpigeon.co.uk

Rare Breeding Birds Panel
www.indaal.demon.co.uk/rbbp.html

Royal Pigeon Racing Association
www.rpra.org

UK Parrot Society
www.theparrotsocietyuk.org

boating

Association of Inland Navigation
Authorities
www.cam.net.uk/home/aina

Association of Waterways Cruising Clubs
www.penpont.demon.co.uk/awcchp.htm

Big Blue Boat Shows
www.bigblue.org.uk

British Waterways
www.britishwaterways.co.uk

Classic Motor Boat Association
www.cmba.classic-marine.co.uk

Inland Waterways Association
www.waterways.org.uk

National Association of Boat Owners
www.nabo.org.uk

Professional Boat Builder Magazine
www.proboat.com

Royal Institution of Naval Architects
www.naval-architects.org

UK Waterways Network
www.ukwaterways.net

bodybuilding

British Natural Bodybuilding Federation
www.bnbf.co.uk

English Federation of Body Builders
www.efbb-npc.co.uk

Flex Magazine
www.flexonline.com

International Federation of Body Builders
www.ifbb.com

Mens Fitness Magazine
www.mensfitness.com

Muscle & Fitness Magazine
www.muscle-fitness.com

National Amateur Body Builders
Association
www.nabbauk.co.uk

Sports Supplements
www.sports-supplements.co.uk

Weider Nutrition
www.weider.ca

bridge

American Contract Bridge League
www.acbl.org

Bridge Today
www.bridgetoday.com/bt

Bridge World
www.bridgeworld.com

Canadian Bridge Federation
www.cbf.ca

English Bridge Union
www.ebu.co.uk

Israeli Bridge Federation
http://tx.technion.ac.il/~herbst/ibf.html

Northern Ireland Bridge Union
www.nibu.co.uk

Scottish Bridge Union
www.sbu.dircon.co.uk

South African Bridge Federation
www.sabf.co.za

Welsh Bridge Union
www.wbu.org.uk

World Bridge Federation
www.bridge.gr

chess

British Chess Federation
www.bcf.ndirect.co.uk

British Chess Magazine
www.bcmchess.co.uk

Garry Kasparov
www.clubkasparov.ru

Internet Chess Club
www.chessclub.com

London Chess Centre
www.chess.co.uk

Scottish Chess Association
www.users.globalnet.co.uk/~sca

This Week in Chess
www.chess.co.uk

World Chess Federation
www.fide.com

collecting

Cards

Cartophilic Society of Great Britain
www.cardclubs.ndirect.co.uk

English Playing Card Society
www.epcs.mcmail.com

International Playing Card Society
www.pagat.com/ipcs

Trade Card Collector's Association
www.tradecardcollectors.com

Coins

British Association of Numismatic Societies
www.coinclubs.freeserve.co.uk

Coin Dealer Directory
www.numis.co.uk

Coin News
www.coin-news.com

Coins & Antiquities Magazine
www.coins-and-antiquities.co.uk

Royal Numismatic Society
www.users.dircon.co.uk/~rns/index.html

Spink & Son
www.spink-online.com

World of Money
www.thebritishmuseum.ac.uk/worldofmoney

Miscellaneous

Airfix Collectors Club
www.djairfix.freeserve.co.uk

Antiquarian Horological Society
www.ahsoc.demon.co.uk

Armourer Magazine
www.armourer.u-net.com

British Matchbox Label & Booklet Society
www.studenter.hb.se/~match/bml&bs

British Watch & Clock Collectors
Association
www.timecap.co.uk

UK Sucrologists Club
www.uksucrologistclub.org.uk

Stamps

Arthur Ryan & Co.
www.gbstamps.co.uk

Association of First Day Cover Collectors
www.gbfdc.co.uk

British Aerophilatelic Federation
www.btinternet.com/~baef

British Library
www.bl.uk

British Library Philatelic Collections
www.bl.uk/collections/philatelic/

Candish McCleevy
www.candlishmccleery.com

David Allen Philatelic Ltd
www.davidallen.co.uk

eBay
www.ebay.co.uk

GB Philatelic Society
www.gbps.org.uk

Hallmark Group
www.hallmark-group.co.uk

Ian Lasok-Smith
www.gbphilately.co.uk

International Direct Ltd
www.inter-direct.co.uk

Jersey Post
www.jerseypost.com

M Osbourne Covers
www.covers-stamps.com

National Postal Museum
www.plus44.com/london44/attractions/national_
postal.html

Peter Tarquin
www.pennyblackuk.com

Philaleaves Ltd
www.philaleaves.force9.co.uk

Philatelic Supplies
www.philatelicsupplies.co.uk

Post Office
www.postoffice.co.uk

Robin Hood Stamp Company
www.robinhood-stamp.co.uk

Royal Philatelic Society London
www.rpsl.org.uk

Stamp websites
www.stampwebsites.co.uk

Stanley Gibbons
www.stanleygibbons.co.uk

The Stampshows Website
www.stampshows.co.uk

UK Philatelic Museums & Libraries
www.gs.dial.pipex.com/museum3.htm

UK Stamp Fairs
www.stampdiary.com

V Roberts
www.postage.co.uk

West Philatelic Auctions
www.wessexphilatelic.com

cookery

Ballymaloe Cookery School
www.ballymaloe-cookery-school.ie

BBC Food & Drink
www.bbc.co.uk/foodanddrink

Cookery Websites
www.cookerywebsites.co.uk

Cooking with Rosie Cookery School
www.rosiedavies.co.uk

Cuisine Net
www.cuisinenet.co.uk

Delia Online
www.deliaonline.com

Five Star Catering
www.fivestarcatering.co.uk

Food of Course
www.foodofcourse.co.uk

Fresh Food Cookbook
www.freshfood.co.uk/cookbook

Gourmet World
www.gourmetworld.co.uk

Jamie Oliver (The Naked Chef)
www.jamieoliver.net

Learn at Leisure
www.learnatleisure.demon.co.uk

Leith's School of Food & Wine
www.leiths.com

Nigella Bites
www.channel4.com/nextstep/nigella

Recipe World
www.recipe-world.com

Royal Thai Cookery School
www.rtsca.com

Tante Marie Cookery School
www.tantemarie.co.uk

The Cooks Thesaurus
www.foodsubs.com

The Cordon Vert Cookery School
www.vegsoc.org/cordonvert

The Gables School of Cookery
www.thegablesschoolofcookery.com

The Seafood Cookery School
www.fishworks.co.uk

Veggie Heaven
www.veggieheaven.com

country pursuits

British Association of Shooting & Conservation
www.basc.org.uk

British Falconers Club
www.users.zetnet.co.uk/bfc

British Field Sports Society
www.bfss.org

CLA Game Fair
www.clagamefair.co.uk

Clay Pigeon Shooting Association
www.cpsa.co.uk

Countryside Alliance
www.countryside-alliance.org

Countrysports
www.countrysports.co.uk

Field Magazine
www.thefield.co.uk

National Association of Regional Game Councils
www.iol.ie/~nargc

National Association of Specialist Anglers
www.cygnet.co.uk/ukfw/nasa

Shooting Gazette
www.countrypursuits.co.uk

Sportsman's Association
www.sa-headquarters.freeserve.co.uk

Sportsman's Association (SAGBNI)
www.sportsmans-association.org

UK Practical Shooting Association
www.ukpsa.co.uk

Welsh Fishing & Trout Association
www.fishing-in-wales.com/wstaa

dancing

Ballroom Dancing Times
www.dancing-times.co.uk

Ceroc
www.ceroc.com

Ceroc Central
www.ceroccentral.com

Ceroc Scotland
www.cerocscotland.com

Country & Western Dancing in the UK
www.cw-dance.bristol-uk.com

DanceSport UK
www.dancesport.uk.com

Evenin' Star
www.eveninstar.co.uk

Imperial Society of Teachers of Dancing (ISTD)
www.istd.org.uk

International Dance Sport Federation
www.idsf.net

International Dance Teachers Association (IDTA)
www.idta.co.uk

Linedance
www.linedance.co.uk

Line Dance 4 All
www.linedance4all.com

Line Dancing
www.linedancing.org.uk

Line Dancing Websites
www.linedancingwebsites.co.uk

Millers Trading Post Ltd
www.flowermill.co.uk/westernwear

Moving Music
www.movingmusic.co.uk

fishing

Angling News
www.angling-news.co.uk

Bankside Fishing Tackle
www.banksidefishing.co.uk

Fishing UK
www.fishing.co.uk

Fishing World
www.fishing.org

Fly Dressers' Guild
www.the-fdg.org

Fly Fishing UK
www.flyfishuk.com

Gardner
www.gardnertackle.co.uk

Glasgow Angling Centre
www.fishingmegastore.com

Grayling Society
www.graylingsociety.org

Harrisons Rods
www.harrisonrods.co.uk

Maver
www.maver.co.uk

National Federation of Anglers
www.fire.org.uk/nfa

RMC Angling
www.rmcangling.co.uk

Salmon & Trout Association
www.salmon-trout.org

Scottish Anglers National Association (SANA)
www.sana.org.uk

Specialist Anglers Conservation Group
www.anglersnet.co.uk/sacg

UK Fly Fishing & Tyers Federation
www.fly-fisherman.org.uk

flying

Aeroclub
www.aeroclub.net

Airspace Magazine
www.raes.org.uk

British Aerobatics Association
www.aerobatics.org.uk

British Disabled Flying Club
www.fly.to/bdfc

British Gliding Association
www.gliding.co.uk

British Microlight Aircraft Association
www.avnet.co.uk/bmaa

Civil Aviation Authority
www.caa.co.uk

Denham Aerodrome
www.egld.com

Flyer
www.flyer.co.uk

Paraglider
www.poweredparaglider.com

Pilot Magazine
www.pilotweb.co.uk

Red Arrows
www.deltaweb.co.uk/reds

World Air Sports Federation
www.fai.org

football

Ian St John's Soccer Camps
www.soccercamps.co.uk

Sunday Football League Directory
www.sunday-football.co.uk

Umbro International Football Festival
www.worldwidesoccer.co.uk

gambling

Blue Sq
www.bluesq.com

British Casino Association
www.british-casinos.co.uk

City Index
www.cityindex.co.uk

Greyhound Racing Board
www.thedogs.co.uk

IG Index
www.igindex.co.uk

Jamba (Carlton TV)
www.jamba.co.uk

Ladbrokes
www.ladbrokes.co.uk

Littlewoods Pools
www.littlewoodspools.com

Mecca Bingo Online
www.meccabingo.com

National Lottery
www.national-lottery.co.uk

Rank Leisure
www.rank.com

Sporting Index
www.sportingindex.com

The Daily Draw
www.thedailydraw.com

Tote
www.tote.co.uk

UK Betting
www.ukbetting.com

Victor Chandler
www.victorchandler.com

William Hill
www.williamhill.co.uk

Zetters
www.zetters.co.uk

games

British Isles Backgammon Association
www.cottagewebs.co.uk/biba

Carta Mundi Cards
www.cartamundi.com

Loquax
www.loquax.co.uk

Monopoly
www.monopoly.com

Scrabble
www.scrabble.com

Trivial Pursuit
www.trivialpursuit.com

World Conker Championships
www.tom-and-ann.demon.co.uk/patch/conker.htm

gardening

Atco
www.atco.co.uk

Barnsdale Gardens (Geoff Hamilton)
www.barnsdalegardens.co.uk

BBC Ground Force
www.bbc.co.uk/groundforce

BBC Home Front in the Garden
www.bbc.co.uk/homefrontgarden

Birstall Garden Centre
www.birstall.co.uk

Black & Decker Online
www.blackanddecker.com

Chelsea Flower Show
www.rhs.org.uk/chelsea

Crocus
www.crocus.co.uk

Cyclamen Society
www.cyclamen.org

Florajac's
www.florajacs.co.uk

Flower & Plant Association
www.flowers.org.uk

Flymo
www.flymo.co.uk

Garden History Society
www.gardenhistorysociety.org

Gardeners' World
www.gardenersworld.beeb.com

Gardening 365
www.oxalis.co.uk

Hampton Court Palace Flower Show
www.rhs.org.uk/hamptoncourt

Hartland
www.hartland.co.uk

Hayter
www.hayter.co.uk

Herb Society
www.herbsociety.co.uk

Heritage Seed Library
www.hdra.org.uk

International Bulb Society
www.bulbsociety.com

Landscape Trust
www.landscape.co.uk

Levington
www.levington.co.uk

Miracle-Gro Online
www.miraclegro.com

National Garden Scheme
www.ngs.org.uk

National Herb Centre
www.herbcentre.co.uk

Permaculture Association
www.permaculture.co.uk

Qualcast
www.qualcast.co.uk

Royal Horticultural Society
www.rhs.org.uk

Royal Horticultural Society Shop
www.grogro.com

Royal National Rose Society
www.roses.co.uk

Secretts
www.secretts.co.uk

Spear & Jackson
www.spear-and-jackson.com

Van Tubergen
www.vantubergen.co.uk

genealogy

Ancestry Research
www.demon.co.uk/ancestors

British Heraldic Archive
www.kwtelecom.com/heraldry

Family Records Centre
www.pro.gov.uk/about/frc

Family Tree Magazine
www.family-tree.co.uk

Federation of Family History Societies
www.ffhs.org.uk

Gendex Genealogical Index
www.gendex.com

Genealogical Services Directory
www.genealogical.co.uk

General Register Office, Northern Ireland
www.nics.gov.uk/nisra/gro

General Register Office, Scotland
www.open.gov.uk/gros

GENUKI, UK & Ireland Geneology
www.genuki.org.uk

Institute of Heraldic & Genealogical Studies
www.ihgs.ac.uk

Irish Family History Foundation
www.mayo-ireland.ie/roots.htm

Mormons Family Search
www.familysearch.org

Public Record Office
www.pro.gov.uk

Scottish Genealogy Society
www.sol.co.uk/s/scotgensoc

Society of Genealogists
www.sog.org.uk

homebrew

Breworld
www.breworld.com

Craft Brewing Association
www.breworld.com/cba

EDME
www.edme.com

horse riding

Association of British Riding Schools
www.equiworld.net/abrs

British Driving Society
www.britishdrivingsociety.co.uk

British Endurance Riding Association
www.british-endurance.org.uk

British Equestrian Trade Association
www.beta-uk.org

British Horse Society
www.bhs.org.uk

Endurance Horse & Pony Society
www.ehps.org.uk

Pony Club
www.pony-club.org.uk

Scottish Equestrian Magazine
www.thescottishequestrian.co.uk

Side Saddle Association
www.equiworld.com/ssa

metal detecting

C Scope
www.cscope.co.uk

Detecnicks
www.detecnicks.co.uk

Federation of Independent Detectorists
www.detectorists.net

UK Detector Net
www.ukdetectornet.co.uk

miscellaneous clubs & associations

Association of Woodturners of Great Britain
www.woodturners.co.uk

British Matchbox Label & Booklet Society
www.studenter.hb.se/~match/bml&bs

British Model Flying Association
www.bmfa.org

British Youth Council
www.byc.org.uk

Country Gentleman's Association
www.thecga.co.uk

Elgar Society
www.elgar.org

English Pool Association
www.epa.org.uk

Gunpowder Plot Society
www.gunpowder-plot.org

Historical Model Railway Society
www.hmrs.org.uk

Hovercraft Club of Great Britain
www.hovercraft.org.uk

International Freemasonry
www.londonfreemasonry.com

Lighthouse Society of Great Britain
www.lsgb.co.uk

London Underground Railway Society
www.lurs.org.uk

Mensa
www.mensa.org

National Federation of Young Farmers
Clubs
www.nfyfc.org.uk

Paintball Zone
www.paintballzone.demon.co.uk

Radio Society of Great Britain
www.rsgb.org

Regent's Park Tennis & Golf
www.regentspark-golf.co.uk

Rotaract Club
www.rotaract.org.uk

Royal British Legion
www.britishlegion.org.uk

Tai Chi Union of Great Britain
www.eb61.dial.pipex.com

Tri-ang Model Railways
www.tri-ang.co.uk

United Kingdom Radio Society
www.ukrs.org

Women's Institute
www.nfwi.org.uk

Womens Royal Voluntary Service (WRVS)
www.wrvs.org.uk

YMCA
www.ymca.org.uk

Youth Clubs UK
www.youthclubs.org.uk

Youth Hostelling Association
www.yha.org.uk

models

Airfix
www.airfix.co.uk

Beatties
www.beatties.net

British Electric Flight Association
www.befa007.freeserve.co.uk

British Model Flying Association
www.bmfa.org

British Model Soldier Society
www.btinternet.com/~model.soldiers

Corgi
www.corgi.co.uk

Hannants
www.hannants.co.uk

Historical Model Railway Society
www.hmrs.org.uk

Hornby
www.hornby.co.uk

Model Yachting Association
www.ukmya.mcmail.com

Scalextric
www.scalextric.co.uk

Tri-ang Model Railways
www.tri-ang.co.uk

motor sports

Association of British Kart Clubs
www.karting.co.uk/ABkC

Association of Racing Kart Schools
www.arks.co.uk

British Superkart Association
www.superkart.mcmail.com

Challenge 2000
www.kartchallenge.com

Daytona
www.daytona.co.uk

Motor Sports Association
www.ukmotorsport.com/racmsa

Motorsports Weekly
www.motorsportsweekly.com

UK Karting
www.karting.co.uk

music

Akai
www.akai.com

Association of Blind Piano Tuners
www.uk-piano.org/abpt

Banks Music Publications
www.banksmusicpublications.cwc.net

Boosey & Hawkes
www.boosey.com

British Flute Society
www.bfs.org.uk

Chamberlain Music
www.chamberlainmusic.com

Chappells
www.uk-piano.org/chappell

Coppernob
www.coppernob.com

Fender
www.fender.com

Gibson
www.gibson.com

Kemble Pianos
www.uk-piano.org/kemble

Marshall Amplification
www.marshallamps.com

Premier Percussion
www.premier-percussion.com

Sheet Music Direct
www.sheetmusicdirect.com

Steinway
www.steinway.com

Yamaha

www.yamaha-music.co.uk

outdoor pursuits

Camping & Caravanning

British Holiday & Home Parks Association
www.ukparks.com

Camping & Caravanning Club
www.campingandcaravanningclub.co.uk

Camping & Outdoor Leisure Association
www.cola.org.uk

Camping UK Directory
www.camping.uk-directory.com

Campsite Guide
www.campsiteguide.com

Caravan Club
www.caravanclub.co.uk

National Caravan Council
www.nationalcaravan.co.uk

Caving & Potholing

National Caving Association
www.nca.org.uk

Climbing

British Mountain Guides
www.bmg.org.uk

British Mountaineering Council
www.thebmc.co.uk

Mountain Rescue
www.mra.org

Mountain Sports Guide
www.mtn.co.uk

Mountaineering Council for Scotland
www.mountaineering-scotland.org.uk

Rockface
www.rockface.co.uk

Scottish Mountaineering Club
www.smc.org.uk

Three Peaks Challenge
www.netdesktop.co.uk/3peaks

UK Climbing
www.ukclimbing.com

Welsh National Mountain Centre
www.pyb.co.uk

Clothes

Cotswold Outdoor
www.cotswold-outdoor.co.uk

Field & Trek
www.field-trek.co.uk

Miscellaneous

Countryside Agency
www.countryside.gov.uk

Duke of Edinburgh's Award Scheme
www.theaward.org

Fell Runners Association
www.fellrunner.org.uk

National Trails
www.nationaltrails.gov.uk

Ordnance Survey
www.ordsvy.gov.uk

Orienteering

British Orienteering Federation
www.cix.co.uk/~bof

Compass Sport Magazine
www.compasssport.com

International Orienteering Federation
www.orienteering.org

Walking

British Walking Federation
www.bwf-ivv.org.uk

English Lakeland Ramblers
www.ramblers.com

Ramblers Association
www.ramblers.org.uk

parachuting

British Collegiate Parachuting Association
www.bcpa.org.uk

British Parachuting Association
www.bpa.org.uk

London Fire Brigade Parachute Team
www.lfbpara.co.uk

Skyline Promotions
www.skylineparachuting.co.uk

Tandem Skydive UK
www.tandemskydive.freeserve.co.uk

United States Parachute Association
www.uspa.org

pets

Academy of Dog Training & Behavior
www.dogtraining-online.co.uk

Aquacare Direct
www.aquacare.co.uk

Bluepet Ltd
www.bluepet.co.uk

Canine Behaviour
www.caninebehaviour.co.uk

Comfy Pet Products
www.comfy-pet.co.uk

Dog Register
www.dog-register.co.uk

Dog World
www.dogworld.co.uk

Erin House Prints
www.erinhouseprints.com

Europa Pet Foods
www.europa-pet-food.co.uk

Exec-Pets
www.exec-pets.co.uk

Forsham Cottage Arks
www.forshamcottagearks.co.uk

Mayhew Animal Home
www.mayhewanimalhome.org

Petwebsites
www.petswebsites.co.uk

Snoozzzeeedog
www.snoozzzeeedog.co.uk

Cats

Cat World
www.catworld.co.uk

Cats Protection League
www.cats.org.uk

Feline Advisory Bureau
www.fabcats.org

Supreme Cat Show
www.chace.demon.co.uk

Whiskas Cat Food
www.whiskas.co.uk

Dogs

Associated Sheep, Police & Army Dog Society
www.aspads.org.uk

Battersea Dogs Home
www.dogshome.org

Border Collie Trust
www.bordercollietrustgb.org.uk

Canine World
www.canineworld.com

Council of Docked Breeds
www.cdb.org

Crossbreed & Mongrel Club
www.crossbreed.freeserve.co.uk

Crufts
www.crufts.org.uk

Dog Club UK
www.dogclub.co.uk

Dogs Online
www.dogsonline.co.uk

Dogs Worldwide
www.dogsworldwide.com

Fanciers Breeder Referral List
www.breedlist.com

Kennel Club
www.the-kennel-club.org.uk

National Canine Defence League
www.ncdl.org.uk

National Dogsitters
www.dogsit.com

National Puppy Register
www.findapup.net

Pedigree Petfoods
www.petcat.co.uk

Fish

British Cichlid Association
www.bca.zetnet.co.uk

British Killifish Association
www.bka.freeuk.com

British Koi Keepers' Society
www.bkks.co.uk

Practical Fishkeeping
www.practicalfishkeeping.co.uk

General

Animail
www.animail.co.uk

British Dragonfly Society
www.dragonflysoc.org.uk

British House Rabbit Association
www.houserabbit.co.uk

Insect World
www.insect-world.com

National Fancy Rat Society
www.nfrs.org

National Gerbil Society
www.gerbils.co.uk

National Hamster Council
www.hamsters-uk.org

Pet Cover
www.petcover.com

Pet Plan Insurance
www.petplan.co.uk

Pets Pyjamas.com
www.pets-pyjamas.co.uk

Rabbits Online
www.rabbitsonline.com

Rabbits UK
www.cs.cf.ac.uk/Rabbits

Serpents Magazine
www.serpents.co.uk

Turtle World
www.downey288.freeserve.co.uk

UK Reptiles Online
www.ukreptiles.com

photography
Cameras & Equipment

Agfa
www.agfa.co.uk

Canon
www.canon.co.uk

Casio
www.casio.co.uk

Contax
www.contaxcameras.com

Cosina
www.cosina.com

Epson
www.epson.com

Fuji Film
www.fujifilm.com

Kodak
www.kodak.co.uk

Konica
www.konica.com

Kyocera Yashica
www.kyu.co.uk

Leica
www.leica-camera.com

Minolta
www.minolta.co.uk

Nikon
www.nikon.co.uk

Olympus
www.olympus.co.uk

Panasonic
www.panasonic.com

Pentax
www.pentax.co.uk

Polaroid
www.polaroid.com

Ricoh
www.ricoh-cameras.co.uk

Rollei
www.rollei.com

Samson
www.samson.com

Sanyo
www.sanyo.co.uk

Sigma
www.sigma-aldrich.com

Sony
www.sony.com

Yashica
www.yashica.com

Magazines & Websites

Amateur Photography UK
www.amphot.co.uk

Boots Photography
www.bootsphoto.com

British Journal of Photography
www.bjphoto.co.uk

Centre for Photographic Art
www.photography.org

Cheese Magazine
www.cheesemagazine.com

Classic Camera
www.marriott.u-net.com/ccm.htm

Digital Photography Review
www.dpreview.com

Focus
www.focus-online.com

Royal Photographic Society
www.rps.org

UK Amateur Photograph
www.amphot.co.uk

Which Camera?
www.whichcamera.co.uk

skates & skateboarding

Real Skate Magazine
www.realskate.com

Skateboard Board Magazine
www.skateboard.com

Skateboard UK
www.sk8uk.co.uk

Slam City
www.slamcity.com

ten pin bowling

British Ten Pin Bowling Association
www.btba.org.uk

SuperBowl
www.superbowl.co.uk

cars

Accessories & Repairs

Allmake Motor Parts
www.allmakemotorparts.co.uk

Alpine Electronics
www.alpine1.com

Autogas UK
www.autogas.co.uk

Autoglass
www.autoglass.co.uk

Britax
www.britax.co.uk

Car Parts World
www.carpartsworld.co.uk

Continental Tyres
www.conti.de

Cooper Tyre & Rubber Company
www.coopertire.com

Duckworth
www.duckworth.co.uk

Elite Registrations
www.elite-registrations.co.uk

Ferodo
www.ferodo.co.uk

Fleet Support Group
www.fsguk.com

Global Registrations
www.globalreg.co.uk

Halfords
www.halfords.co.uk

Hammerite
www.hammerite-automotive.com

Kenwood
www.kenwood-electronics.co.uk

Kwik-Fit
www.kwik-fit.com

Michelin
www.michelin.com

Motor World
www.motor-world.co.uk

Motorola
www.mot.com

National Tyre Distributors Association
www.ntda.co.uk

National Tyres
www.national.co.uk

New Reg Personalised Registration Numbers
www.reg.co.uk

Parts Direct
www.partsdirect.co.uk

Pirelli
www.pirelli.co.uk

RAC Trackstar
www.ractrackstar.com

Registration Transfers
www.regtransfers.co.uk

Roaduser
www.roaduser.co.uk

Tracker
www.tracker-network.co.uk

Trafficmaster
www.trafficmaster.co.uk

Tyresave
www.tyresave.co.uk

UK Registrations
www.reg.co.uk

Unipart
www.unipart.co.uk

Buying, Selling & Auctions

Autobytel UK
www.autobyteluk.com

Autofinder
www.autofinder.net

British Car Auctions Group
www.bca-group.com

Fish4 Cars
www.fish4cars.co.uk

Jam Jar
www.jamjar.com

Lex Retail
www.lexretail.co.uk

Motor Auction Consortium
www.carworld.co.uk/auction/mac.htm

National Car Auctions
www.carworld.co.uk/auction/nca.htm

Parkers
www.parkers.co.uk

Scottish Car Auctions
www.scottishcarauctions.co.uk

UK Motor Vehicle Auctions
www.auctions.co.uk/cars

Magazines & Websites

Auto Exchange
www.autoexchange.co.uk

Auto Express
www.autoexpress.co.uk

Auto Trader
www.autotrader.co.uk

Autobytel
www.autobytel.co.uk

Autofinder
www.autofinder.net

Automobile
www.hartlana.co.uk

Automotive Body Repair News
www.abrn.com

Automotive Online
www.automotive-online.com

AutoWired
www.autowired.co.uk

BBC Top Gear
www.topgear.com

BMW Car
www.bmwcarmagazine.com

British Car Auctions
www.bca-group.com

Car
www.carmagazine.co.uk

CarNet
www.carnet.co.uk

Classic Car Directory
www.classicdirect.co.uk

Classic Car World
www.classiccarworld.co.uk

Classic Motor
www.classicmotor.co.uk

Drive
www.drive.com

Fleet NewsNet
www.automotive.co.uk

Haynes
www.haynes.co.uk

Learner Drivers UK
www.learners.co.uk

MG Enthusiast
www.mgcars.org.uk/mgmag

Motor World
www.motor-world.co.uk

Motoring UK
www.motoring-uk.co.uk

MotorTrader
www.motortrader.com

Power On Wheels
www.power-on-wheels.co.uk

ShopQ
www.shopq.co.uk

Top Gear
www.topgear.beeb.com

Tyre Trade News
www.tyretradenews.co.uk

Tyres-Online
www.tyres-online.co.uk

WhatCar?
www.whatcar.co.uk

Which? - Motoring
www.which.net/motoring

World Off Road
www.worldoffroad.com

Manufacturers

AC
www.accars.co.uk

Alfa Romeo
www.alfaromeo.com

Aston Martin
www.astonmartin.com

Audi
www.audi.co.uk

Bentley
www.rolls-royceandbentley.co.uk

BMW
www.bmw.co.uk

Bristol
www.bristolcars.co.uk

Cadillac
www.cadillaceurope.com

Caterham
www.caterham.co.uk

Chevrolet
www.chevrolet.com

Chrysler
www.chrysler.co.uk

Citroen
www.citroen.co.uk

Daewoo
www.daewoo.com

Dennis Group
www.dennis-group.co.uk

Ferrari
www.ferrari.com

Fiat
www.fiat.co.uk

Ford
www.ford.co.uk

General Motors
www.gm.com

Honda
www.honda.co.uk

Hyundai
www.hyundai-car.co.uk

Isuzu
www.isuzu.zo.uk

Jaguar
www.jaguar.com/uk

Jeep
www.jeep.co.uk

Jensen
www.jensen-motors.com

Kia
www.kia.com

Lamborghini
www.lamborghini.it

Land Rover
www.landrover.co.uk

Lexus
www.lexus.co.uk

London Taxis
www.london-taxis.co.uk

Lotus
www.lotuscars.co.uk

Maserati
www.maserati.it/engquattroporte.htm

Mazda
www.mazda.co.uk

Mercedes Benz
www.mercedes-benz.co.uk

MG
www.mgcars.com

Mini
www.mini.co.uk

Mitsubishi
www.mitsubishi-cars.co.uk

Morgan
www.morgan-motor.co.uk

Nissan
www.nissan.co.uk

Opel
www.opel.com

Peugeot
www.peugeot.co.uk

Porsche
www.porsche.com

Proton
www.proton.co.uk

Renault
www.renault.co.uk

Rolls Royce
www.rolls-royceandbentley.co.uk

Rover
www.rovercars.com

Saab
www.saab.co.uk

SEAT
www.seat.com

Skoda
www.skoda-auto.com

Subaru
www.subaru.co.uk

Suzuki
www.suzuki.co.uk

Toyota
www.toyota.co.uk

TVR
www.tvr-eng.co.uk

Vauxhall
www.vauxhall.co.uk

Volkswagen
www.vw.co.uk

Volvo
www.volvocars.volvo.co.uk

Westfield
www.westfield-sportscars.co.uk

Owners' Clubs

Aston Martin
www.amoc.org

Austin Healey Club
www.austin-healey-club.co.uk

Ferrari
www.ferrariownersclub.co.uk

Jensen
www.british-steel.org

Jensen Interceptor
www.jioc.org

Mini Cooper Register
www.minicooper.org

Morris Minor
www.morrisminor.co.uk

Rolls Royce
www.rroc.org

Petrol

Esso
www.esso.co.uk

Mobil
www.mobil.co.uk

Shell
www.shell.com

Texaco
www.texaco.co.uk

TotalFinaElf
www.totalfinaelf.com

dating agencies

Dateline
www.dateline.co.uk

Drawing Down the Moon
www.drawingdownthemoon.co.uk

Executive Club
www.thematchmaker.co.uk

Sirius
www.clubsirius.com

disability

Shaw Trust
www.shaw-trust.org.uk

driving schools

BSM
www.bsm.co.uk

Institute of Advanced Motoring
www.iam.org.uk

UK Learner Drivers
www.learners.co.uk

family life

Advisory Centre For Education
www.ace-ed.org.uk

Association of Breastfeeding Mothers
http://home.clara.net/abm

Babyworld
www.babyworld.co.uk

BBC Parenting Resource
www.bbc.co.uk/education/health/parenting

Child of Achievement
www.childofachievement.co.uk

Community Hygiene Concern
www.chc.org

Families Need Fathers
www.fnf.org.uk

Family Planning Association
www.fpa.org.uk

La Leche League
www.lalecheleague.org

National Childbirth Trust
www.nct-online.org

National Family & Parenting Institute
www.nfpi.org

One Parent Families
www.oneparentfamilies.org.uk

Parent News
www.parents-news.co.uk

Parent Soup
www.parentsoup.com

Parenting Education & Support Forum
www.parenting-forum.org.uk

Parentline
www.parentlineplus.org.uk

Parentline Plus
www.parentlineplus.org.uk

Serene
www.our-space.co.uk/serene.htm

hairdressers, beauty salons & image consultants

Andrew Collinge Hairdressing
www.andrewcollinge.com

Charles Worthington
www.cwlondon.com

Daniel Galvin
www.daniel-galvin.co.uk

Elizabeth Arden Red Door Salons
www.reddoorsalons.com

House of Colour
www.houseofcolour.co.uk

Jo Hansford
www.johansford.com

Toni & Guy
www.toniandguy.co.uk

Trevor Sorbie
www.trevorsorbie.com

Vidal Sassoon
www.vidalsassoon.co.uk

health & fitness

Dragons Health Club
www.dragons.co.uk

LA Fitness
www.lafitness.co.uk

The Sanctuary Spa
www.thesanctuary.co.uk

The Third Space
www.thethirdspace.com

Clubs

Cannons Health Clubs
www.cannons.co.uk

David Lloyd Leisure
www.davidlloydleisure.co.uk

Esporta
www.esporta.co.uk

Greens Health & Fitness
www.greensonline.co.uk

Harbour Club
www.harbourclub.co.uk

Holmes Place
www.holmesplace.co.uk

Diet

Cambridge Diet
www.cambridge-diet.co.uk

Rosemary Conley
www.rosemary-conley.co.uk

Slimming World
www.slimming-world.co.uk

Weightwatchers
www.weightwatchers.com

Health Farm

Champneys
www.central-chamber.co.uk

Forestmere
www.forestmere.co.uk

Henlow Grange
www.henlowgrange.co.uk

Nirvana Spa
www.nirvana-spa.co.uk

Sopwell House
www.sopwellhouse.co.uk

Naturism

British Naturist Society
www.british-naturism.org.uk

H&E
www.h-and-e.co.uk

Pilates

Body Control Pilates Group
www.bodycontrolpilates.com

Pilates
www.pilates.co.uk

Pilates Foundation
www.pilatesfoundation.com

Smoking

ASH
www.ash.org.uk

Giving Up Smoking (Health Education Authority)
www.givingupsmoking.co.uk

No Smoking Day
www.nosmokingday.org.uk

QUIT
www.quit.org.uk

Yoga

British Wheel of Yoga
www.bwy.org

home life
Cleaning & Laundry

Corby Press
www.corbypress.com

Dynorod
www.dyno.com

Earth Friendly
www.ecos.com

Finish
www.homesolutionsnews.com/rbdocs/uk/finish

Persil
www.persil.co.uk

Scotchcare
www.scotchcare-services.co.uk

White Knight
www.white-knight.co.uk

Estate Agents

Asserta
www.assertahome.com

Bradford & Bingley
www.bb-ea.co.uk

Bushells
www.bushells.com

Chancellors
www.chancellors.co.uk

Chestertons
www.chestertons.co.uk

CityLet
www.citylet.com

Cluttons
www.cluttons.com

Connells
www.connells.co.uk

Copping Joyce
www.coppingjoyce.co.uk

Drivers Jonas
www.djonas.co.uk

Easier
www.easier.co.uk

Egerton
www.egertonproperty.co.uk

Felicity J Lord
www.fjlord.co.uk

Foxtons
www.foxtons.co.uk

Friend & Falcke
www.friendandfalcke.co.uk

Goldschmidt Howland
www.goldschmidt-howland.co.uk

Haart
www.haart.co.uk

Hamptons
www.hamptons.co.uk

Humberts
www.humberts.co.uk

Jackson-Stops & Staff
www.jackson-stops.co.uk

John D Wood
www.johndwood.co.uk

King Sturge
www.kingsturge.co.uk

Knight Frank
www.knightfrank.co.uk

London Property Guide
www.londonpropertyguide.co.uk

London Property News
www.lpn.co.uk

National Homes Network
www.nhn.co.uk

National Property Register
www.national-property-register.co.uk

Richard Ellis
www.richardellis.co.uk

Right Move
www.rightmove.co.uk

Savills
www.fpdsavills.co.uk

Spicer McColl
www.spicer.co.uk

Strettons
www.strettons.co.uk

Strutt & Parker
www.struttandparker.co.uk

Winkworth
www.winkworth.co.uk

Heating

Baxi Heating
www.baxi.com

British Gas
www.gas.co.uk

Calor Gas
www.calorgas.co.uk

Corgi
www.corgi-gas.co.uk

Energy Saving Trust
www.est.org.uk

Energy Shop
www.energyshop-plc.co.uk

Potterton
www.potterton.co.uk

Robinson Willey
www.robinson-willey.co.uk

Valor
www.valor.co.uk

Home Improvements

National Home Improvement Council
www.nhic.org.uk

House Builders

Alfred McAlpine
www.alfred-mcalpine.co.uk

Antler Homes
www.antlerhomes.co.uk

Ashwood Homes
www.ashwoodhomes.co.uk

Banner Homes
www.banner-homes.co.uk

Barratt Homes
www.ukpg.co.uk/barratt

Beechwood Homes
www.beechwood.co.uk

Bewley Homes
www.bewley.co.uk

Bloor Homes
www.bloorhomes.com

Bryant Homes
www.bryant.co.uk

Charles Church
www.charles-church.co.uk

Country Life
www.countrylife.demon.co.uk

Countryside Residential
www.countrysideresidential.co.uk

Crownwood Developments
www.crownwooddevelopments.co.uk

David Wilson Homes
www.dwh.co.uk

Fairclough Homes
www.faircloughhomes.com

Fairview
www.fairview.co.uk

Gainsborough
www.gainsbc.co.uk

George Wimpey
www.wimpey.co.uk

Goldcrest Homes
www.goldcresthomes.plc.uk

Hazelmere
www.hazelmerehomes.co.uk

Laing
www.laing.co.uk

Linden Homes
www.lindenhomes.co.uk

McAlpine
www.alfred-mcalpine.co.uk

McLean Homes
www.wimpey.co.uk/mclean

Michael Shanly Homes
www.michaelshanly.co.uk

Persimmon Homes
www.persimmon.plc.uk

Rialto Homes
www.rialtohomes.co.uk

Robertson Residential
www.robertson.co.uk

St James Homes
www.stjameshomes.co.uk

Tarmac
www.tarmac.co.uk

Taylor Woodrow
www.taywood.co.uk

Thirlstone Home Development
www.thirlstone.co.uk

Ward Homes
www.ward-homes.co.uk

Westbury Homes
www.westbury-homes.co.uk

Wilcon
www.wilcon.co.uk

Wimpey Homes
www.wimpey.co.uk

Housekeeping

GH Institute
www.goodhousekeeping.co.uk

Housekeeping Today
www.housekeeping-today.co.uk

Jeeves Housekeeping
www.jeeveshousekeeping.co.uk

United Kingdom Housekeepers
Association
www.ukha.co.uk

Removals & Storage

Abbey Self-Storage
www.abbey-self-storage.co.uk

Association of Relocation Agents
www.relocationagents.com

Baggage Express
www.baggage-express.com

Bishops
www.bishopsmove.com

Bishops Move
www.bishops-move.co.uk

Capital Movers
www.capital-worldwide.com

European Removals
www.europeanremovals.com

House Removals.com
www.houseremovals.com

I Have Moved!
www.ihavemoved.com

Interpac
www.interpac.co.uk

Moves
www.moves.co.uk

Pickfords
www.pickfords.co.uk

Sterling International Movers
www.sterlingmovers.com

Teacrate
www.teacrate.com

Transeuro
www.transeuro.com

Transeuro Worldwide Movers
www.transeuro.com

Repairs & Servicing

Hotpoint, Creda, Cannon
www.theservicecentre.co.uk

Whirlpool
www.whirlpool.co.uk

Safety & Security

Ability Security Systems
www.ability-security.co.uk

Ademco Microtech
www.ademco-microtech.co.uk

ADT
www.adt.co.uk

Banham
www.banham.com

Bates Alams
www.batesalarms.co.uk

Bradbury Group Ltd
www.bradburyuk.com

Chubb
www.chubb.co.uk

CIS
www.cis-security.co.uk

Crime Prevention Services
www.preventcrime.co.uk

Crown Protection Services
www.security-guards.com

First Security
www.first-security.co.uk

Health & Safety Executive
www.hse.gov.uk

Index Security Systems Ltd
www.indexsecurity.co.uk

Ingersoll
www.nt-architectural-products.co.uk

Institute of Home Safety
www.instituteofhomesafety.co.uk

Jacksons Fine Fencing
www.jacksons-fencing.co.uk

Lorrainne Electronics Surveillance
www.lorraine.co.uk

M R Security
www.mrsecurity.co.uk

National Inspection Council for Electrical
Installation Contracting
www.niceic.org.uk

National Key Holding
www.nationalkeyholding.co.uk

Neighbourhood Watch
www.nwatch.org.uk

Onwatch CCTV
www.onwatchcctv.co.uk

Reliance High Tech
www.relitech.co.uk

RF Concepts
www.rfconcepts.co.uk

RoSPA
www.rospa.co.uk

Safety Systems & Alarm Inspection Board
www.ssaib.co.uk

Secom
www.secom.plc.uk

Security Surveyors Group
www.crimeseen.co.uk

Security Websites
www.securitywebsites.co.uk

Selectamark Security Systems
www.selectamark.co.uk

Utilities

Amerada
www.amerada.co.uk

British Energy
www.british-energy.com

British Gas
www.gas.co.uk

Centrica
www.centrica.co.uk

Direct Power
www.directpower.co.uk

Eastern Energy
www.easternenergy.co.uk

London Electricity
www.london-electricity.co.uk

MEB
www.meb.co.uk

National Grid
www.nationalgrid.com

National Power
www.national-power.com

North West Water
www.nww.co.uk

Northern Ireland Electricity
www.nie.co.uk

Npower
www.npower.com

NU-Tility
www.nu-tility.com

Powergen
www.powergen.co.uk

Scottish Hydro-Electric
www.hydro.co.uk

Scottish Nuclear
www.snl.co.uk

ScottishPower
www.scottishpower.co.uk

Servowarm
www.servowarm.co.uk

Severn Trent
www.severn-trent.com

South West Water
www.swwater.co.uk

Sutton & East Surrey Water
www.waterplc.com

SWALEC
www.swalec.com

Sweb plc
www.sweb.co.uk

Thames Water
www.thames-water.com

Transco
www.transco.uk.com

TXU Energy
www.txuenergi.co.uk

Virgin Energy
www.virgin.com/energy

Wessex Water
www.wessexwater.plc.uk

magazines & websites

Antiques Trade Gazette
www.atg-online.com

Baby Directory
www.babydirectory.com

Babyworld
www.babyworld.co.uk

BBC Good Homes
www.goodhomes.beeb.com

Beeb.com
www.beeb.com

Beme
www.beme.com

Big Issue
www.bigissue.com

Charlotte Street
www.charlottestreet.com

Cosmopolitan
www.cosmomag.com

Country Life
www.countrylife.co.uk

Docklands & City
www.docklandsandcity.com

Elle
www.ellemag.com

Esquire
www.esquiremag.com

FHM
www.fhm.co.uk

Good Housekeeping
www.goodhousekeeping.co.uk

GQ
www.gq-magazine.co.uk

Handbag.com
www.handbag.com

Hello!
www.hello-magazine.co.uk

House & Garden
www.houseandgarden.co.uk

House Beautiful
www.housebeautiful.co.uk

Islam Direct
www.islamdirect.com

Jewish Online
www.jewishonline.org.uk

Jewish.net
www.jewish.net

Kitchen Specialists Association
www.ksa.co.uk/consumer

Kitchens, Bedrooms & Bathrooms
Magazine
www.dmg.co.uk/kbbmag

Life
www.pathfinder.com/life

Loaded
www.loaded.co.uk

Magazine Shop
www.magazineshop.co.uk

Maxim
www.maximmag.com

Men's Health
www.menshealth.com

Mother & Baby
www.motherandbaby.co.uk

National Enquirer
www.nationalenquirer.com

New Woman
www.newwomanonline.co.uk

Parent News
www.parents-news.co.uk

Playboy
www.playboy.com

Private Eye
www.private-eye.co.uk

Punch
www.punch.co.uk

Readers' Digest
www.readersdigest.co.uk

Royalty
www.royalty-magazine.com

Spectator
www.spectator.co.uk

Tatler
www.tatler.co.uk

The Oldie
www.theoldie.co.uk

Totally Jewish
www.totallyjewish.com

UFO
www.ufomag.co.uk

Vanity Fair
www.vanityfair.co.uk

Viz
www.viz.co.uk

Vogue
www.vogue.co.uk

World of Interiors
www.worldofinteriors.co.uk

Zoom
www.zoom.co.uk

military associations

American Legion
www.legion.org

Bomber Command Historical Society
www.hellzapoppin.demon.co.uk

Burma Star Association
www.burmastar.org.uk

Far East Prisoners of War
www.fepow.org.uk

Friends of War Memorials
www.war-memorials.com

Officers' Pensions Society
www.officerspensionsoc.co.uk

Royal Auxiliary Air Force
www.rauxaf.mod.uk

Royal Canadian Legion
www.legion.ca

Scottish National War Memorial
www.snwm.org

Service Pals
www.servicepals.com

motorcycles

Autocom
www.autocom.co.uk

Bike Trader Interactive
www.biketrader.co.uk

BMW
www.bmw.co.uk

British Motor Racing Circuits
www.bmrc.co.uk

British Motorcyclists Federation
www.bmf.co.uk

British Speedway Promoters
www.british-speedway.co.uk

BSA Owners' Club UK
www.bsaoc.demon.co.uk

CSM Motorcycle Training
www.csm.uk.com

Ducati
www.ducati.com

Ducati Owners Club GB
www.docgb.org

Federation of European Motorcyclists'
Associations
www.mag-uk.org/fema

Harley-Davidson
www.harley-davidson.co.uk

Honda
www.honda.co.uk

Honda Owners Club GB
www.hoc.org.uk

Kawasaki
www.kawasaki.com

Moto Guzzi
www.motoguzziclub.co.uk

Moto Guzzi Club GB
http://freespace.virgin.net/motoguzzi.clubgb

Motorbikes Online
www.motorbikes-online.com

Motorcycle Industry Association
www.mcia.co.uk

Motorcycle Sport
www.bikenet.co.uk

Motorcycle UK
www.motorcycle-uk.com

Motorcycle World Magazine
www.motorcycleworld.co.uk

Norton Owner Club GB
www.noc.co.uk

Norton Owners' Club
www.noc.co.uk

Piaggio
www.piaggio.com

Scootering Magazine
www.scootering.com

Suzuki
www.suzuki.co.uk

Suzuki Owners Club
www.suzuki-club.co.uk

Triumph
www.triumph.co.uk

Triumph Owners Motorcycle Club
www.tomcc.demon.co.uk

TVR
www.tvr-eng.co.uk

Vespa
www.vespa.com

Yamaha
www.yamaha-motor.co.uk

new age

British Feng Shui Society
www.fengshuisociety.org.uk

Findhorn Foundation
www.findhorn.org

Foundation for International Spiritual
Unfoldment
www.fisu.org

International Centre for Reiki Training
www.reiki.org

Raven Lodge of Shamanism
www.shamana.co.uk

Tarot World Cards
www.tarotworld.com

religion

Buddhist

Buddhist Society (UK)
www.buddsoc.org.uk

Centre for Buddhist Studies
www.bris.ac.uk

International Zen Association
www.zen-izauk.org

Middle Way Journal
www.thebuddhistsociety.org.uk

Christian

Anglican
www.anglican.org/online

Archbishop of Canterbury
www.archbishopofcanterbury.org

Baptist Church
www.baptist.org.uk

Carmelite Friars UK
www.carmelite.org

Catholic Church (in England & Wales)
www.catholic-ew.org.uk

Catholic Church (Scotland)
www.catholic-scotland.org.uk

Christadelphian
www.christadelphian.org.uk

Christian Fellowship Church
www.cfc-net.org

Church of England
www.church-of-england.org

Church of Jesus Christ Latter Day Saints
www.ldscn.com

Church of Scotland
www.cofs.org.uk

Church Society
www.churchsociety.org

Congregational Federation
www.congregational.org.uk

Free Church of Scotland
www.freechurch.org

Jehovah's Witnesses
www.watchtower.org

Jesus Army
www.jesus.org.uk

Latter-day Saints (Mormons)
www.lds.org.uk

Mennonite Church
www.mennolink.org

Methodist Church
www.methodist.org.uk

Mormons
www.mormon.org

Order of St Benedict
www.osb.org

Religious Society of Friends (Quakers)
www.quaker.org

Retreat Association
www.retreats.org.uk

Salvation Army
www.salvationarmy.org.uk

Scientology
www.scientology.org.uk

Scripture Union
www.scripture.org.uk

Seventh Day Adventist
www.adventist.org.uk

Unitarian
www.unitarian.org.uk

United Free Church of Scotland
www.ufcos.org.uk

United Pentecostal Church
www.upcogbi.freeserve.co.uk

Vatican
www.vatican.va

World Council of Churches
www.wcc-coe.org

Islam

Federation of Students Islamic Societies
www.fosis.org.uk

Islam
www.islamic.org.uk

Islamic Centre England
www.ic-el.org

Islamic Foundation
www.islamic-foundation.org.uk

Islamic Unity Society
www.ius.org.uk

Muslim Council of Britain
www.mcb.org.uk

World Assembly of Muslim Youth
www.wamy.co.uk

Young Muslims UK
www.ymuk.com

Jewish

International Council of Jewish Women
www.icjw.org.uk

Jewish Board of Deputies
www.bod.org.uk

Judaism
www.jewish.co.uk

Maccabi Union
www.maccabi.org.uk

Reform Synagogues
www.refsyn.org.uk

Union of Liberal & Progressive Synagogues
www.ulps.org

Minority Faiths

Bahai Faith
www.bahai.com

British Humanist Association
www.humanism.org.uk

Hare Krishna UK
www.iskcon.org.uk

International Society for Krishna
Consciousness
www.religioustolerance.org/hare.htm

Order of Bards, Ovates & Druids
www.druidry.org

Pagan Federation
www.paganfed.demon.co.uk

Spiritualists' National Union
www.snu.org.uk

Sikh

British Organization of Sikh Students
www.waheguru.demon.co.uk

Sikh Spirit
www.sikhspirit.com

Sikhism UK
www.sikhism.org.uk

retirement

Anchor Homes
www.anchor.org.uk

Association of Retired & Persons over 50
www.arp.org.uk

Elderly Accommodation Counsel
www.e-a-c.demon.co.uk

Occupational Pensions Regulatory
Authority
www.stakeholder.opra.gov.uk

Retirement Matters Ltd
www.retirement-matters.co.uk

weddings

A1 Stretch Limos
www.a1stretch.com

Candles on the Web Ltd
www.candlesontheweb

City Weddings
www.city-weddings.co.uk

Confetti
www.confetti.co.uk

Creative Cakes by Elizabeth Lyle
www.elizabethlylecakes.com

E and L Insurance
www.eandl.co.uk/wedding-insurance

Exclusive by Design
www.exclusivebydesign.co.uk

FAB International UK Ltd.
www.fabcarimports.com

Fantasy Waistcoats
www.fantasywaistcoats.com

Forever Memories
www.forevermemories.co.uk

Groomservice
www.groomservice.co.uk

Guild of Wedding Photographers
www.gwp-uk.co.uk

Kiss the Bride
www.kissthebride.co.uk

Margaret Lee
www.margaretlee.co.uk

Merllin Fireworks Ltd
www.merlin-fireworks.co.uk

Mint & Magnolia
www.mintandmagnolia.com

Mozfarian Jewellers
www.mozafarian.com

Picture Palace Wedding Service
www.picturepalace.co.uk

Pronuptia
www.pronuptia.co.uk

Rainbow Club Ltd
www.rainbowclub.co.uk

Sharon Cunningham Couture
www.sc-couture.co.uk

Sposa Bella Manufacturing
www.sposabella.co.uk

Stevies Gowns
www.steviesgownsbridalwear.com

Suzanne Leverington
www.suzanneleverington.co.uk

The White Company
www.thewhiteco.com

V an B Chauffeur Service
www.limohire.com

Wedding Day Websites
www.weddingdaywebsites.co.u

Wedding Store UK
www.weddingstore.co.uk

Museums, Libraries & Information

careers guidance

Careers Research & Advisory Centre
www.crac.org.uk

Careers Services National Association
www.careers-uk.com

Channel 4 Careers
www.channel4.com/brilliantcareers

Institute of Career Guidance
www.icg-uk.org

Prospects
www.prospects.ac.uk

University of London Careers Service
www.careers.lon.ac.uk

encyclopaedias

Britannica
www.britannica.co.uk

Encarta
www.encarta.msn.com

Encyclopaedia Smithsonian
www.si.edu/resource/faq/start.htm

Grolier
www.grolier.com

Probert
www.probert-encyclopaedia.co.uk

history

Anne Frank Educational Trust
www.afet.org.uk

Britannia History
www.britannia.com/history

British Association of Paper Historians
www.baph.freeserve.co.uk

Channel 4 Black & Asian History
www.blackhistorymap.com

Economic History Society
www.ehs.org.uk

English Civil War Society
www.english-civil-war-society.org/public_html

English Heritage
www.english-heritage.org.uk

First Empire Magazine
www.firstempire.ltd.uk

Galpin Society
www.music.ed.ac.uk/euchmi/galpin

Historical Association
www.history.org.uk

History – BBC Online
www.bbc.co.uk/history

History Today Magazine
www.historytoday.com

Institute of Historical Research
www.ihrinfo.ac.uk

Journal of Design History
www.oup.co.uk/design

Journal of Victorian Culture
www.indiana.edu/~victoria/jvc.html

Local History Magazine
www.local-history.co.uk

Making History (BBC)
www.bbc.co.uk/education/archive/makinghistory

Manorial Society of Great Britain
www.msgb.co.uk

Oral History Society
www.essex.ac.uk/sociology/oralhis.htm

Society for History of Mathematics
www.dcs.warwick.ac.uk/bshm

Society for the Promotion of Roman Studies
www.sas.ac.uk/icls/Roman/Default.htm

libraries

Aberdeen University Library
www.abdn.ac.uk/library

Balliol College Library
www.balliol.ox.ac.uk/library/library.html

Barbican
www.barbican.co.uk

Bodleian Library, Oxford
www.bodley.ox.ac.uk

British Film Institute National Library
www.bfi.org.uk/nationallibrary

British Library
www.bl.uk

Cambridge University Library
www.lib.cam.ac.uk

Corporation of London Records Office (CLRO)
www.corpoflondon.gov.uk

Edinburgh University Library
www.lib.ed.ac.uk

John Rylands Library
www.rylibweb.man.ac.uk

Library of Congress
www.loc.gov

London & South Eastern Library Region
www.viscount.org.uk

London Library
www.londonlibrary.co.uk

National Archives of Ireland
www.nationalarchives.ie

National Art Library (Victoria & Albert Museum)
www.nal.vam.ac.uk

National Library of Scotland
www.nls.uk

National Library of Wales
www.llgc.org.uk

National Library of Women
www.lgu.ac.uk/fawcett/main.htm

Natural History Museum Library
www.nhm.ac.uk/library

Science Museum Library
www.sciencemuseum.org.uk/library/index.asp

maps

Association for Geographic Information (AGI)
www.agi.org.uk

Australian National Mapping Agency
www.auslig.gov.au

A-Z Maps
www.a-zmaps.co.uk

British Cartographic Society
www.cartography.org.uk

British Geological Survey
www.bgs.ac.uk

Committee of the National Mapping Agencies of Europe
www.cerco.org

Geomatics Canada
www.geocan.nrcan.gc.ca

Harvey
www.harveymaps.co.uk

Land Information New Zealand
www.linz.govt.nz

Mapblast
www.mapblast.com

Maporama
www.maporama.co.uk

Multimap
www.multimap.com

Multi-purpose European Ground-Related Information Network
www.megrin.org

National Map Centre
www.mapstore.co.uk

Ordnance Survey
www.ordsvy.gov.uk

Ordnance Survey Ireland
www.irlgov.ie/osi

Ordnance Survey of Northern Ireland
www.nics.gov.uk/doe/ordnance

Shell Geostar
www.shellgeostar.com

Society of Cartographers
www.soc.org.uk

Stanfords
www.stanfords.co.uk

Street Map
www.streetmap.co.uk

US Geological Survey
www.usgs.gov

museums

Andrew Carnegie Birthplace Museum
www.carnegiemuseum.co.uk

Armed Forces Museum
www.nms.ac.uk

Ashmolean Museum
www.ashmol.ox.ac.uk

Bank of England Museum
www.bankofengland.co.uk

Bass Museum
www.bass-museum.com

Beamish Open Air Museum
www.beamish.org.uk

Bear Museum, Petersfield
www.bearmuseum.co.uk

Birmingham & Midland Transport Museum
www.bammot.org.uk

Birmingham Railway Museum
www.vintagetrains.co.uk/brm.htm

Black Country Living Museum
www.bclm.co.uk

Bletchley Park
www.bletchleypark.org.uk

Brewers Quay & The Timewalk
www.brewers-quay.co.uk

Bristol City Museum & Art Gallery
www.bristol-city.gov.uk/museums

Britain At War Experience
www.britainatwar.com

British Lawnmower Museum
www.dspace.dial.pipex.com/town/square/gf86

British Museum
www.british-museum.ac.uk

British Road Transport Museum
www.mbrt.co.uk

Broadfield House Glass Museum
www.dudley.gov.uk

Bronte Parsonage Museum
www.bronte.org.uk

Brooklands Museum
www.brooklands.org.uk

Cabinet War Rooms
www.iwm.org.uk/cabinet.htm

Caernarfon Air Park
www.users.globalnet.co.uk/~airworld

Cambridge Museum of Technology
www.cam.net.uk/home/steam

Chertsey Museum
www.chertseymuseum.org.uk

Clan Cameron Museum
www.clan-cameron.org/museum.html

Clan Donnachaidh Museum
www.donnachaidh.com

Clink Prison Museum
www.clink.co.uk

Cobbaton Combat Collection
www.cobbatoncombat.co.uk

Cowper & Newton Museum
www.olio.demon.co.uk/cnmhome.html

Creetown Gem and Rock Museum
www.gemrock.net

Cutty Sark
www.cuttysark.org.uk

Design Museum
www.southwark.gov.uk/tourism

Dickens House Museum
www.dickensmuseum.com

Dinosaur Museum
www.dinosaur-museum.org.uk

Discovery Point
www.rrs-discovery.co.uk

Dover Museum
www.designmuseum.org

Dunaskin Open Air Museum
www.dunaskin.org.uk

Eastleigh Museum
www.hants.gov.uk/museum/eastlmus

Eden Camp Modern History Museum
www.edencamp.co.uk

Elgin Museum
www.elginmuseum.demon.co.uk

Elmbridge Museum
www.surrey-online.co.uk

Eureka The Museum For Children
www.eureka.org.uk

Fitzwilliam Museum
www.fitzmuseum.cam.ac.uk

Florence Nightingale
www.florence-nightingale.co.uk

Fort Grey
www.museum.guernsey.net

Freud Museum
www.freud.org.uk

Galleries of Justice
www.galleriesofjustice.org.uk

Geffrye Museum
www.geffrye-museum.org.uk

Gracie Fields Museum
www.rochdale.gov.uk/Leisure/LocalHist.asp?URL
=GracieFields

Grampian Transport Museum
www.gtm.org.uk

Grantown Museum
www.grantown-on-spey.co.uk/museum.htm

Green Howards Regimental Museum
www.greenhowards.org.uk

Gressenhall Norfolk Rural Life Museum
www.norfolk.gov.uk/tourism/museums/nrlm.htm

Hancock Museum
www.ncl.ac.uk/hancock

Haynes Motor Museum
www.haynesmotormuseum.co.uk

Heritage Motor Centre
www.heritage.org.uk

HMS Belfast
www.iwm.org.uk/belfast/

Horniman Museum
www.horniman.demon.co.uk

Hunterian Museum & Art Gallery
www.gla.ac.uk/museum

Imperial War Museum
www.iwm.org.uk

Ironbridge Museum Trust, Telford
www.ironbridge.org.uk

Jane Austen Centre
www.janeausten.co.uk

Jane Austen Museum
www.janeaustenmuseum.org.uk

Jewish Museum
www.jewmusm.ort.org

Kew Bridge Steam Museum
www.kbsm.org

London Toy & Model Museum
www.londontoy.com

London Transport Museum
www.ltmuseum.co.uk

Macclesfield Silk Museum
www.silk-macclesfield.org

Maidstone Museum
www.museum.maidstone.gov.uk

Manchester Museum
www.mcc.ac.uk/museum

Manchester Museum of Science & Industry
www.msim.org.uk

Mangapps Farm Railway Museum
www.mangapps.co.uk

Mary Rose
www.maryrose.org

Michael Faraday's Museum
www.ri.ac.uk

Midland Air Museum
www.midlandairmuseum.org.uk

Museum of Army Flying
www.flying-museum.org.uk

Museum of British Road Transport
www.mbrt.co.uk

Museum of Childhood Memories
www.vam.ac.uk/vastatic/nmc

Museum of Classical Archaeology
www.classics.cam.ac.uk/ark.html

Museum of Costume
www.museumofcostume.co.uk

Museum of East Anglian Life
www.suffolkcc.gov.uk/Central/meal

Museum of East Asian Art
www.east-asian-art.co.uk

Museum of Garden History
www.museumgardenhistory.org

Museum of London
www.museum-london.org.uk

Museum of Scotland
www.museum.scotland.net

Museum of the History of Science
www.mhs.ox.ac.uk

Museum of the Moving Image
www.bfi.org.uk/momi

Museum of Welsh Life
www.nmgw.ac.uk

Museums of the Potteries
www.stoke.gov.uk/museums

National Army Museum
www.national-army-museum.ac.uk

National Coal Mining Museum
www.ncm.org.uk

National Maritime Museum
www.nmm.ac.uk

National Motor Museum
www.beaulieu.co.uk

National Museum of Photography, Film & TV
www.nmpft.org.uk

National Museums & Galleries on Merseyside
www.nmgm.org.uk

National Museums of Scotland
www.nms.ac.uk

National Railway Museum
www.nmsi.ac.uk/nrm

National Tramways Museum
www.tramway.co.uk

National Waterways Museum at Gloucester
www.nwm.org.uk

Natural History Museum
www.nhm.ac.uk

Pitt Rivers Museum, Oxford
www.prm.ox.ac.uk

Potteries Museum & Art Gallery
www.stoke.gov.uk/museums/pmag

Ragged School Museum
www.ics-london.co.uk/rsm

River & Rowing Museum
www.rrm.co.uk

Roman Baths Museum
www.romanbaths.co.uk

Royal Airforce Museum
www.cosford.rafmuseum.com

Royal Albert Memorial Museum & Art Gallery, Exeter
www.exeter.gov.uk/tourism

Royal Armouries Museum, Leeds
www.armouries.org.uk

Royal Cornwall Museum
www.royalcornwallmuseum.org.uk

Royal Navy Submarine Museum
www.rnsubmus.co.uk

Royal Ulster Constabulary Museum, Belfast
www.ruc.police.uk

Royal Yacht Britannia
www.royalyachtbritannia.co.uk

Science Museum
www.nmsi.ac.uk

Second World War Experience Centre
www.war-experience.org

Sedgwick Museum of Geology
www.esc.cam.ac.uk

Sherlock Holmes Museum
www.sherlock-holmes.co.uk

Shetland Museum
www.shetland-museum.org.uk

Sikh Museum
www.sikhmuseum.org

Sir John Soane's Museum
www.soane.org

Somerset House
www.somerset-house.org.uk

Southampton Maritime Museum
www.southampton.gov.uk/leisure/heritage/maritime.htm

Spitfire & Hurricane Memorial
www.spitfire-museum.com

St Albans Museum
www.stalbans.gov.uk/tourism

St Barbe Museum
www.st-barbe-museum.demon.co.uk

St.Helens Transport Museum
www.sthtm.freeserve.co.uk

Tank Museum
www.tankmuseum.co.uk

Techniquest
www.tquest.org.uk

Thackray Medical Museum
www.thackraymuseum.org

Tunbridge Wells Museum
www.tunbridgewells.gov.uk/museum

Verdant Works
www.verdant-works.co.uk

Victoria & Albert Museum
www.vam.ac.uk

Whitby Museum
www.durain.demon.co.uk

Windermere Steamboat Museum
www.steamboat.co.uk

Wordsworth Museum
www.wordsworth.org.uk

Working Silk Museum
www.humphriesweaving.co.uk

York Castle Museum
www.york.gov.uk/heritage/museums

York Dungeon
www.yorkshirenet.co.uk/yorkdungeon

Yorkshire Museum
www.york.gov.uk/heritage/museums/yorkshire

opinion polls & market research

Audit Bureau of Circulation
www.abc.org.uk

British Market Research Association
www.bmra.org.uk

Gallup Organisation
www.gallup.com

Mintel.com
www.mintel.co.uk

Mori
www.mori.com

NetValue
http://uk.netvalue.com

NOP Research
www.nopres.co.uk

phone numbers

192.com
www.192.com

BT Online Phonebook
www.bt.com/directory-enquiries

Business Pages
www.businesspages.co.uk

Phonenumbers.net
www.phonenumbers.net

Telephone Code Changes
www.numberchange.org

Telephone Directories on the Web
www.teldir.com

Thomson Directories

www.thomsonlocal.com

Yellow Pages
www.yell.co.uk

reference

Ask a Librarian
www.earl.org.uk/ask

Association for Information Management
www.aslib.co.uk

Bartleby.com
www.bartleby.com

Book Industry Communications
www.bic.org.uk

BUBL Information Service
www.bubl.ac.uk

Dictionary
www.dictionary.com

FTSE
www.ftse.com

Jane's
www.janes.com

Kelly's Guide
www.kellysonline.net

Oxford English Dictionary
www.oed.com

Roget's Thesaurus
www.thesaurus.com

Scoot
www.scoot.co.uk

The Weather Channel
www.weather.com

Up My Street
www.upmystreet.com

USGS National Mapping Information
www.mapping.usgs.gov

Whitakers Almanack
www.whitakersalmanack.co.uk

X-Refer
www.xrefer.com

Yellow Pages (US)
www.yell.com

weather

BBC Weather Centre
www.bbc.co.uk/weather

Belgium
www.meteo.oma.be

France
www.meteo.fr

Germany
www.dwd.de

Guardian Weather
www.guardianunlimited.co.uk/weather

ITN
www.itn.co.uk/weather

Meteorological Office
www.met-office.gov.uk

Netherlands
www.knmi.nl

Online Weather
www.onlineweather.com

Royal Meteorological Society
www.royal-met-soc.org.uk/

Ski Club of Great Britain (Snow Reports)
www.skiclub.co.uk

USA
www.nws.noaa.gov

Weathercall
www.weathercall.co.uk

World Meteorological Organisation
www.wmo.ch

Yahoo! Weather
www.uk.weather.yahoo.com

news

Alertnet
www.alertnet.org

BBC
www.bbc.co.uk/news

CNN
www.cnn.com

Drudge Report
www.drudgereport.com

IRN
www.irn.co.uk

ITN
www.itn.co.uk

News Unlimited
www.newsunlimited.co.uk

NewsNow
www.newsnow.co.uk

PA News
www.pa.press.net

PA News Centre
www.pa.press.net/weather

PR Newswire
www.prnewswire.com

Reuters
www.reuters.com

Sky
www.sky.com/news

Teletext
www.teletext.co.uk

Universal Press Syndicate
www.uexpress.com

newspapers

British Local

Aberdeen & District Independent
www.aberdeen-indy.co.uk

Aberdeen Evening Express
www.thisisnorthscotland.co.uk

Andover Advertiser
www.andoveradvertiser.co.uk

Ascot Express
www.ascotexpress.co.uk

Ayrshire Post
www.inside-scotland.co.uk/ayrshire

Ballyclare Gazette
www.ulsternet-ni.co.uk

Banbury Guardian
www.banburyguardian.co.uk

Barnoldswick & Earby Times
www.eastlancsonline.co.uk

Barnsley Chronicle
www.barnsley-chronicle.co.uk

Barry & District News
www.thisisbarry.co.uk

Basildon Evening Echo
www.thisisessex.co.uk

Basingstoke Gazette
www.basingstokegazette.co.uk

Bath Chronicle
www.thisisbath.com

Belfast Telegraph
www.belfasttelegraph.co.uk

Belper News
www.belpernews.co.uk

Bexhill Observer
www.bexhillobserver.co.uk

Bexley News Shopper
www.newsshopper.co.uk

Bicester Advertiser
www.thisisoxfordshire.co.uk

Birmingham Post & Mail
www.go2birmingham.co.uk

Blackburn Citizen
www.thisislancashire.co.uk

Blackpool & Fylde Citizen
www.thisislancashire.co.uk

Blackpool Gazette
www.blackpool.com

Blairgowrie Advertiser
www.inside-scotland.co.uk/perthshire/index.html

Bognor Regis Journal & Guardian
www.jandg.co.uk

Bolton Evening News
www.thisislancashire.co.uk

Bournemouth Daily Echo
www.daily-echo.co.uk

Bradford Star
www.thisisbradford.co.uk

Bradford Telegraph & Argus
www.telegraph-and-argus.co.uk

Braintree Witham & Dunmow Times
www.thisisessex.co.uk

Brentwood Weekly News
www.thisisessex.co.uk

Brighton Evening Argus
www.argus-btn.co.uk

Bristol Evening Post
www.epost.co.uk

Bristol Journal
www.newscom.co.uk

Bristol Western Daily Press
www.westpress.co.uk

Bromley News Shopper
www.newsshopper.co.uk

Bromsgrove Standard
www.bromsgrovestandard.co.uk

Buckingham Advertiser
www.buckinghamonline.co.uk

Bucks Free Press
www.thisisbuckinghamshire.co.uk

Bucks Herald
www.bucksherald.co.uk

Burnley Citizen Group
www.thisislancashire.co.uk

Burnley Express
www.eastlancsnews.co.uk

Bury Free Press
www.buryfreepress.co.uk

Bury Times
www.thisislancashire.co.uk

Business Gazette
www.businessgazette.co.uk

Cambridge Evening News
www.cambridge-news.co.uk

Carlisle News & Star
www.news-and-star.co.uk

Carrickfergus Advertiser
www.ulsternet-ni.co.uk

Castle-Point Rayleigh Standard
www.thisisessex.co.uk

Chelmsford Woodham Weekly News
www.thisisessex.co.uk

Cheltenham Independent
www.thisisgloucestershire.co.uk

Cheshire Guardian Series
www.thisischeshire.co.uk

Chester Chronicle Newspapers
www.cheshirenews.co.uk

Chichester Observer
www.chiobserver.co.uk

Chorley Citizen
www.thisislancashire.co.uk

Citizen (Gloucester)
www.thisisgloucestershire.co.uk

Clacton, Frinton & Walton Gazette
www.thisisessex.co.uk

Clitheroe Advertiser & Times
www.eastlancsnews.co.uk/clithhome

Colchester Coastal Express
www.thisisessex.co.uk

Colne Times
www.eastlancashireonline.co.uk

Congleton Chronicle
www.beartown.co.uk

Congleton Guardian
www.thisischeshire.co.uk

Consett & Stanley Advertiser
www.thiisthenortheast.co.uk

Cornish Guardian
www.thisiscornwall.co.uk

Cornishman
www.thisiscornwall.co.uk

Courier (Dundee)
www.thecourier.co.uk

Coventry Evening Telegraph
www.go2coventry.co.uk

Craven Herald & Pioneer
www.thisisbradford.co.uk

Crawley News
www.icsurreyonline.icnetwork.co.uk

Crewe & Nantwich Guardian
www.thisischeshire.co.uk

Cumberland News (Carlisle)
www.cumberland-news.co.uk

Cumbria Life
www.cumbrialife.co.uk

Daily Express
www.express.co.uk

Darlington & Stockton Times
www.thisisthenortheast.co.uk

Darlington Northern Echo
www.thisisthenortheast.co.uk

Daventry Express
www.daventryonline.co.uk

Derby Evening Telegraph
www.thisisderbyshire.co.uk

Derbyshire Times
www.derbyshiretimes.co.uk

Dorking & Leatherhead Advertiser
www.dorkingadvertiser.co.uk

Dundee Courier
www.thecourier.co.uk

Dundee Evening Telegraph
www.dcthomson.co.uk/mags/tele

Dundee Weekly News
www.dcthomson.co.uk/mags/weekly

East Anglian Daily Times
www.eadt.co.uk

East Grinstead Courier
www.thisiskentandsussex.co.uk

East Grinstead Observer
www.eastgrinsteadobserver.co.uk

East London Advertiser
www.leevalley.co.uk/ela

Eastbourne Herald
www.eastbourneherald.co.uk

Eastwood Advertiser
www.eastwoodadvertiser.co.uk

Edinburgh Echo
www.edinburghecho.co.uk

Epsom & Banstead Herald
www.epsomherald.co.uk

Essex Chronicle Series
www.thisisessex.co.uk

Essex County Newspapers
www.thisisessex.xo.uk

Essex County Standard
www.thisisessex.xo.uk

Essex Weekly News
www.thisisessex.co.uk

Evening Argus (Brighton)
www.argus-btn.co.uk

Evening Herald (Plymouth)
www.plymouth-online.co.uk

Evening Press (York)
www.thisisyork.co.uk

Evening Standard
www.thisislondon.co.uk

Evening Telegraph (Peterborough)
www.peterboroughet.co.uk

Evesham, Cotswold, Stratford Journal
www.newsquestmidlands.co.uk

Express & Star Online (West Midlands)
www.westmidlands.com

Falkirk Herald
www.falkirkherald.co.uk

Gateshead Post
www.gateshead-post.co.uk

Gazette Series
www.gazetteseries.co.uk

Glasgow Evening Times
www.eveningtimes.co.uk

Glasgow Herald
www.theherald.co.uk

Gloucestershire Citizen
www.thisisgloucestershire.co.uk

Gloucestershire Echo
www.thisisgloucestershire.co.uk

Goole Times
www.btinternet.com/~gooletimes

Grimsby Evening Telegraph
www.grimsby-online.co.uk

Guardian Series Newspapers
www.thisischeshire.co.uk

Guernsey Press (Guernsey Evening &
Weekly Press)
www.guernsey-press.com

Halstead Gazette & Advertiser
www.thisiseesex.co.uk

Hampshire Chronicle
www.hampshirechronicle.co.uk

Hampstead & Highgate Gazette
www.hamhigh.co.uk

Harborough Mail
www.harborough.co.uk

Harlow Star
www.herts-essex-news.co.uk

Harrogate Advertiser
www.harrogate-advertiser-series.co.uk

Hartlepool Mail
www.hartlepool-mail.co.uk

Harwich & Manningtree Standard
www.thisiseesex.co.uk

Hastings Observer
www.observeronline.co.uk

Hemel Hempstead Gazette
www.hemelonline.co.uk

Hendon Times Group
www.thisislocallondon.co.uk

Herald & Post (Newcastle upon Tyne)
www.herald-and-post.co.uk

Hereford Times
www.thisisherefordshire.co.uk

Hertfordshire Mercury
www.herts-essex-news.co.uk

Herts & Essex News
www.herts-essex-news.co.uk

Herts & Essex Observer
www.herts-essex-news.co.uk

Hinckley Times
www.hinckley-times.co.uk

Hitchin & Stevenage Advertiser
www.theadvertiser.demon.co.uk

Horncastle News
www.horncastlenews.co.uk

Hornsea Post
www.hornseapost.co.uk

Hucknall Dispatch
www.hucknall-dispatch.co.uk

Huddersfield Daily Examiner
www.ichuddersfield.icnetwork.co.uk

Hull Daily Mail
www.hulldailymail.co.uk

Hunts Post
www.huntspost.co.uk

Isle of Man Independent
www.isle-of-man-newspapers.com

Isle of Wight County
www.iwcp.co.uk

Jersey Evening Post
www.jerseyeveningpost.com

Johnston Press
www.johnstonpress.co.uk

Keighley News
www.keighleynews.co.uk

Kenilworth Weekly News
www.kenilworthonline.co.uk

Kent & Sussex Courier
www.thisiskentandeastsussex.co.uk

Kent Messenger
www.kent-online.co.uk

Kilmarnock Standard
www.inside-scotland.co.uk

Knutsford Guardian
www.thisischeshire.co.uk

Lancashire Evening Post
www.lep.co.uk

Lancashire Evening Telegraph
www.thisislancashire.co.uk

Lancaster & Morecambe Citizen
www.thisislancashire.co.uk

Lancaster Guardian Series
www.thisislancashire.co.uk

Larne Gazette
www.ulsternet-ni.co.uk

Leamington Observer
www.leamington-now.com

Leamington Spa Courier
www.leamingtononline.co.uk

Leatherhead Advertiser
www.leatherheadadvertiser.co.uk

Leicester Mail
www.thisisleicestershire.co.uk

Leicester Mercury
www.leicestermercury.co.uk

Leigh Reporter
http://wiganonline.co.uk

Leigh, Tyldesley & Atherton Journal
www.thisislancashire.co.uk

Lewisham News Shopper
www.newsshopper.co.uk

Lincolnshire Echo
www.lincolnshire-live.co.uk

Lincolnshire Target
www.thisislincolnshire.co.uk

Liverpool Daily Post
www.liverpool.com/post

Liverpool Echo
www.liverpool.com/echo

Llangollen Courier
www.courier-llan.u-net.com

London Evening Standard
www.thisislondon.co.uk/dynamic/index.html

London Jewish News
www.ljn.co.uk

Louth Leader
www.louthleader.co.uk

Luton Herald & Post
www.lutononline.co.uk

Lynn News
www.lynnnews.co.uk

Maidenhead Advertiser
www.maidenhead-advertiser.co.uk

Maldon & Burnham Standard
www.thisisessex.co.uk

Malvern Gazette
www.newsquestmidlands.co.uk/malvern

Manchester Evening News
www.manchesteronline.co.uk

Mansfield Chad/Chronicle & Advertiser
www.chad.co.uk

Market Rasen Mail
www.marketrasentoday.co.uk

MegaStar
www.megastar.co.uk

Metro
www.metro.co.uk

Mid Devon Gazette
www.middevongazette.co.uk

Milton Keynes Citizen
www.miltonkeynes.co.uk

Morecambe Visitor
www.morecambeonline.co.uk

New Zealand News UK
www.nznewsuk.co.uk

Newark Advertiser
www.newarkadvertiser.co.uk

Newbury Weekly News
www.newburynews.co.uk

Newcastle Evening Chronicle
www.evening-chronicle.co.uk

Newcastle Herald & Post
www.herald-and-post.co.uk

Newcastle Journal
www.the-journal.co.uk

Newcastle Sunday Sun
www.sundaysun.co.uk

News & Star (Carlisle)
www.news-and-star.co.uk

Newton & Goldborne Guardian
www.thisischeshire.co.uk

North Devon Journal
www.northdevonjournal.co.uk

North East Evening Gazette
(Middlesbrough)
www.tees.net

North Eastern Evening Gazette
www.tees.net

North Wales Newspapers
www.nwnews.co.uk

North West Evening Mail
www.nwemail.co.uk

Northampton Chronicle & Echo
www.northamptonchronicleecho.co.uk

Northants Evening Telegraph
www.northamptonshireeveningtelegraph.co.uk

Northern Echo
www.thisisthenortheast.co.uk

Northern Echo (Darlington)
www.thisisthenortheast.co.uk

Northwich & District Guardian
www.ecn.co.uk

Nottingham Evening Post
www.thisisnottingham.co.uk

Ormskirk Advertiser
www.ormskirkadvertiser.co.uk

Oxford Mail
www.thisisoxfordshire.co.uk

Oxford Star
www.thisisoxfordshire.co.uk

Peterborough Evening Telegraph
www.peterboroughet.co.uk

Petersfield Post
www.thepost.co.uk

Plymouth Evening Herald
www.thisisplymouth.co.uk

Plymouth Western Morning News
www.thisisplymouth.co.uk

Portsmouth Journal
www.journal.co.uk

Portsmouth News
www.thenews.co.uk

Reading Chronicle
www.readingchronicle.co.uk

Reading Evening Post
www.getreading.co.uk

Reading Newspaper Company
www.rnc.co.uk

Redditch Advertiser/Alcester Chronicle
www.redditch-now.com

Rhyl, Prestatyn & Abergele Journal
www.nwn.co.uk

Rochdale Observer
www.rochdaleobserver.co.uk

Rugby Advertiser
www.rugbyonline.com

Rugby Observer
www.rugby-now.com

Runcorn & Widnes World
www.thisiswirral.co.uk

Rye & Battle Observer
www.ryeandbattleobserver.co.uk

Sale & Altrincham Messenger
www.thisistrafford.co.uk

Salisbury Journal
www.salisburyjournal.co.uk

Scotland on Sunday
www.scotlandonsunday.com

Scunthorpe Evening Telegraph
www.thisisscunthorpe.co.uk

Sevenoaks Chronicle
www.thisiskentandeastsussex.co.uk

Sheffield Star & Telegraph
www.sheffweb.co.uk

Shetland News
www.shetland-news.co.uk

Shetland Times
www.shetland-times.co.uk

Shetland Today
www.shetlandtoday.co.uk

Shields Gazette
www.shields-gazette.co.uk

Shropshire Star
www.shropshirestar.com

Skegness News
www.skegnesstoday.co.uk

Slough Express
www.sloughexpress.co.uk

Slough Observer
www.thisisslough.com

Somerset County Gazette
www.countygazette.co.uk

South Bucks Express
www.southbucksexpress.co.uk

South Wales Argus
www.southwalesargus.co.uk

South Wales Evening Post
www.thisissouthwales.co.uk

Southend Evening Echo
www.thisisessex.co.uk

Southend Observer
www.thisisessex.co.uk

Southern Daily Echo (Southampton)
www.dailyecho.co.uk

Southport Visiter
www.southportvisiter.co.uk

St Albans & District Review
www.thisishertfordshire.co.uk

St Albans Observer
www.thisishertfordshire.co.uk

St Helen's Reporter
www.wiganonline.co.uk

St Helen's Star
www.thisislancashire.co.uk

Star (Sheffield)
www.sheffweb.co.uk

Stornoway Gazette
www.stornoway-gazette.com

Stratford Herald
www.stratford-herald.co.uk

Stratford Standard
www.stratford-now.com

Stretford & Urmston Messenger
www.thisistrafford.co.uk

Stroud News & Journal
www.newscom.co.uk

Suffolk Now
www.suffolk-now.co.uk

Sunday Herald
www.sundayherald.com

Sunday Mercury
www.go2birmingham.co.uk

Sunday Post
www.sundaypost.com

Sunderland Echo
www.sunderland-echo.co.uk

Surrey Advertiser
www.surreyad.co.uk

Surrey Mirror Series
www.surreymirror.co.uk

Sussex Express
www.sussexexpress.co.uk

Swindon Evening Advertiser
www.thisiswiltshire.co.uk

Swindon Messenger
www.newscom.co.uk

Swindon Star
www.adver.co.uk

Torquay Herald Express
www.torquay-online.co.uk

Tyrone Courier
www.ulsternet-ni.co.uk

Ulster Gazette
www.ulsternet-ni.co.uk

Ulster Herald
www.ulsterherald.com

Warrington Mercury
www.thisischeshire.co.uk

Warwick Courier
www.warwickonline.co.uk

Watford Observer
www.watfordobserver.co.uk

Western Morning News
www.westernmorningnews.co.uk

Worcester Evening News
www.thisisworcestershire.co.uk

Yorkshire Evening Post
www.yorkshire-evening-post.co.uk

Yorkshire Post
www.ypn.co.uk

British National

Daily Mail
www.dailymail.co.uk

Daily Record
www.record-mail.co.uk

Daily Star
www.megastar.co.uk

Daily Telegraph
www.telegraph.co.uk

Financial Mail on Sunday
www.thisismoney.com

Financial Times
www.ft.com

Guardian
www.guardian.co.uk

Independent
www.independent.co.uk

Mirror
www.mirror.co.uk

News of the World
www.newsoftheworld.com

Observer
www.observer.co.uk

Racing Post
www.racingpost.co.uk

Scotsman
www.scotsman.com

Sun
www.thesun.co.uk

Sunday Mail
www.record-mail.co.uk

Sunday Mirror
www.sundaymirror.co.uk

Sunday People
www.people.co.uk

Sunday Times
www.sunday-times.co.uk

Times
www.the-times.co.uk

Foreign – Australia

Australia Daily
www.ausdaily.net.au

Australian Financial Review
www.afr.com.au

Canberra Times
www.canberratimes.com.au

Sydney Morning Herald
www.smh.com.au

The Australian Newspaper
www.theaustralian.com.au

West Australian News Review
www.perth-wa.com

Western Australian Business News
www.businessnews.com.au

Foreign – Austria

Kurier
www2.kurier.at

Foreign – Bangladesh

Daily Star
www.dailystarnews.com

Foreign – Belgium

Good Morning
www.yweb.com/goodmorningnews

Foreign – Canada

Edmonton Journal Extra
www.edmontonjournal.com

Globe & Mail
www.globeandmail.ca

Montreal Gazette
www.montrealgazette.com

Ottawa Citizen
www.ottawacitizen.com

Toronto Star
www.thestar.com

Vancouver Sun
www.vancouversun.com

Foreign – China

China Post
www.chinapost.gov.cn

China Today
www.chinatoday.com

South China Morning Post
www.scmp.com

Foreign – Cyprus

Cyprus News
www.cynews.com

Foreign – Denmark

Copenhagen Post
www.cphpost.dk

Foreign – Egypt

Egyptian Gazette
www.egy.com

Middle East Times
www.metimes.com

Foreign – France

Paris Match
www.parismatch.com

Foreign – Gibraltar

Gibraltar Chronicle
www.gibnet.com/chron

Foreign – Hungary

Budapest Sun
www.centraleurope.com

Foreign – India

Hindu
www.hinduonnet.com

Times of India
www.timesofindia.com

Foreign – Indonesian

Indonesian Observer
www.indoexchange.com/indonesian-observer

Foreign – Iran

Iran Daily
www.iran-daily.com

Foreign – Ireland

Clare Champion
www.clarechampion.ie

Derry People & Donegal News
www.donegalnews.com

Examiner
www.examiner.ie

Ireland on Sunday
www.irelandonsunday.com

Ireland Today
www.ireland-today.ie

Irish Echo
www.irishecho.com

Irish Independent
www.independent.ie

Irish News
www.irishnews.com

Irish Post
www.irishpost.co.uk

Irish Times
www.irish-times.com

Irish World
www.theirishworld.com

Kerry's Eye
www.iol.ie/kerryseye

Leinster Times & The Nationalist
www.lowwwe.com/nationalist

Limerick Leader
www.limerick-leader.ie

Limerick Post
www.limerickpost.ie

Mayo Gazette
www.mayogazette.com

Mayo News
www.mayonews.ie

Munster Express
www.munster-express.ie

Saoirse
http://ireland.iol.ie/~saoirse

Waterford Today
www.waterford-today.ie

Foreign – Israel

Jerusalem Post
www.jpost.co.il

Foreign – Japan

Asahi Shinbun
www.asahi.com/english

Foreign – Jordon

Jordan Times
www.jordantimes.com

Foreign – Kenya

East African Standard
www.eastandard.net

Foreign – Korea

Korea Herald
www.koreaherald.co.kr

Foreign – Kuwait

Kuwait Times
www.paaet.edu.kw/ktimes

Foreign – Lebannon

Daily Star
www.dailystar.com.lb

Foreign – Netherlands

Nederlander
www.netherlander.com

Foreign – New Zealand

Christchurch Press
www.press.co.nz

Otago Daily Times
www.odt.co.nz

Foreign – Nigeria

Guardian
www.ngrguardiannews.com

Foreign – Norway

Norway Post
www.norwaypost.no

Foreign – Pakistan

Herald
www.xiber.com

Foreign – Philippines

Philippine Star
www.philstar.com

Foreign – Russia

Pravda
www.pravda.ru

Foreign – Singapore

Zaobao
www.zaobao.com

Foreign – South Africa

WOZA
www.woza.co.za

Foreign – Sri Lanka

Island
www.island.lk

Foreign – Taiwan

China Times
www.chinatimes.com.tw/english

Foreign – Tanzania

Express
www.theexpress.com

Foreign – Thailand

Nation
www.nationgroup.com

Foreign – Turkey

Hurriyet
www.hurriyet.com.tr

Foreign – Uganda

Monitor
www.africanews.com/monitor

Foreign – USA

Arizona Republic
www.azcentral.com

Baltimore Sun
www.sunspot.net

Boston Globe
www.boston.com/globe

Chicago Sun-Times
www.suntimes.com

Chicago Tribune
www.chicagotribune.com

Cincinnati Enquirer
www.enquirer.com/today

Cincinnati Post
www.cincypost.com

Dallas Morning News
www.dallasnews.com

Denver Post
www.denverpost.com

Denver Rocky Mountain News
www.rockymountainnews.com

Detroit Free Press
www.freep.com

Detroit News
www.detnews.com

Fort Lauderdale Sun-Sentinel
www.sun-sentinel.com

Fort Worth Star-Telegram
www.star-telegram.com

Hollywood Reporter
www.hollywoodreporter.com

Houston Chronicle
www.chron.com

International Herald Tribune (USA)
www.iht.com

Kansas City Star
www.kcstar.com

Los Angeles Times
www.latimes.com

Miami Herald
www.herald.com

Milwaukee Journal Sentinel
www.onwis.com

Minneapolis Star Tribune
www.startribune.com

New York Daily News
www.nydailynews.com

New York Newsday
www.newsday.com

New York Post
www.nypostonline.com

New York Times
www.nytimes.com

Orlando Sentinel
www.orlandosentinel.com

Philadelphia Inquirer
www.phillynews.com/inq

Pittsburgh Tribune Review
www.triblive.com

Portland Oregonian
www.oregonian.com

Salt Lake Tribune
www.sltrib.com

San Francisco Chronicle
www.sfgate.com/chronicle

San Francisco Examiner
www.examiner.com

Seattle Times
www.seattletimes.com

Tampa Tribune
www.tampatrib.com

USA Today
www.usatoday.com

Wall Street Journal
www.wsj.com

Washington Post
www.washingtonpost.com

Washington Times
www.washtimes.com

Foreign – Vietnam

Saigon Times
www.saigon-news.com

Special Interest

Canadian Jewish News
www.cjnews.com

Christian Science Monitor
www.csmonitor.com

Jewish Chronicle
www.thejc.com

Jewish Telegraph
www.jewishtelegraph.com

Personal Finance

banks & building socieities

Abbey National
www.abbeynational.co.uk

Alliance & Leicester
www.alliance-leicester.co.uk

Allied Irish
www.aib.ie

Banc Cymru
www.bankofwales.co.uk

Bank of Ireland
www.bank-of-ireland.co.uk

Bank of Scotland
www.bankofscotland.co.uk

Bank of Wales
www.bankofwales.co.uk

BankNet
www.mkn.co.uk/bank

Barclaycard
www.barclaycard.co.uk

Barclays
www.barclays.co.uk

Bath
www.bibs.co.uk

Birmingham Midshires
www.askbm.co.uk

Bradford & Bingley
www.bradford-bingley.co.uk

Bristol & West
www.bristol-west.co.uk

Cahoot
www.cahoot.com

Cambridge Building Society
www.cambridge-building-society.co.uk

Capital
www.capitalbank.co.uk

Cash Centres
www.cashcentres.co.uk

Cater Allen (Isle of Man)
www.focusiom.com/CATER.htm

Cheltenham & Gloucester
www.cheltglos.co.uk

Chesham
www.cheshamsoc.co.uk

Co-op
www.co-operativebank.co.uk

Darlington
www.darlington.co.uk

Dunfermline Building Society
www.dunfermline-bs.co.uk

ECU
www.ecu.co.uk/group

Egg
www.egg.com

Express Finance
www.express-finance.co.uk

First Active
www.firstactive.co.uk

First Direct
www.firstdirect.co.uk

First Trust
www.ftbni.co.uk/ft

First-e
www.first-e.com

Fleming
www.fleming.co.uk/premier

Forexia
www.forexia.com

Granville
www.granville.co.uk

Grindlays
www.pb.grindlays.com

Halifax
www.halifax.co.uk

Hambros
www.hambrosbank.com

Hamilton
www.hdb.co.uk

Hays
www.hays-banking.co.uk

HFC
www.hfcbank.co.uk

Home & Capital Trust
www.homecapital.co.uk

HSBC
www.hsbc.com

ICC
www.icc.ie

Jyske
www.jbpb.com

Lambeth
www.lambeth.co.uk

Leeds & Holbeck
www.leeds-holbeck.co.uk

Leek
www.leek-united.co.uk

Legal & General
www.landg.com

Lloyds TSB
www.lloydstsb.co.uk

Lombard
www.lombard.co.uk/banking

Loughborough Building Society
www.theloughborough.co.uk

Market Harborough
www.mhbs.co.uk

Marsden
www.marsdenbs.co.uk

Melton Mowbray Building Society
www.mmbs.co.uk

Nationwide
www.nationwide.co.uk

NatWest
www.natwest.co.uk

Newbury Building Society
www.newbury.co.uk

Northern
www.nbonline.co.uk

Northern Rock
www.northernrock.co.uk

Norwich & Peterborough
www.npbs.co.uk

Nottingham Building Society
www.nottingham-bs.co.uk

Personal Loan Corporation
www.loancorp.co.uk

Prudential
www.pru.co.uk

Royal Bank of Canada (Channel Islands)
www.royalbankci.com

Royal Bank of Scotland
www.rbs.co.uk

Save & Prosper
www.prosper.co.uk

Scottish Financial Enterprise
www.sfe.org.uk

Secure Trust
www.securetrustbank.com

Skipton Building Society
www.skipton.co.uk

Smile
www.smile.co.uk

Staffordshire
www.staffordshirebuildingsociety.co.uk

Standard
www.sbl.co.uk

Standard Life
www.standardlifebank.com

Stroud & Swindon
www.stroudandswindon.co.uk

Sunbank
www.sunbank.co.uk

Teachers'
www.teachersbs.co.uk

Triodos
www.triodos.co.uk

Universal
www.universal.uk.com

Virgin Direct
www.virgin-direct.co.uk

West Bromwich Building Society
www.westbrom.co.uk

Woolwich
www.woolwich.co.uk

Yorkshire
www.ybs.co.uk

credit cards

Advanta
www.rbsadvanta.co.uk

American Express
www.americanexpress.co.uk

Barclaycard
www.barclaycard.co.uk

Capital One
www.capitalone.co.uk

CharityCard
www.charitycard.org

Diners Club
www.dinersclub.com

Football Club Credit Cards
www.footballcard.co.uk

Goldfish
www.goldfish.com

Marbles
www.marbles.com

Mastercard
www.mastercard.com

MBNA
www.mbna.com

Scottish Widows
www.scottishwidows.co.uk

Switch
www.switch.co.uk

Visa
www.visa.com

insurance

A1 Insurance
www.a1insurance.co.uk

AA Insurance
www.aainsurance.co.uk

Abacus Direct
www.abacusdirect.co.uk

Abbey Online
www.abbey-online.co.uk

Admiral
www.cmg.co.uk

Allied Dunbar
www.allieddunbar.co.uk

Anglia Countrywide
www.anglia-countrywide.co.uk

AutoDirect (HSBC)
www.autodirect.co.uk

AXA
www.axa.co.uk

Britannic Assurance
www.britannic.co.uk

BUPA
www.bupa.co.uk

Canada Life
www.canadalife.com

Carquote
www.carquote.co.uk

Central Direct
www.central-insurance.co.uk

CGU
www.cgu-direct.co.uk

Chubb
www.chubb.com

Churchill
www.churchill.co.uk

Columbus
www.columbusdirect.co.uk

Commercial Union
www.commercial-union.co.uk

Co-op
www.cis.co.uk

Cornhill
www.cornhill.co.uk

Cornhill Direct
www.cornhilldirect.co.uk

County
www.county-insurance.co.uk

DAS
www.das.co.uk

Denplan
www.denplan.co.uk

Dial Direct
www.ddirect.co.uk

Diamond
www.diamond.uk.com

Direct
www.digs.co.uk

Direct Line
www.directline.com

Eagle Star
www.eaglestar.co.uk

Elephant
www.elephant.co.uk

Endsleigh
www.endsleigh.co.uk

Equitable Life
www.equitable.co.uk

Firebond
www.firebond.co.uk

Hibernian Group
www.hibernian.ie

Hiscox
www.hiscox.com

Hogg Robinson
www.hoggrobinson.com

Home Quote
www.home.quote.co.uk

HSBC Insurance Brokers
www.insurancebrokers.hsbc.com

InterSure
www.intersure.co.uk

Lancaster
www.lancaster-ins.co.uk

Legal & General
www.legal-and-general.co.uk

Lloyds TSB
www.insurance.co.uk

MCM Group
www.mcmgroup.co.uk

National Mutual
www.nationalmutual.co.uk

NFU Mutual
www.nfumutual.co.uk

Norwich Union
www.norwich-union.co.uk

Old Mutual
www.oldmutual.com

Pearl
www.pearl.co.uk

Pet Plan
www.petplan.co.uk

PPP/Columbia
www.columbiahealthcare.co.uk

Preferential
www.preferential.co.uk

Privilege Cars
www.privilege.co.uk

Prospero Direct
www.prospero.co.uk

Prudential
www.pru.co.uk

Royal & Sun Alliance
www.royal-and-sunalliance.com

Royal Liver
www.royal-liver.com

Saga
www.saga.co.uk

Scottish Amicable
www.scottishamicable.com

Scottish Widows
www.scottishwidows.co.uk

Screentrade
www.screentrade.com

Sedgwick Group
www.sedgwick.com

Skandia Life
www.skandia.co.uk

Sportscover
www.sportscover.co.uk

Standard Life
www.standardlife.co.uk

Sun Life
www.sunlife.co.uk

Sun Life of Canada
www.sunbank.co.uk

Swinton
www.swinton.co.uk

Swiss Life (UK)
www.swisslife.co.uk

Trade Indemnity
www.tradeindemnity.com

UK Friendly
www.ukfriendly.co.uk

Western Provident
www.wpahealth.co.uk

Willis Corroon Group
www.willis.com

Woolwich Insurance Services
www.woolwich-insurance.co.uk

World Cover Direct
www.worldcover.co.uk

World Trekker
www.worldtrekker.com

Worldwide Travel
www.wwtis.co.uk

Zurich
www.zurich.com

investment funds

Aberdeen Asset Management
www.aberdeen-asset.com

Aberdeen Unit Trust Managers
www.aberdeen-knowhow.com

ABN AMRO Asset Management
www.invweek.co.uk/abn

AIB Asset Management
www.aibgovett.com

Baring Asset Management
www.baring-asset.com

Capel Cure Sharp
www.capelcuresharp.co.uk

Cazenove Fund Management
www.cazenove.com

City of London Investment Group
www.citlon.co.uk

Credit Suisse Asset Management
www.csamfunds.co.uk

Edinburgh Fund Managers
www.edfd.com

Ely Fund Managers
www.ely.uk.com

Fidelity
www.fidelity.co.uk

Finsbury Asset Management
www.finsbury-asset.co.uk

Flemings
www.fleming.co.uk

Foreign & Colonial
www.fandc.co.uk

Framlington
www.framlington.com

Friends Provident
www.friendsprovident.co.uk

Gartmore Investment
www.gartmore.co.uk

Gerrard Group
www.gerrard.com

Global Asset Management
www.ukinfo.gam.com

GNI Fund Management
www.gnifm.com

Henderson
www.henderson.co.uk

Herald Investment Management
www.heralduk.com

Hill Samuel
www.hillsamuel.co.uk

Invesco
www.invesco.co.uk

Investec Guinness Flight
www.investecguinnessflight.com

ISA Shop
www.isa-shop.co.uk

ITS Investment Trusts
www.itsonline.co.uk

Jupiter
www.jupiteronline.co.uk

Liverpool Victoria Friendly Society
www.lvbestbond.co.uk

M&G Group
http://mandg.co.uk

National Savings
www.nationalsavings.co.uk

Norwich Union
www.norwich-union.co.uk

Perpetual Investment
www.perpetual.co.uk

Pictet Group
www.pictet.com

Pinnacle
www.allmortgages.co.uk

PPM UK
www.ppm-uk.com

Premier Asset Management
www.premierfunds.co.uk

Royal Skandia
www.royalskandia.com

Sabre Fund Management
www.sabrefund.com

Save & Prosper
www.prosper.co.uk

Schroders
www.schroder.co.uk

Scottish Amicable
www.scottishamicable.com

Scottish Investment Trust
www.sit.co.uk

Scottish Life International
www.sli.co.im

Scottish Mutual International
www.smi.ie

Scottish Provident
www.scotprov.co.uk

Scottish Value Management
www.scottish-value.co.uk

Threadneedle Investments
www.threadneedle.co.uk

Virgin
www.virginmoney.com/isa

magazines & websites

Bloomberg
www.bloomberg.com

Business Money
www.business-money.com

CAROL
www.carol.co.uk

Citywatch
www.citywatch.co.uk

Direct Debit
www.directdebit.co.uk

Euromoney Online
www.euromoney.com

Hemmington Scott
www.hemscott.co.uk

Interactive Investor International
www.iii.co.uk

International Fund Investment
www.ifiglobal.com

Investment & Pensions Europe
www.ipeurope.co.uk

Investment Trust Newsletter
www.trustnews.co.uk

Investors Chronicle
www.investorschronicle.co.uk

Investors Internet Journal
www.iij.co.uk

Line One Money Zone
www.lineone.net/moneyzone

Money Money Money
www.moneymoneymoney.co.uk

Moneyweb
www.moneyweb.co.uk

MoneyWorld UK
www.moneyworld.co.uk

Motley Fool
www.fool.co.uk

Mrs Cohen
www.mrscohen.com

Offshore Investor
www.offshore-investor.com

Pensions World
www.pensionsworld.co.uk

Quicken.com
www.quicken.com

mortgages

Chase De Vere
www.cdvmortgage.co.uk

Home & Capital Trust
www.homecapital.co.uk

John Charcol
www.johncharcol.co.uk

Midlands Insurance Services
www.midlandsinsurance.freeserve.co.uk

Moneynet
www.moneynet.co.uk

Mortgage Help Desk UK
www.mortgageman.u-net

Mortgage Intelligence
www.mortgage-intelligence.co.uk

Mortgage Shop
www.mortgage-shop.co.uk

MTS Mortgage Company
www.mtsmortgage.co.uk

Royal & SunAlliance Investments
www.rsa-investments.co.uk

stockbrokers

Barclays Stockbrokers
www.barclays-stockbrokers.com

Brewin Dolphin
www.brewin.co.uk

Capel-Cure Sharp
www.capelcuresharp.co.uk

Cazenove & Co
www.cazenove.co.uk

Charles Schwab Europe
www.schwab-worldwide.com

Charles Stanley
www.charles-stanley.co.uk

CMC Group
www.cmcplc.com

Credit Suisse First Boston de Zoete & Bevan
www.csamfunds.co.uk

Durlacher Corporation
www.durlacher.co.uk

E*TRADE United Kingdom
www.etrade.co.uk

Edward Jones
www.edwardjones.com

European Stockbrokers
www.europeanstockbrokers.co.uk

GNI
www.gni.co.uk

Greig Middleton
www.greigmiddleton.co.uk

James Brearley & Sons
www.jbrearley.co.uk

Killik & Co.
www.killik.co.uk

Mercury Asset Management
www.mercury-asset-management.co.uk

Rudolf Wolff
www.rwolff.com

Salomon Smith Barney
www.sbil.co.uk

Selftrade
www.selftrade.com

TD Waterhouse
www.tdwaterhouse.co.uk

advertising & marketing •
agriculture •
animal health •
art & crafts •
arts & entertainment •
communications •
education •
emergency services •
employment •
engineering & electrical •
finance •
flying •
food & drink •
furniture •
general •
government •
healthcare •
law •
libraries & museums •
livery companies & guilds •
management & human resources •
manufacturing •
pharmaceutical •
printing & publishing •
property •
retail •
shipping •
transport •
travel & tourism •
utilities •

advertising & marketing

Advertising Association
www.adassoc.org.uk

Association of Qualitative Research
Practitioners
www.aqrp.co.uk

British Web Design & Marketing
Association
www.bwdma.co.uk

Chartered Institute of Marketing
www.cim.co.uk

Incorporated Society of British Advertisers
www.isba.org.uk

Institute of Practitioners in Advertising
www.ipa.co.uk

agriculture

Grain and Feed Trade Association (GAFTA)
www.gafta.com

National Farmers' Union
www.nfu.org.uk

animal health

British Equine Veterinary Association
www.beva.org.uk

British Small Animal Veterinary Association
www.bsava.ac.uk

British Veterinary Association
www.bva.co.uk

British Veterinary Nursing Association
www.vetweb.co.uk/sites/bvna

Royal College of Veterinary Surgeons
www.rcvs.org.uk

Society of Practising Veterinary Surgeons
www.spvs.org.uk

art & crafts

Association of Guilds of Weavers, Spinners
& Dyers
www.wsd.org.uk

British Woodworkers Federation
www.bwf.org.uk

Company of Master Jewellers
www.company-of-master-jewellers.co.uk

International Feltmakers Association
www.feltmakers.com

National Association of Goldsmiths
www.progold.net

arts & entertainment

Association of British Theatre Technicians
www.abtt.org.uk

Association of Mouth & Foot Painting
Artists Worldwide
www.amfpa.com

British Society of Master Glass Painters
www.bsmgp.org.uk

Broadcasting Entertainment
Cinematograph & Theatre Union (BECTU)
www.bectu.org.uk

Cartoonists' Guild
www.pipemedia.net/cartoons

Directors' Guild of Great Britain
www.dggb.co.uk

Equity British Actors' Union
www.equity.org.uk

Fine Art Trade Guild
www.fineart.co.uk

Guild of Television Cameramen
www.gtc.org.uk

Incorporated Society of Musicians
www.ism.org

London Association of Art & Design
Education
www.laade.org

Magic Circle
www.themagiccircle.co.uk

Musicians Union
www.musiciansunion.org.uk

Piano Tuners' Association
www.pianotuner.org.uk

Producers Alliance for Cinema & Television
www.pact.co.uk

Production Managers' Association
www.pma.org.uk

Society of Television Lighting Directors
www.stld.org.uk

communications

Communications Workers Union (CWU)
www.cwu.org

Radio Officers' Association
www.roassn.org

education

Association of Christian Teachers
www.christian-teachers.org

Association of University Administrators
www.aua.ac.uk

215

Association of University Teachers
www.aut.org.uk

National Association of School Masters Union of Women Teachers (NASUWT)
www.teachersunion.org.uk

National Union of Teachers (NUT)
www.teachers.org.uk

Professional Association of Nursery Nurses
www.pat.org.uk

emergency services

Ambulance Service Association
www.ambex.co.uk

Association of Police Authorities
www.apa.police.uk

Fire Brigade Union
www.fbu-ho.org.uk

Metropolitan Police Federation
www.metfed.org.uk

Police Federation for Northern Ireland
www.policefed-ni.org.uk

Police Federation of England & Wales
www.polfed.org

Scottish Police Federation
www.spf.org.uk

employment

Association of Direct Labour Organisations
www.adlo.org.uk

Equal Opportunities Commission
www.eoc.org.uk

Federation of Recruitment & Employment Services
www.rec.uk.com/home.htm

engineering & electrical

Agricultural Engineers Association
www.aea.uk.com

Amalgamated Engineering & Electrical (AEEU)
www.aeeu.org.uk

The Armed Forces Communications & Electronics Association
www.afcea.org.uk

Associated Society of Locomotive Engineers & Fireman
www.aslef.org.uk

Association of Consulting Engineers
www.acenet.co.uk

Association of Electrical & Mechanical Trades
www.aemt.co.uk

British Association of Professional Draftsmen
www.drafter.co.uk

Federation of the Electronics Industry
www.fei.org.uk

Institute of Chartered Engineers
www.ice.org.uk

finance

Accounting Standards Body
www.asb.org.uk

Arson Prevention Bureau
www.arsonpreventionbureau.org.uk

Association of Accounting Technicians
www.aat.co.uk

Association of British Insurers
www.abi.org.uk

Association of Chartered Certified Accountants
www.acca.co.uk

Association of Consulting Actuaries
www.aca.org.uk

Association of Corporate Treasurers
www.corporate-treasurers.co.uk

Association of Fundraising Consultants
www.afc.org.uk

Association of Independent Financial Advisers
www.aifa.net

Association of Insurers & Risk Managers
www.airmic.com

Association of International Accountants
www.aia.org.uk

Association of Investment Trust Companies
www.aitc.co.uk

Association of Private Client Investment Managers & Stockbrokers
www.apcims.org

Association of Unit Trusts & Investment Funds (AUTIF)
www.investmentfunds.org.uk

British Bankers Association
www.bba.org.uk

British Insurance & Investment Brokers Association
www.biba.org.uk

Building Societies Association
www.bsa.org.uk

Chartered Institute of Bankers
www.cib.org.uk

Chartered Institute of Public Finance & Accountancy
www.cipfa.org.uk

Chartered Institute of Taxation
www.tax.org.uk

Chartered Insurance Institute
www.cii.co.uk

Council of Mortgage Lenders
www.cml.org.uk

European Central Securities Depositories Association
www.ecsda.com

Factors & Discounters Association
www.factors.org.uk

Financial Accounting Standards Board
www.fasb.org

Financial Reporting Council
www.frc.org.uk

Financial Services Authority
www.fsa.gov.uk

Financial Services Consumer Panel
www.fs-cp.org.uk

Guernsey Financial Services Commission
www.gfsc.guernseyci.com

Guild of Film Production Accountants & Financial Administrators
www.gfpa.org.uk

Institute of Actuaries
www.actuaries.org.uk

Institute of Chartered Accountants of England
www.iceaw.org.uk

Institute of Chartered Accountants of Scotland
www.icas.org.uk

Institute of Financial Accountants
www.ifa.org.uk

Institute of Internal Auditors
www.iia.org.uk

Insurance Institute of London
www.iilondon.co.uk

International Federation of Accountants
www.ifac.org

International Underwriting Association of London
www.iua.co.uk

Investors Compensation Scheme (ICS)
www.the-ics.org.uk

Jersey Financial Services Commission
www.jerseyfsc.org

London Investment Bank Association
www.liba.org.uk

National Association of Pension Funds
www.napf.co.uk

Securities Institute
www.securities-institute.org.uk

Society of Insolvency Practitioners
www.spi.org.uk

Society of Investment Professionals
www.uksip.org

United Kingdom Shareholders' Association
www.uksa.org.uk

flying

British Airline Pilots Association
www.balpa.org.uk

British Women Pilots' Association
www.bwpa.demon.co.uk

food & drink

Allied Brewers Traders Association
www.breworld.com/abta

Army Catering Corps Association
www.regiments.org/milhist/uk/corps/ACC.htm

Brewers & Licensed Retailers Association
www.blra.co.uk

British Sandwich Association
www.martex.co.uk/bsa

Catering Equipment Distributors Association
www.ceda.co.uk

Federation of Bakers
www.bakersfederation.org.uk

Gin & Vodka Association of Great Britain
www.ginvodka.org

Institute of Brewing
www.breworld.com/iob

Institute of Food Research
www.ifrn.bbsrc.ac.uk

Institute of Food Science & Technology
www.ifst.org

International Brewers' Guild
www.breworld.com/brewersguild

International Flight Catering Association
www.ifca.co.uk

National Association of Catering Butchers
www.haighs.com/nacb.htm

National Association of Master Bakers
www.masterbakers.co.uk

National Federation of Fish Friers
www.federationoffishfriers.co.uk

National Pasta Association
www.ilovepasta.org

National Soft Drink Association
www.nsda.org

Restaurant Association
www.ragb.co.uk

Scotch Whisky Association
www.scotch-whisky.org.uk

Traidcraft
www.traidcraft.co.uk

Worshipful Company of Bakers
www.bakers.co.uk

furniture

Association of Master Upholsterers & Soft Furnishers
www.upholsterers.co.uk

Association of Suppliers to the Furniture Industry
www.asfi.org

British Antique Furniture Restorers Association
www.bafra.org.uk

British Contract Furnishing Association
www.bcfa.org.uk

British Furniture Manufacturers
www.bfm.org.uk

Kitchen Specialists Association
www.ksa.co.uk

general

British Office Systems & Stationery Federation
www.bossfed.co.uk

British Security Industry Association
www.bsia.co.uk

Butlers Guild
www.butlersguild.com

Motor Schools Association
www.msagb.co.uk

National Hairdressers Federation
www.the-nhf.org

Public & Commercial Services Union
www.pcs.org.uk

Trades Union Congress (TUC)
www.tuc.org.uk

Transport & General Workers Union
www.tgwu.org.uk

government

Association of Directors of Social Services
www.adss.org.uk

Association of First Division Civil Servants
www.fda.org.uk

Chartered Institute of Environmental Health Officers
www.cieh.org.uk/cieh

Unison
www.unison.org.uk

healthcare

Ancillary

Association of British Healthcare Industries
www.abhi.org.uk

Association of Professional Ambulance Personnel
www.apap.org.uk

British Dietetic Association
www.bda.uk.com

British Healthcare Trade Association
www.bhta.com

Carers Online
www.carersonline.org.uk

NHS Confederation
www.nhsconfed.org.

Complementary

Association of Reflexologists
www.aor.org.uk

British Acupuncture Council
www.acupuncture.org.uk

British Chiropractic Association
www.chiropractic-uk.co.uk

British Homeopathic Dental Association
www.bhda.org

British Medical Acupuncture Society
www.medical-acupuncture.co.uk

British Osteopathic Association
www.osteopathy.org

Canadian Chiropractic Association
www.ccachiro.org

Chiropractors' Association of Australia
www.caa.com.au

General Chiropractic Council
www.gcc-uk.org

International Chiropractors Association
www.chiropractic.org

International Federation of Aromatherapists
www.ifa.org.au

Society of Chiropodists & Podiatrists
www.feetforlife.org

Society of Teachers of the Alexander Technique
www.stat.org.uk

UK Aromatherapy Practitioners & Suppliers
www.fragrant.demon.co.uk/ukaromas.html

Dentistry

British Dental Association
www.bda-dentistry.org.uk

British Dental Trade Association
www.bdta.org.uk

British Endodontic Society
www.derweb.ac.uk/bes

British Society for Restorative Dentistry
www.derweb.ac.uk/bsrd

British Society of Dentistry for the
Handicapped
www.bsdh.org.uk

Dental Practice Board
www.dentanet.org.uk

General Dental Council
www.gdc-uk.org

Medicine & Surgery

American Medical Association
www.ama-assn.org

Anatomical Society
www.anatsoc.org.uk

Association of Clinical Pathologists
www.pathologists.org.uk

Association of Operating Department
Practitioners
www.aodp.org

Association of Police Surgeons
www.apsweb.org.uk

British Association of Accident &
Emergency Medicine
www.baem.org.uk

British Association of Emergency Medical
Technicians
www.baemt.org.uk

British Association of Paediatric Surgeons
www.baps.org.uk

British Association of Plastic Surgeons
www.baps.co.uk

British Medical Association
www.bma.org.uk

British Ophthalmic Anaesthesia Society
www.boas.org

Clinical Trial Managers Association
www.ctma.org.uk

General Medical Council
www.gmc-uk.org

Hospital Consultants & Specialists
Association
www.hcsa.com

Medical Defence Union
www.the-mdu.com

Medical Protection Society
www.mps.org.uk

Physiological Society
www.physoc.org

Royal College of Anaesthetists
www.rcoa.ac.uk

Royal College of General Practitioners
www.rcgp.org.uk

Royal College of Obstetricians &
Gynaecologists
www.rcog.org.uk

Royal College of Physicians, Edinburgh
www.rcpe.ac.uk

Royal College of Surgeons, Edinburgh
www.rcsed.ac.uk

Royal College of Surgeons, England
www.rcseng.ac.uk

Nursing & Midwifery

British Nursing Association
www.bna.co.uk

English National Board for Nursing,
Midwifery & Health Visiting
www.enb.org.uk

Federation of Independent Nursing
Agencies
www.fina-nursing.com

Infection Control Nurses Association
www.icna.co.uk

In-flight Nurses Association
www.gmb.dircon.co.uk/ifna

National Association of Theatre Nurses UK
www.natn.org.uk

National Board for Nursing, Midwifery &
Health Visiting for Northern Ireland
www.n-i.nhs.uk/nipec

National Board of Nursing, Midwifery &
Health Visiting in Scotland
www.nbs.org.uk

National HIV Nurses Association
www.fons.org/nhivna

Royal College of Nursing
www.rcn.org.uk

Royal College of Nursing Scotland
www.rcnscotland.org

Scottish National Board for Nursing,
Midwifery & Health Visiting
www.nbs.org.uk

United Kingdom Central Council for
Nursing, Midwifery & Health Visiting
www.ukcc.org.uk

Welsh National Board for Nursing,
Midwifery & Health Visiting
www.wnb.org.uk

Physiotherapy

Chartered Society of Physiotherapy
www.csphysio.org.uk

Psychology

Association of Psychological Therapists
www.apt.uk.com

British Association for Behavioural &
Cognitive Psychotherapies
www.babcp.org.uk

British Association of Psychotherapists
www.bap-psychotherapy.org

British Psychological Society
www.bps.org.uk

Speech Therapy

Royal College of Speech & Language
Therapists
www.rcslt.org

law

Academy of Experts
www.academy-experts.org

Association of Personal Injury Lawyers
www.apil.com

Chartered Institute of Patent Agents
www.cipa.org.uk

International Association for the Protection
of Industrial Property
www.aippi.org

Law Society
www.law-services.org.uk

libraries & museums

British Association for Information & Library
Education & Research
www.bailer.ac.uk

Council for Museums, Archives & Libraries
www.resource.gov.uk

Library & Information Commission
www.lic.gov.uk

Library Association
www.la-hq.org.uk

Museums Association
www.museumsassociation.org

Society of Archivists
www.archives.org.uk

livery companies & guilds

Company of Water Conservators
www.waterlco.co.uk

Mercer's Company
www.mercers.co.uk

Worshipful Collection of Clock Makers
www.clockmakers.org

Worshipful Company of Bakers
www.bakers.co.uk

Worshipful Company of Barbers
www.barbers.org.uk

Worshipful Company of Carpenters
www.thecarpenterscompany.co.uk

Worshipful Company of Curriers
www.btinternet.com/~kestrels

Worshipful Company of Engineers
www.engineerscompany.org.uk

Worshipful Company of Fan Makers
www.fanmakers.co.uk

Worshipful Company of Farriers
www.wcf.org.uk

Worshipful Company of Framework
Knitters
www.frameworkknitters.co.uk

Worshipful Company of Goldsmiths
www.thegoldsmiths.co.uk

Worshipful Company of Grocers
www.grocershall.co.uk

Worshipful Company of Information
Technologists
www.wcit.org.uk

Worshipful Company of Ironmongers
www.ironhall.co.uk

Worshipful Company of Makers of Playing
Cards
www.epcs.mcmail.com/worshipful.html

Worshipful Company of Marketors
www.marketors.fsnet.co.uk

Worshipful Company of Professional
Turners
www.rpturners.co.uk

Worshipful Company of Scientific
Instrument Makers
www.wcsim.co.uk

Worshipful Company of Spectaclemakers
www.spectaclemakers.com

Worshipful Company of Stationers &
Newspaper Makers
www.stationers.org

Worshipful Company of Upholders
www.upholders.co.uk

Worshipful Company of Wax Chandlers
www.waxchandlershall.co.uk

Worshipful Company of World Traders
www.world-traders.org

Worshipful Society of Apothecaries
www.apothecaries.org

management & human resources

Association for Consultants & Trainers
www.act-assn.dircon.co.uk

Institution of Professionals Managers & Specialists (IPMS)
www.ipms.org.uk

manufacturing

Association of Plastic Manufacturers
www.apme.org

Association of Play Industries
www.ipma.uk.com

Association of Suppliers to the British Clothing Industry
www.asbci.co.uk

British Aerosol Manufacturers Association
www.bama.co.uk

British Apparel & Textile Confederation
www.brainstorm.co.uk/TANC/Winners/Report/batc.html

Institute of Packaging
www.iop.co.uk

Institute of Paper
www.instpaper.org.uk

International Federation of Chemical, Energy, Mine & General Workers Unions
www.icem.org

Knitting, Footwear & Textile Workers (KFAT)
www.kfat.org.uk

Tobacco Manufacturers' Association
www.the-tma.org.uk

pharmaceutical

Association of the British Pharmaceutical Industry
www.abpi.org.uk

Boots Pharmacists' Association
omnisbpa.members.beeb.net

British Association of European Pharmaceutical Distributors
www.api.org.uk

National Pharmaceutical Association
www.npa.co.uk

Royal Pharmaceutical Society of Great Britain
www.rpsgb.org.uk

Scottish Pharmaceutical General Council
www.spgc.org.uk

printing & publishing

Booksellers Association
www.booksellers.org.uk

British Association of Picture Libraries
www.bapla.org.uk

British Printing Industries Federation
www.bpif.org.uk

Graphic & Printworkers Union (GPMU)
www.gpmu.org.uk

Independent Publishers Guild
www.ipg.uk.com

Institute of Printing
www.globalprint.com/uk/iop

National Association of Paper Merchants
www.napm.org.uk

National Union of Journalists (NUJ)
www.nuj.org.uk

Newspaper Society
www.newspapersoc.org.uk

Periodical Publishers Association
www.ppa.co.uk

Press Association
www.pa.press.net

Printmakers Council
www.printmaker.co.uk/pmc

Scottish Newspaper Publishers Association
www.snpa.org.uk

Screen Printers Association
www.martex.co.uk/screen-printing

Society of Editors
www.ukeditors.com

Society of Freelance Editors & Proofreaders
www.sfep.org.uk

Society of Indexers
www.socind.demon.co.uk

Writers Guild of Great Britain
www.writers.org.uk/guild

property

Association of Residential Letting Agents
www.arla.co.uk

British Association of Landscape Industries
www.bali.co.uk

Chartered Institute of Building
www.ciob.org.uk

Confederation of Roofing Contractors
www.corc.co.uk

Construction Employers Federation
www.cefni.co.uk

221

Federation of Master Builders
www.fmb.org.uk

Glass & Glazing Federation
www.ggf.org.uk

Guild of Architectural Ironmongers
www.martex.co.uk/gai

Housebuilders Federation
www.hbf.co.uk

Incorporated Society of Valuers & Auctioneers
www.isva.co.uk

Institute of Building Control
www.building-control.org

Institution of Structural Engineers
www.istructe.org.uk

National Association of Estate Agents
www.naea.co.uk

National Federation of Builders
www.builders.org.uk

National Housebuilders Council (NHBC)
www.nhbc.co.uk

National Housing Federation
www.housing.org.uk

Royal Institution of Chartered Surveyors
www.rics.org.uk

retail

Alliance of Independent Retailers
www.indretailer.co.uk

Balloon Association
www.nabas.co.uk

Booksellers Association of Great Britain & Northern Ireland
www.booksellers.org.uk

British Antique Dealers Association
www.bada.org

British Association of Toy Retailers
www.batr.co.uk

British Footwear Association
www.shoeworld.co.uk

British Jewellers Association
www.bja.org.uk

British Toy & Hobby Association
www.btha.co.uk

Giftware Association
www.giftware.org.uk

Independent Footwear Retailers Association
www.shoeshop.org.uk

LAPADA: Association of Art & Antique Dealers
www.lapada.co.uk

Union of Shop, Distributive & Allied Workers (USDAW)
www.poptel.org.uk/usdaw

shipping

British Marine Industries Federation
www.bigblue.org.uk

Shipbuilders & Shiprepairers Association
www.ssa.org.uk

transport

Association of Car Fleet Operators
www.acfo.org

Chartered Institute of Transport
www.citrans.org.uk

Institute of the Motor Industry
www.motor.org.uk

Transport Salaried Staffs Association
www.tssa.org.uk

travel & tourism

ABTA
www.abtanet.com

Association of European Travel Agents International
www.aeta.co.uk

Association of Independent Tour Operators
www.aito.co.uk

Association of National Tourist Offices
www.tourist-offices.org.uk

Hotel & Catering International Management Association
www.hcima.org.uk

Railway Industry Association
www.riagb.org.uk

utilities

British Water
www.britishwater.co.uk

CORGI (Gas Installers)
www.corgi-gas.co.uk

Electricity Association
www.electricity.org.uk

Institute of Plumbing
www.plumbers.org.uk

Water UK
www.water.org.uk

Science & Nature

astronomy

American Astronomical Society
www.aas.org

Armagh Observatory
www.arm.ac.uk/home.html

Armagh Planetarium
www.armagh-planetarium.co.uk

Astronomy Now
www.astronomynow.com

British Astronomical Society
www.ast.cam.ac.uk/~baa

British National Space Centre
www.bnsc.gov.uk

Buzz Aldrin
www.buzzaldrin.com

Consortium for European Research on
Extragalactic Surveys
www.jb.man.ac.uk/research/gravlens/data/ceres.
html

European Space Agency
www.esrin.esa.it

Greenwich Mean Time
www.gmt2000.co.uk

Hubble Space Telescope
www.stsci.edu

International Meteor Organisation
www.imo.net

Jodrell Bank
www.jb.man.ac.uk

Kennedy Space Centre
www.ksc.nasa.gov

NASA
www.nasa.gov

National Space Science Centre
www.nssc.co.uk

Royal Astronomical Society
www.ras.org.uk

Royal Observatory Edinburgh
www.roe.ac.uk

Royal Observatory, Greenwich
www.rog.nmm.ac.uk

Sky at Night
www.bbc.co.uk/skyatnight

Society for Popular Astronomy
www.popastro.com

Starchaser Foundation
www.starchaser.co.uk

State Research Centres of Russian
Federation
www.extech.msk.su/src_eng

University of London Observatory
www.ulo.ucl.ac.uk

conservation

Advisory Committee on Protection of the
Sea
www.acops.org

Animal Aid
www.animalaid.org.uk

Atlantic Salmon Trust
www.atlanticsalmontrust.org

Bat Conservation Trust
www.bats.org.uk

Bird Life International
www.birdlife.net

Born Free Foundation
www.bornfree.org.uk

British Deer Society
www.bds.org.uk

British Dragonfly Society
www.dragonflysoc.org.uk

British Hedgehog Preservation Society
www.software-technics.co.uk/bhps

Flora Locale
www.floralocale.org

Game Conservancy Trust
www.game-conservancy.org.uk

Hawk & Owl Trust
www.hawkandowl.org

International Wildlife Coalition
www.iwc.org

Marine Conservation Society
www.mcsuk.org

National Birds of Prey Centre
www.nbpc.co.uk

National Federation of Badger Groups
www.nfbg.org.uk

National Ferret Welfare Society
http://homepage.ntlworld.com/ferreter

National Seal Sanctuary
www.sealsanctuary.co.uk

Nature Conservation Bureau
www.naturebureau.co.uk

Orangutan Foundation UK
www.orangutan.org.uk

Parrot Line
www.parrotline.org

Rainforest Action Network
www.ran.org

Raptor Conservation
www.raptor.uk.com

Scottish Natural Heritage
www.snh.org.uk

Slimbridge Wildfowl & Wetlands Centre
www.wwt.org.uk/visit/slimbridge

Wetland Centre
www.wetlandcentre.org.uk

Whale & Dolphin Conservation Society
www.wdcs.org.uk

Whale Foundation
www.whale-foundation.org

Wildfowl & Wetlands Trust
www.wwt.org.uk

Wildlife Trust
www.wildlifetrust.org.uk

World Society for the Protection of Animals
www.wspa.org.uk

World Wide Fund for Nature
www.panda.org

WWF International
www.panda.org

WWF UK
www.wwf-uk.org

Young People's Trust for the Environment &
Nature Consrevation
www.yptenc.org.uk

magazines & websites

Alpha Galileo
www.alphagalileo.org

Astronomy
www.astronomy.com

Birds of Britain
www.birdsofbritain.co.uk

Birdwatch
www.birdwatch.co.uk

Chemistry & Industry Magazine
www.chemind.org

Chemistry UK
www.u-net.com/ukchem

Delphi Magazine
www.itecuk.com/delmag

Developers Review
www.itecuk.com/devrev

Ecologist
www.gn.apc.org/ecologist

Elemental Discoveries
www.camsoft.com/elemental

Journal of Natural History
www.tandf.co.uk/jnls/nah.htm

National Geographic
www.nationalgeographic.com

Nature
www.nature.com

Naturenet
www.naturenet.net

New Civil Engineer
www.nceplus.co.uk

New Electronics
www.neon.co.uk

New Scientist
www.newscientist.co.uk

Physics World
www.physicsweb.org

Planet Ark
www.planetark.org

Science Frontiers
www.science-frontiers.com

Science News
www.sciencenews.org

Science Online
www.scienceonline.org

Scientific American
www.sciam.com

Stephen Hawking
www.hawking.org.uk

Tomorrow's World (BBC)
www.bbc.co.uk/tw

Walking with Dinosaurs
www.bbc.co.uk/dinosaurs

societies & institutions

Amateur Entomologists' Society
www.theaes.org

Association for Science Education
www.ase.org.uk

Association for Women in Science &
Engineering
www.awise.org

Association of British Fungus Groups
www.abfg.org

British Antarctic Survey
www.antarctica.ac.uk

British Association for the Advancement of
Science
www.britassoc.org.uk

British Bee Keepers Association
www.bbka.org.uk

British Geological Survey
www.bgs.ac.uk

British Horological Institute
www.bhi.co.uk

British Mycological Society
www.britmycolsoc.org.uk

British Ornithologists' Union
www.bou.org.uk

British UFO Research Association
www.bufora.org.uk

Central Science Laboratory
www.csl.gov.uk

Council for Science & Technology
www.cst.gov.uk

Engineering & Physical Sciences Research
Council
www.epsrc.ac.uk

Field Studies Council
www.field-studies-council.org

Forensic Science Society
www.forensic-science-society.org.uk

Geological Society
www.geolsoc.org.uk

Human Cloning Foundation
www.humancloning.org

Human Genetic Advisory Commission
www.hgc.gov.ukk

Independent Cat Society
www.welcome.to/tipcs

Institute of Biology
www.iob.org

Institute of Biomedical Sciences
www.ibms.org

Institute of Broadcast Sound
www.ibs.org.uk

Institute of Hydrology
www.nwl.ac.uk/ih

Isaac Newton Institute
www.newton.cam.ac.uk

Jane Goodall Institute
www.janegoodall.org

Linnean Society of London
www.linnean.org

Mammal Society
www.abdn.ac.uk/mammal

National Bird of Prey Centre
www.nbpc.co.uk

National Institute of Agricultural Botany
www.niab.com

National NDT Centre
www.aeat.co.uk/ndt

Natural Resources Institute
www.nri.org

Office of Science & Technology
www.dti.gov.uk/ost

Palaeontological Association
www.palass.org

Paleontological Society
www.paleosoc.org

Plantlife
www.plantlife.org.uk

Primate Society of Great Britain
www.psgb.org

Roslin Institute
www.ri.bbsrc.ac.uk

Royal Academy of Engineering
www.raeng.org.uk

Royal Botanic Gardens
www.rbgkew.org.uk

Royal Entomological Society
www.royensoc.co.uk

Royal Geographical Society
www.rgs.org

Royal Society
www.royalsoc.ac.uk

Royal Society of Chemistry
www.rsc.org

Scientists of Global Responsibility
www.sgr.org.uk

Scottish Ornithologists' Club
www.the-soc.org.uk

Society for Experimental Biology
www.sebiology.org

Society for Interdisciplinary Studies
www.knowledge.co.uk/sis

Society for Underwater Exploration
www.underwaterdiscovery.org

Tree Register
www.tree-register.org

UK Science Park Association
www.ukspa.org.uk

World Nuclear Association
www.world-nuclear.org

Zoological Society of London
www.zsl.org

ZOOS

Banham Zoo
www.banhamzoo.co.uk

Blackpool
www.blackpoolzoo.org.uk

Bristol
www.bristolzoo.org.uk

Chester
www.chesterzoo.org.uk

Colchester
www.colchester-zoo.uk

Dublin
www.dublinzoo.ie

Dudley
www.dudleyzoo.org.uk

Edinburgh
www.edinburghzoo.org.uk

Howletts Wild Animal Park
www.howletts.net

Knowsley Safari Park
www.knowsley.com

London
www.londonzoo.co.uk

Longleat Safari Park
www.longleat.co.uk

Marwell
www.marwell.org.uk

Mole Hall Wildlife Park
www.molehall.co.uk

National Sea Life Centre
www.sealife.co.uk

Paignton
www.paigntonzoo.org.uk

Paradise Wildlife Park
www.pwpark.com

Twycross
www.twycrosszoo.com

West Midlands Safari Park
www.wmsp.co.uk

Whipsnade
www.londonzoo.co.uk/whipsnade

Shopping

antiques & auctions

Antique Dealers Directory
www.antique-dealers-directory.co.uk

Antiques Bulletin Online
www.antiquesbulletin.com

Antiques Roadshow
www.bbc.co.uk/antiques

Antiques Trade Gazette
www.atg-online.com

Antiques UK
www.antiques-uk.co.uk

Antiques Wesites
www.antiqueswebsites.co.uk

Antiques-Net
www.antiques-net.co.uk

Association of Art & Antique Dealers
(LAPADA)
www.lapada.co.uk

BBC Online
www.bbc.co.uk/antiques

Bonhams
www.bonhams.com

British Antique Furniture Restorers'
Association
www.bafra.org.uk

British Horological Institute
www.bhi.co.uk

Bushwood Antiques
www.bushwood.co.uk

Chappell's and the Antiques Centre
www.chappells-antiques.co.uk

Chinasearch
www.chinasearch.uk.com

Christie's
www.christies.com

Daltons Antiques
www.daltons.com

David Martin-Taylor Antiques
www.davidmartintaylor.com

Dodge & Son
www.dodgeandson.co.uk

Godson & Coles
www.godsonandcoles.co.uk

Kemberly Antique Clocks
www.kdclocks.co.uk

Lassco Ltd
www.lassco.co.uk

Lots Road Galleries
www.lotsroad.com

Mallett
www.mallett.co.uk

Olympia Fine Art & Antiques Fairs
www.olympia-antiques.co.uk

Philips
www.philips-auctions.com

Portobello Antiques Market
www.portobelloroad.co.uk

Pugh's Farm Antiques
www.pughs-antiques-export.com

QXL.com
www.qxl.com

Salvo
www.salvo.co.uk

Sothebys
www.sothebys.com

Stanley Gibbons
www.stanleygibbons.com

The Art Loss Register Ltd
www.artloss.com

Wallis & Wallis
www.wallisandwallis.co.uk

beds & bedding

Dunlopillo
www.dunlopillo.co.uk

Relyon
www.relyon.co.uk

Rest Assured
www.rest-assured.co.uk

Sealy
www.sealyuk.co.uk

Silent Night
www.silentnight.co.uk

Sleep Council
www.sleepcouncil.org.uk

Slumberland
www.slumberland.co.uk

books

AlphabetStreet
www.alphabetstreet.co.uk

Amazon
www.amazon.co.uk

Barnes & Noble
www.barnesandnoble.com

BBC Shop
www.bbcshop.com

Blackwell's
www.blackwells.co.uk

Bol
www.bol.co.uk

Book Club Associates
www.bca.co.uk

Bookzone
www.bookzone.co.uk

Borders
www.borders.com

Cook Book Shop
www.cooks-book-shop.co.uk

Countrybooks
www.countrybookshop.co.uk

Dillons
www.dillons.co.uk

Dorling Kindersley
www.dk.com/uk

Hammicks
www.thebookplace.com

Heffers
www.heffers.co.uk

Internet Bookshop
www.bookshop.co.uk

James Thin
www.jamesthin.co.uk

John Menzies
www.john-menzies.co.uk

John Smith
www.johnsmith.co.uk

Ottakar's
www.ottakars.co.uk

Penguin
www.penguin.co.uk

Talking Book Club
www.talkingbookclub.co.uk

Tesco
www.tesco.com/books

The Book Place
www.thebookplace.com

The Children's Bookshop
www.childrensbookshop.com

The Red House
www.redhouse.co.uk

Waterstones
www.waterstones.co.uk

WH Smith
www.whsmith.co.uk

World Books
www.worldbooks.co.uk

Zwemmer
www.zwemmer.co.uk

china & glass

Chinacraft
www.chinacraft.co.uk

Dartington Crystal
www.dartington.co.uk

Lladró
www.lladro.com

Poole Pottery
www.poolepottery.co.uk

Portmeirion
www.portmeirion.com

Royal Doulton
www.royal-doulton.com

Spode China
www.spode.co.uk

Wedgwood
www.wedgwood.co.uk

clothes

Alexandra
www.alexandra.co.uk

Aquascutum
www.aquascutum.co.uk

Armani
www.armaniexchange.com

Artigiano
www.artigiano.co.uk

Austin Reed
www.austinreed.co.uk

Ben Sherman
www.bensherman.co.uk

Benetton
www.benetton.com

Bernini
www.bernini.co.uk

Betty Barclay
www.bettybarclay.co.uk

Boden
www.boden.co.uk

Boxfresh
www.boxfresh.co.uk

Brooks Brothers
www.brooks-brothers.net

Browns
www.brownsfashion.com

Burtons
www.burtonmenswear.co.uk

C & A
www.c-and-a.com

Caractere
www.caractere.it

Charles Tyrwhitt
www.ctshirts.co.uk

Ciro Citterio
www.cirocitterio.com

Cotswold
www.cotswold-outdoor.co.uk

Cotton Moon
www.cottonmoon.co.uk

Cyrillus
www.cyrillus.co.uk

Diesel
www.diesel.co.uk

DKNY
www.donnakaran.com

Dockers
www.dockers.com

Donaldson
www.donaldson.be

Dorothy Perkins
www.dorothyperkins.co.uk

Dressmart.com
www.dressmart.com

Eddie Bauer
www.eddiebauer.co.uk

Elvi
www.elvi.co.uk

Empire Stores
www.empirestores.co.uk

Evans
www.evans.ltd.uk

Fat Face
www.fatface.co.uk

Fenn Wright & Manson
www.fwm.co.uk

FireTrap
www.firetrap.co.uk

Frank Usher
www.frankusher.co.uk

Freemans
www.freemans.co.uk

French Connection
www.frenchconnection.com

French Sole
www.frenchsole.com

Gap
www.gap.com

Gap Kids
www.gapkids.com

Georgina von Etzdorf
www.georginavonetzdorf.co.uk

Gianfranco Ferre
www.gianfrancoferre.com

Givenchy
www.givenchy.com

Grattan
www.grattan.co.uk

GUS
www.shoppersuniverse.com

Gymboree
www.gymboree.com

H & M Hennes
www.hm.com

Hackett
www.hackett.co.uk

Harvie & Hudson
www.harvieandhudson.com

Hawkshead
www.hawkshead.com

Henri Lloyd
www.henrilloyd.com

High & Mighty
www.highandmighty.co.uk

Jaeger
www.jaeger.co.uk

James Meade
www.jamesmeade.com

Kaleidescope
www.kaleidoscope.co.uk

Kays
www.kaysnet.com

Kelsey Tailors
www.kelseytailors.co.uk

Kingshill
www.kingshilldirect.co.uk

L L Bean
www.llbean.com

La Redoute
www.redoute.co.uk

Lands' End
www.landsend.co.uk

Laura Ashley
www.laura-ashley.com

Levis
www.eu.levi.com

Liberty
www.liberty-of-london.com

Look Again
www.lookagain.co.uk

Lycra
www.lycra.com

Madhouse
www.madhouse.co.uk

Marks & Spencer
www.marksandspencer.com

Marshalls
www.marshalls.co.uk

Monsoon
www.monsoon.co.uk

Morgan
www.morgan.fr

Moschino
www.moschino.it

Moss Bros
www.mossbros.co.uk

Muji
www.mujionline.com

Next
www.next.co.uk

Oasis
www.oasis-stores.com

Oilily
www.oililyusa.com

Olsen
www.olsen.de

Osh Kosh B'Gosh
www.oshkoshbgosh.com

Paul Smith
www.paulsmith.co.uk

Pepe Jeans
www.pepejeans.com

Peruvian Connection
www.peruvianconnection.com

Prada
www.prada.com

Principles
www.principles.co.uk

Pringle
www.pringle-of-scotland.co.uk

QS
www.qsgroup.co.uk

Racing Green
www.racinggreen.co.uk

Red or Dead
www.redordead.co.uk

Reiss
www.reiss.co.uk

River Island
www.riverisland.com

Scotch Corner
www.scotch-corner.co.uk

Sophia Swire
www.sophiaswire.com

Ted Baker
www.tedbaker.co.uk

The Clothes Store
www.theclothesstore.com

Thomas Pink
www.thomaspink.co.uk

Tie Rack
www.tie-rack.co.uk

Timberland
www.timberland.com

Tommy Hilfiger
www.tommypr.com

Top Man
www.topman.co.uk

TopShop
www.tops.co.uk

Virgin Clothing Company
www.virginclothing.co.uk

Wealth of Nations
www.wealthofnations.co.uk

Wrangler
www.wrangler.com

Children

Childrenswear Websites
www.childrenswearwebsites.co.uk

Clothes 4 Boys
www.clothes4boys.co.uk

Hopscotch
www.hopscotchmailorder.co.uk

Jokids
www.jokids.com

Lads & Lasses
www.ladsandlasses.co.uk

Patricia Smith
www.patriciasmith.co.uk

Poppy Ltd
www.poppy-children.co.uk

Raindrops
www.raindrops.co.uk

Schoolwear Centre
www.schoolwear-centre.co.uk

Snazzykids
www.snazzykids.co.uk

The Children's Warehouse
www.childrens-warehouse.com

The Kids Window
www.thekidswindow.co.uk

Trotters
www.trotters.co.uk

Vertbaudet
www.vertbaudet.co.uk

computers & electrical

Carphone Warehouse
www.carphonewarehouse.com

Comet
www.comet.co.uk

C-Pen
www.cpen.com

Currys
www.dixons.com/about_currys.html

Dixons
www.dixons.co.uk

Duracell
www.duracell.com

Ever Ready
www.everready.co.uk

Hewlett Packard
www.hp.com

Hi-Fidelity
www.hi-fidelity.co.uk

Home Electronics Show
www.livexpo.co.uk

Link
www.the-link.co.uk

Matsushita
www.meluk.co.uk

PC World
www.pcworld.co.uk

Powerhouse
www.powerhouse-retail.co.uk

Roberts Radios Direct
www.wesellradios.co.uk

Robertsons
www.robertsons-online.co.uk

Simply
www.simply.co.uk

Time
www.timecomputers.com

cosmetics & perfumes

Avon
www.uk.avon.com

BeneFit
www.benefitcosmetics.com

Biore
www.biore.com

Bloom Cosmetics
www.bloomcosmetics.com

Bobbi Brown
www.bobbibrowncosmetics.com

Body Shop
www.thebodyshop.co.uk

Bonne Bell
www.bonnebell.com

Boots
www.wellbeing.com

Cacharel
www.cacharel.com

Chanel
www.chanel.com

Clarins
www.clarins-paris.com

Clinique
www.clinique.com

Color Me Beautiful
www.colorme.com

Colorlab
www.colorlab-cosmetics.com

Cover Girl
www.covergirl.com

Crabtree & Evelyn
www.crabtree-evelyn.com

Culpeper
www.culpeper.co.uk

Darphin
www.darphin.fr/en/index2.html

Dior
www.dior.com

Dr Hauschka
www.drhauschka.com

Elizabeth Arden
www.elizabetharden.com

Eve Lom
www.evelom.co.uk

Givenchy
www.givenchy.com

Gucci
www.gucci.com

Hard Candy
www.hardcandy.com

Hugo Boss
www.hugo.com

Issey Miyake
www.isseymiyake.com

Jean Paul Gaultier
www.jpgaultier.fr

Joey New York
www.joeyny.com

Jurlique
www.jurlique.com.au

Lacoste
www.lacoste.com/index_uk.htm

Lancaster
www.lancaster-beauty.com

Lancome
www.lancome.com

Laura Mercier
www.lauramercier.com

L'Oreal
www.loreal.com

Lush
www.lush.co.uk

Liz Earle
www.lizearle.com

Mac
www.maccosmetics.com

Mary Kay
www.marykay.com

Max Factor
www.maxfactor.com

Maybelline
www.maybelline.com

MUM Roll On
www.mum-online.co.uk

Nars
www.narscosmetics.com

Nu Skin
www.nuskin.com

Oil of Olay
www.olay.com

Paco Rabanne
www.pacorabanne.com

Philosophy
www.philosophy.com

Profaces
www.profaces.com

Ren
www.ren.ltd.uk

Revlon
www.revlon.com

Shiseido
www.shiseido.co.uk

Sisley
www.sisley.tm.fr

Space NK
www.spacenk.co.uk

Stila
www.stilacosmetics.com

Sundari
www.sundari.com

Tommy Hilfiger
www.tommypr.com

Yves Saint Laurent
www.yslonline.com

department stores

Allders
www.allders.co.uk

Argos
www.argos.co.uk

Bentalls
www.bentalls.co.uk

Bhs
www.bhs.co.uk

Debenhams
www.debenhams.co.uk

Fortnum & Mason
www.fortnumandmason.co.uk

Harrods
www.harrods.com

House of Fraser
www.houseoffraser.co.uk

Index
www.indexshop.com

John Lewis
www.johnlewis.co.uk

Liberty
www.liberty-of-london.com

Marks & Spencer
www.marksandspencer.com

Selfridges
www.selfridges.co.uk

Woolworths
www.woolworths.co.uk

flooring

Allied Carpets
www.alliedcarpets.co.uk

Amtico
www.amtico.co.uk

Axminster
www.axminster-carpets.co.uk

Brintons
www.brintons.co.uk

British Wool Marketing Board
www.britishwool.org.uk

Carpet Information Centre
www.carpetinfo.co.uk

Carpetright
www.carpetright.co.uk

Duralay
www.duralay.co.uk

Marley
www.marley.co.uk

Ryalux
www.ryalux.com

Stoddard
www.stoddardintl.co.uk

Weston Carpets
www.weston-carpets.co.uk

Wilton
www.wiltoncarpets.com

flowers

August
www.augustflorist.co.uk

Clareflorist
www.clareflorist.co.uk

Flowergram
www.flowergram.co.uk

Flowers Direct
www.flowersdirect.co.uk

Interflora
www.interflora.co.uk

Jane Packer
www.jane-packer.co.uk

Teleflorist
www.teleflorist.co.uk

William Hayford
www.william-hayford.co.uk

furniture & upholstery

Chaplins
www.chaplins.co.uk

Conran Shop
www.conran.co.uk

Designers Guild
www.designersguild.com

Ducal
www.ducal-furniture.co.uk

Ercol
www.ercol.com

Fogarty
www.fogarty.co.uk

G Plan
www.morrisfurniture.co.uk/gplan

General Trading Company
www.general-trading.co.uk

Habitat
www.habitat.net

Harris Carpets
www.harriscarpets.co.uk

Holding Company
www.theholdingcompany.co.uk

Ikea
www.ikea.com

Indian Ocean Trading Company
www.indian-ocean.co.uk

Iron Bed Company
www.ironbed.co.uk

Kingdom of Leather
www.kingdomofleather.co.uk

Laura Ashley
www.laura-ashley.com

Ligne Roset
www.ligne-roset.co.uk

Marks & Spencer
www.marks-and-spencer.co.uk

McCord
www.mccord.uk.com

MFI Homeworks
www.mfi.co.uk

Multiyork
www.multiyork.co.uk

Parker Knoll
www.parkerknoll.co.uk

Purves & Purves
www.purves.co.uk

Sharps
www.sharps.co.uk

The Garden Shop
www.thegardenshop.co.uk

The Holding Company
www.theholdingcompany.co.uk

Wesley Barrell
www.wesley-barrell.co.uk

World of Leather
www.worldofleather.com

gifts & stationery

Birthdays
www.birthdays.co.uk

Cards Galore
www.cardsgalore.co.uk

Charles Letts
www.letts.co.uk

Charles Rennie Mackintosh Store
www.rennie-mackintosh.co.uk

Choc Express
www.chocexpress.com

Hallmark Cards
www.hallmark.com

Lastminute.com
www.lastminute.com

Links
www.linksoflondon.com

Papermate
www.papermate.co.uk

Past Times
www.past-times.com

Pen Shop
www.penshop.co.uk

Prince's Trust Shop
www.princestrustshop.co.uk

Red Letter Days
www.redletterdays.co.uk

Smythson of Bond Street
www.smythson.com

Thorntons
www.thorntons.co.uk

Victorinox
www.victorinox.com

Voucher Express
www.voucherexpress.com

healthcare, beauty & personal hygiene

Alka Seltzer
www.alka-seltzer.com

BaByliss
www.babyliss.co.uk

Bic
www.bicworld.com

Bioforce
www.bioforce.co.uk

Bodyform
www.bodyform.co.uk

Boots
www.wellbeing.com

Braun
www.braun.com

Camilla Hepper
www.camillahepper.co.uk

Cibavision
www.cibavision.co.uk

Colgate
www.colgate.com

Denman Brushes
www.denmanbrush.com

Durex
www.durex.com

Gillette
www.gillette.com

Kimberly Clark
www.kimberly-clark.com

Lanes
www.laneshealth.com

Listerine
www.listerine.com

L'Oreal
www.loreal.com

Macleans
www.macleans.co.uk

Nelsons
www.nelsons.co.uk

Nicorette
www.nicorette.co.uk

Nicotinell
www.nicotinell.co.uk

Nivea
www.nivea.co.uk

Nurofen
www.nurofen.com

Opal
www.opal-london.com

Oral B
www.oralb.com

Palmers Cocoa Butter
www.palmerscocoabutter.com

Potter's Herbal Medicines
www.pottersherbals.co.uk

Rennies
www.rennie.co.uk

Seven Seas
www.seven-seas.ltd.uk

Slendertone
www.slendertone.co.uk

Solgar
www.solgar.com

Strepsils
www.strepsils.com

Tampax
www.tampax.com

Tisserand
www.tisserand.com

Vitabiotics
www.vitabiotics.com

Wella
www.wella.co.uk

Wilkinson Sword
www.wilkinson-sword.co.uk

home entertainment

Aiwa
www.aiwa.co.uk

Akai
www.akai.com

Alpine
www.alpine-europe.com

Astra
www.ses-astra.com/uk

Bang & Olufsen
www.bang-olufsen.com

Hitachi
www.hitachi.com

JVC
www.jvc-europe.com

Marantz
www.marantz.com

Naim
www.naim-audio.com

Phillips
www.phillips.com

Richer Sounds
www.richersounds.com

Sharp
www.sharp.co.uk

Sony
www.sony.com

TAG McLaren Audio
www.tagmclarenaudio.com

Technics
www.technics.com

home improvements & products

Adrienne Chinn Design Company
www.adriennechinn.co.uk

Amway
www.amway.com

Anglian Home Improvements
www.anglianhome.co.uk

Aqualisa
www.aqualisa.co.uk

Axminster Power Tools
www.axminster.co.uk

B&Q
www.diy.co.uk

BAC Windows
www.bacwindows.co.uk

Ballingers
www.ballingers.co.uk

Black & Decker
www.blackanddecker.com

Bostik
www.bostik.com

British Bathroom Council
www.british-bathrooms.org.uk

British Coatings Federation
www.coatings.org.uk

British Stone
www.british-stone.com

Casa Paint Company
www.casa.co.uk

Coldshield
www.coldshield.com

Cookson's Tools
www.cooksons.com

Crown
www.crownpaints.co.uk

De Walt
www.dewalt.com

DIY Fixit
www.diyfixit.co.uk

DIY Tools
www.diytools.co.uk

Do It Yourself Websites
www.doityourselfwebsites.co.uk

Dolphin
www.dolphin-fitted-bathrooms.co.uk

Draper Tools
www.draper.co.uk

Dulux
www.dulux.co.uk

Duwit
www.duwit.com

Everest
www.everest.co.uk

Farrow & Ball Ltd
www.farrow-ball.co.uk

Focus
www.focusdiy.co.uk

Focus Do-it-All
www.focusdoitall.co.uk

Genty Fine Decorations Ltd
www.genty.co.uk

Graham & Brown
www.grahambrown.com

Great Mills
www.greatmills.co.uk

Hammerite
www.hammerite.com

Harris
www.lgharris.co.uk

Homebase
www.homebase.co.uk

Ideal Standard
www.ideal-standard.co.uk

Interior Design Websites
www.interiordesignwebsites.co.uk

Iso Design-Blind
www.isodesign-blind.com

Its All Greek
www.itsallgreek.co.uk

Jali Ltd
www.jali.co.uk

Jewson
www.jewson.co.uk

Makita
www.ukindustry.co.uk/makita

Maris Interiors Ltd
www.maris-regions.co.uk

Meddings Machine Tools
www.meddings.co.uk

Mica Hardware
www.micahardware.co.uk

National Tile Association
www.nta.org.uk

Osram
www.osram.co.uk

Paint Research Association
www.pra.org.uk

Paul Carter
www.paulcarter.co.uk

Polycell
www.polycell.co.uk

Potterton
www.potterton.co.uk

Quickgrip
www.quickgrip.co.uk

Rawlplug
www.rawlplug.co.uk

Rytons Building Products
www.rytons.com

Sanderson
www.sanderson-uk.com

Scott & Sargeant
www.scosarg.co.uk

Screwfix
www.screwfix.com

Shortland
www.shortland.co.uk

Showerlux
www.showerlux.com

Spring Ram
www.ultrastyl.com

Stanley Tools
www.stanleyworks.com

Stannah Stairlifts
www.stannah.co.uk

Sue Foster Fabrics
www.suefoster.co.uk

The Bed Drape Company
www.thebeddrapecompany.co.uk

The K & N Waite Construction Group
www.roomsbydesign.com

TLC Direct
www.tlc-direct.co.uk

Toolfast Supplies
www.toolfast.co.uk

Travis Perkins
www.travisperkins.co.uk

Trend
www.trendm.co.uk

Trevor Moore Designs Ltd
www.belowstairskitchens.co.uk

Unibond
www.unibond.co.uk

Universal Fittings
www.universal-fittings.co.uk

Vent Axia
www.vent-axia.com

Wallpaper Direct
www.wallpaperdirect.co.uk

Wallpaper Online
www.wallpaperonline.co.uk

Warehouse Direct
www.whdirect.co.uk

Weatherseal
www.weatherseal.co.uk

Wickes
www.wickes.com

Wilkinsons
www.wilko.co.uk

Zenith Windows
www.zenithwindows.co.uk

Zoffany
www.zoffany.com

jewellers

Adler
www.adler.ch

Alexanders
www.alexanders-the-jewellers.co.uk

Asprey & Garrard
www.asprey-garrard.com

Bogaert
www.bogaertjewellery.com

Boodle & Dunthorne
www.boodles.co.uk

Cartier
www.cartier.com

De Beers
www.adiamondisforever.com

Ernest Jones
www.ernestjones.co.uk

Goldsmiths
www.goldsmiths.co.uk

Graff
www.graff-uk.com

H Samuel
www.hsamuel.co.uk

Hamilton & Inches
www.hamiltonandinches.com

Harriet Glen Design
www.hgd.co.uk

Hirsh
www.hirsh.co.uk

Jewellery Now
www.JewelleryNow.co.uk

Jewellery Websites
www.jewellerywebsites.co.uk

Lladró
www.lladro.com

Longines
www.longines.com

Mayfair Jewellers
www.mayfairjewellers.com

N Bloom & Son
www.nbloom.co.uk

Say It With Jewels
www.sayitwithjewels.com

Silver UK
www.silver.uk.com

Theo Fennell
www.theofennell.co.uk

Tiffany
www.tiffany.com

Wright & Teague
www.wrightandteague.com

kitchens & appliances

AEG
www.aeg.com

Aga Rayburn
www.aga-rayburn.co.uk

Arena Kitchens
www.arena-kitchens.co.uk

Atag
www.atag.co.uk

Baumatic
www.baumatic.co.uk

Belling
www.belling.co.uk

Bosch
www.boschappliances.co.uk

Brabantia
www.brabantia.com

Breville
www.breville.co.uk

Bristan Ltd
www.bristan.com

Burbidge
www.burbidge.co.uk

Cannon
www.cannongas.co.uk

Carrs Silverware
www.carrs-of-sheffield.com

CCI Kitchens & Bedrooms
www.ccikitchens.co.uk

Cookers Direct
www.cookers-direct.co.uk

Country Kitchens Bedrooms & Bahrooms
www.ckbb.co.uk

Creda
www.creda.co.uk

Cucina Direct
www.cucinadirect.co.uk

De Dietrich
www.DeDietrich.co.uk

Divertimenti
www.divertimenti.co.uk

Dualit
www.dualit.com

Dyson
www.dyson.com

Ekos Kitchens
www.ekos-kitchen.co.uk

Electrolux
www.electrolux.co.uk

Franke
www.franke.co.uk

Gaggia
www.gaggia.it

Hoover
www.hoover.co.uk

Hotpoint
www.hotpoint.co.uk

Indesit
www.indesit.co.uk

In-Sinks
www.kitchen-sinks.co.uk

Intoto Kitchens
www.intoto.co.uk

Keek Kitchen Appliances
www.keek.co.uk

Kerwood Kitchens
www.kerwoodkitchens.co.uk

Kitchen Websites
www.kitchenwebsites.co.uk

Krups
www.krups.co.uk

Lakeland
www.lakelandlimited.co.uk

Le Creuset
www.lecreuset.com

Magnet
www.magnet.co.uk

Miele
www.miele.co.uk

Mitsubishi Electric
www.mitsubishi.co.uk

Moben
www.moben.co.uk

Moulinex
www.moulinex.co.uk

Neff
www.neff.co.uk

New Kitchens Ltd
www.newkitchens.ltd.uk

Ocean
www.oceancatalogue.co.uk

Osbourne Interiors
www.osborne-interiors.co.uk

Panasonic
www.panasonic.co.uk

Paula Rosa
www.paularosa.com

Philips
www.philips.com

Redring
www.redring.co.uk

Roots Kitchens & Bedrooms
www.rootskitchens.co.uk

Russell Hobbs
www.russell-hobbs.com

Salter Housewares
www.salterhousewares.co.uk

Scott & Sargeant Cookshop
www.scottsargeant.com

Servis
www.servisuk.co.uk

Sheffield Steel
www.made-in-sheffield.com

Siemens
www.siemensappliances.co.uk

Smeg
www.smeguk.com

Stoves
www.stoves.co.uk

Technics
www.technics.co.uk

Tefal
www.tefal.co.uk

The English Kitchen Company
www.the-english-kitchen-company.co.uk

Toshiba
www.toshiba.co.uk

Vax
www.vax.co.uk

Villeroy & Boch
www.villeroyboch.com

Viners
www.viners.co.uk

Whirlpool
www.whirlpool.co.uk

Wining Designs South Ltd.
www.winningdesigns.co.uk

Zanussi
www.zanussi.co.uk

lighting

Abacus
www.abacus-lighting.com

Anglepoise
www.anglepoise.co.uk

Christopher Wray
www.christopher-wray.com

Mathmos
www.mathmos.co.uk

lingerie

Agent Provocateur
www.agentprovocateur.com

Berlei
www.berlei.com

Bravissimo
www.bravissimo.com

Charnos
www.charnos.co.uk

Contessa
www.contessa.org.uk

Damart
www.damartonline.co.uk

Gossard
www.gossard.co.uk

Janet Reger
www.janetreger.com

Laetitia Allen
www.laetitiaallen.com

Playtex
www.playtex.com

Pretty Polly
www.prettypolly.co.uk

Triumph
www.triumph-international.com

Victoria's Secret
www.victoriassecret.com

Wonderbra
www.wonderbra.co.uk

luggage

Antler
www.antler.co.uk

Louis Vuitton
www.vuitton.com

Samsonite
www.samsonite.com

Tanner Krolle
www.tannerkrolle.com

magazines & websites

Daltons Weekly
www.daltons.co.uk

Empire Direct
www.empiredirect.co.uk

Exchange & Mart
www.ixm.co.uk

Goldfish Guide
www.goldfishguide.com

Loot
www.loot.com

Shops on the Net
www.sotn.co.uk

ShopSmart
www.shopsmart.com

Which?
www.which.net

markets & malls

Barclaysquare
www.barclaysquare.co.uk

Bicester Village
www.bicester-village.co.uk

Bluewater
www.bluewater.co.uk

Central Milton Keynes
www.cmkshop.co.uk

Covent Garden
www.coventgardenmarket.co.uk

Freeport
www.freeportplc.com

Galleria Outlet Centre
www.factory-outlets.co.uk

Jermyn Street
www.jermynstreet.com

Meadowhall Centre
www.meadowhall.co.uk

Outlet Centres International
www.outletcentres.com

Shops on the Net
www.sotn.co.uk

ShopSmart
www.shopsmart.com

Whitgift
www.whitgiftshopping.co.uk

mother & baby

Avent
www.avent.co.uk

Babies R Us
www.babiesrus.co.uk

Baby Gap
www.babygap.com

Bebe Confort
www.bebeconfort.com

Blooming Marvellous
www.bloomingmarvellous.co.uk

Britax
www.britax.co.uk

Bumpsadaisy
www.bumpsadaisy.co.uk

Chicco
www.chiccousa.com

Cosatto
www.cosatto.com

Formes
www.formes.com

Graco
www.graco.co.uk

Huggies
www.huggies.com

Johnson's
www.yourbaby.com

JoJo Maman Bebe
www.jojomamanbebe.co.uk

Klippan
www.klippan.co.uk

Mamas & Papas
www.mamasandpapas.co.uk

Mothercare
www.mothercare.com

Nappies Direct
www.nappies-direct.co.uk

National Childbirth Trust
www.nct-online.org

Pampers
www.pampers.com

Pegasus Pushchairs
www.allterrain.co.uk

Playtex
www.playtex.com

Real Nappy Association
www.realnappy.com

Urchin
www.urchin.co.uk

music, games & video

Blackstar
www.blackstar.co.uk

Blockbuster
www.blockbuster.co.uk

Boxman
www.boxman.co.uk

Britannia Music Club
www.britmusic.co.uk

Carlton Video
www.carltonvideo.co.uk

CD Now
www.cdnow.com

Computer Exchange
www.cex.co.uk

DVDplus
www.dvdplus.co.uk

EIL
www.eil.com

Game
www.game-retail.co.uk

Gameplay
www.gameplay.com

HMV
www.hmv.com

Jungle.com
www.jungle.com

Music & Games
www.musicandgames.com

Nice Price
www.niceprice.net

Odeon Filmstore
www.filmstore.com

Our Price
www.ourprice.co.uk

Streets Online
www.infront.co.uk

Tower Records
www.towerrecords.co.uk

Virgin Megastore
www.virginmega.com

WH Smith
www.whsmith.co.uk

Yalplay
www.yalplay.com

photography

Dixons
www.dixons.co.uk

Jessops
www.jessops.co.uk

Olan Mills
www.olanmills.com

Photo Me
www.photo-me.co.uk

shoes & accessories

Accessorize
www.accessorize.co.uk

Arc Rite Weilding & Safety Ltd
www.arc-rite.co.uk

Barker Shoes
www.barker-shoes.co.uk

Barratts
www.barratts.co.uk

Birkenstock
www.birkenstock.co.uk

Cheaney
www.cheaney.co.uk

Church & Co
www.buckinghamgate.com/bgate

Claire's Accessories
www.claires.com

Clarks
www.clarks.co.uk

Dainty Feet
www.womens-small-shoes.com

DASCO
www.shoeworld.co.uk/dasco

Dolcis
www.dolcis.co.uk

Dr Martens
www.drmartens.com

Dunkelman & Son
www.dunkelman.com

Ecco
www.ecco-shoes.co.uk

Faith
www.faith.co.uk

Florida Group Ltd
www.vandalshoes.com

Footwear Websites
www.footwearwebsites.co.uk

Gina Shoes
www.ginashoes.com

Gordon Scott
www.gordonscott.co.uk

Gucci
www.gucci.com

Hush Puppies
www.hushpuppiesshoes.com

James Lock
www.lockhatters.co.uk

Jeremy Law of Scotland
www.moccasin.co.uk

Jimmy Choo
www.jimmychoo.com

Jones Bootmaker
www.jonesbootmaker.com

Joseph Cheany & Sons
www.cheaney.co.uk

Lulu Guiness
www.luluguinness.com

Mulberry
www.mulberry-england.co.uk

Oakley
www.oakley.com

Office
www.office.co.uk

R J Draper & Co. Ltd
www.draper-of-glastonbury.com

Ray-Ban
www.rayban.com

Rockport Shoes
www.walking-shoes.com

Sak
www.thesak.com

Sergio Rossi
www.sergiorossi.com

Skechers
www.skechers.com

Skin Trade (Dr Martens)
www.skintrade.co.uk

Timberland
www.timberland.com

Timpson
www.timpson.com

Tods
www.tods.com

Whitehouse & Cox
www.whitehouse-cox.co.uk

Wolford
www.wolfordboutique-centralmode-london.co.uk

specialist

Ann Summers
www.annsummers.co.uk

Anything Left Handed
www.anythingleft-handed.co.uk

Dubai Duty Free
www.dubaidutyfree.com

Innovations
www.innovations.co.uk

The Left Hand
www.thelefthand.com

sports & outdoor

Allsports
www.allsportsretail.co.uk

Altberg Boots
www.altberg.co.uk

Barbour
www.barbour.com

Berghaus
www.berghaus.com

Blacks
www.blacks.co.uk

Bromley Bike
www.bromleybike.com

Cycle Centre
www.cyclestore.co.uk

Danskin
www.danskin.com

Edge2Edge
www.edge2edge.co.uk

Edinburgh Bicycle
www.edinburgh-bicycle.com

Ellesse
www.ellesse.com

Ellis Brigham
www.ellis-brigham.com

Farlows
www.farlows.co.uk

Fila
www.fila.com

Hawkshead
www.hawkshead.com

Intersport
www.intersport.co.uk

James Lock
www.lockhatters.co.uk

JD Sports
www.jdsports.co.uk

JJB Sports
www.jjb.co.uk

Kitbag.com
www.kitbag.com

ProLine
www.proline-sports.co.uk

Rohan
www.rohan.co.uk

Snow and Rock
www.snowandrock.co.uk

Sports Connection
www.sportsconnection.co.uk

Sweatshop
www.sweatshop.co.uk

tobacco

AE Lloyd & Son
www.aelloyd.com

Alfred Dunhill Pipes
www.whitespot.co.uk

Belphil London Cigars
www.belphillondoncigars.com

Burlington Bertie Cigars
www.bbertie-cigars.com

Davidoff
www.davidoff.com

James J Fox & Robert Lewis Cigars
www.jjfox.co.uk

Rizla
www.rizla.co.uk

toys

Action Man
www.actionman.com

Barbie
www.barbie.com

Brio
www.brio.co.uk

Corgi
www.corgi.co.uk

Crayola
www.crayola.com

Dawson & Son
www.dawson-and-son.com

Early Learning Centre
www.earlylearningcentre.co.uk

English Teddy Bear
www.teddy.co.uk

FAO Schwartz
www.faoschwarz.com

Fisher Price
www.fisher-price.com

Hamleys
www.hamleys.co.uk

Hasbro
www.hasbro.com

Hobbycraft
www.hobbycraft.co.uk

Hornby
www.hornby.co.uk

Knex
www.knex.co.uk

Lego
www.lego.com

Little Tikes
www.adventuretoys.co.uk/littletikes.asp

Matchbox
www.matchboxtoys.com

Mattel
www.mattel.com

Paddington Bear
www.paddingtonbear.co.uk

Playmobil
www.playmobil.de

Pokemon
www.pokemon.com

Polly Pocket
www.pollypocket.co.uk

Quadro
www.quadro-toys.co.uk

Scalextric
www.scalextric.co.uk

Tiger Toys
www.tigertoys.co.uk

Tomy
www.tomy.co.uk

Toy City
www.toycity.com

Toys R Us
www.toysrus.co.uk

TP Activity Toys
www.tptoys.com

Wicksteed
www.wicksteed.co.uk

Woolworths
www.woolies.co.uk

wallcovering

Armourcoat
www.armourcoat.co.uk

Coleman Brothers
www.colemanbros.co.uk

Coloroll
www.coloroll.co.uk

Farrow & Ball
www.farrow-ball.co.uk

Graham & Brown Wallcoverings
www.grahambrown.com

Monkwell
www.monkwell.com

watches

Baume & Mercier
www.baume-et-mercier.com

Breitling
www.breitling.com

Casio
www.casio.co.uk

Citizen
www.citizenwatch.com

Jaeger le coultre
www.jaeger-lecoultre.com

Longines
www.longines.com

Omega
www.omega.ch

Panerai
www.panerai.com

Patek Philippe
www.patek.com

Rado
www.rado.com

Rotary
www.rotarywatches.com

Seiko
www.seiko.co.uk

Sekonda
www.sekonda.com

Swatch
www.swatch.com

TAG Heuer
www.tagheuer.com

Timex
www.timex.com

Tissot
www.tissot.ch

aikido	hang/paragliding	shinty
american football	hockey	shooting
angling	horseracing	show jumping
archery	hovering	skeleton
arm wrestling	hurling	skiing
athletics	ice hockey	snooker
australian rules	inline & roller skating	snooker & billiards
football	international games	softball
badminton	ju jitsu	sombo
ballooning	judo	speedway
baseball	kendo	sportswear &
basketball	korfball	equipment
baton twirling	lacrosse	squash
biathlon	luge	stoolball
bobsleigh	magazines &	sub aqua
boccia	websites	surfing
body building	motor cycling	swimming
bowls	motor racing	table tennis
boxing	mountaineering	taekwando
canoeing	netball	tang soo do
caving	orienteering	target sports
combat	petanque	tchoukball
cricket	pentathlon	ten pin bowling
curling	personalities	tennis
cycling	pigeon racing	trampolining
darts	polo	triathlon
dragon boat racing	powerboat racing	tug-of-war
equestrianism	promotion &	volleyball
exercise & fitness	education	walking
extreme sports	racketball	water polo
fencing	roller skating	water skiing
football	roller hockey	weightlifting
gaelic games	rounders	weightlifting &
gliding	rowing	strength
golf	rugby	windsurfing
greyhounds	rugby fives	winter sports
gymnastics	sailing	wrestling
handball	sailing & watersports	

249

aikido

The British Aikido Association
www.aikido-baa.org.uk

The British Aikido Board
www.bab.org.uk

The National Aikido Federation
www.nataikidofed.org.uk

american football

Bath University American Football Club
www.bath.ac.uk/~su5bees

Birmingham University Lions
www.eteamz.com/birminghamlions

Bristol Aztecs American Footbal League
www.bristolaztecs.co.uk/home.htm

Bristol Combined University Bullets
www.eteamz.com/bristolbullets

British American Football Referees
Association
www.bafra.org

British Collegiate American Football
League
www.bcafl.org

Cardiff Cobras
www.comp.glam.ac.uk/students/rgwingfi/cobras.
html

Derby Braves
www.braves.co.uk

Hertfordshire Hurricanes
www.hurricanes.org.uk

National Football League
www.nfl.com

Sky Sports American Football
www.sky.co.uk/sports/nfl

Super Bowl
www.superbowl.com

The British Youth American Football
Association
www.isport.uk.com/amfootball/byafa

UCH Sharks
www.eteamz.com/uchsharks

UEA Pirates
www.ueapirates.hostinguk.com

angling

National Federation of Anglers
www.the-nfa.org.uk

archery

Grand National Archery Association
www.gnas.org

International Archery Association
www.archery.org

Northern Ireland Archery Association
www.nias.co.uk

Scottish Archery Association
www.scottisharchery.org.uk

arm wrestling

British Arm Wrestling Federation
www.armwrestling.co.uk

athletics

Amateur Athletics Association
www.englandathletics.co.uk

Athletics Board of Ireland
www.ble.ie

British Athletics Federation
www.british-athletics.co.uk

British Triathlon Association
www.britishtriathlon.org

British Wheelchair Sports Foundation
www.britishwheelchairsports.org

English Federation Of Disability Sport
www.efds.co.uk

English Schools Athletics Association
www.esaa.net

European Athletic Federation
www.eaa-athletics.ch

Health Development Agency
www.hea.org.uk

International Amateur Athletics Federation
www.iaaf.org

International Paralympic Committee
www.paralympic.org

International Pentathlon Union
www.pentathlon.org

International Triathlon Union
www.triathlon.org

London Marathon
www.london-marathon.co.uk

National Coaching Foundation
www.ncf.org.uk

Runner's World
www.runnersworld.co.uk

Scottish Athletics Federation
www.saf.org.uk

Sports Aid
www.sportsaid.org.uk

Youth Sport Trust
www.youthsport.net

australian rules football

British Australian Rules Football League
www.barfl.co.uk

badminton

Badminton Association of England
www.baofe.co.uk

Badminton UK
www.badmintonuk.ndo.co.uk

English Schools' Badminton Association
www.esba.co.uk

International Badminton Federation
www.intbadfed.org

Scottish Badminton Union
www.scotbadminton.demon.co.uk

World Badminton Federation
www.worldbadminton.com

ballooning

British Association of Balloon Operators
www.babo.org.uk

British Balloon & Airship Club
www.bbac.org

baseball

Baseball
www.baseball.com

Baseball Softball UK
www.baseballsoftballuk.com

British Baseball Federation
www.bbf.org

Great Britain National Baseball Team
www.gbbaseball.co.uk

International Baseball Federation
www.baseball.ch

Major League Baseball
www.mlb.com

basketball

Basketball Players Association
www.woods.demon.co.uk/BPA

British Basketball League
www.bbl.org.uk

Budweiser Basketball League UK
www.basketball-league.co.uk

English Basketball Association
www.basketballengland.org.uk

Global Basketball News
www.eurobasket.com

International Basketball Federation
www.fiba.com

National Basketball Association
www.nba.com

NBA
www.nba.com

Scottish Basketball Association
www.isport.uk.com/basketball/sba

Scottish Basketball League
www.basketball-scotland.com

XXL Basketball
www.xxl.co.uk

baton twirling

British Baton Twirling Sports Association
www.bbtsa.co.uk

biathlon

British Cycling Federation
www.bcf.uk.com

International Biathlon Union
www.ibu.at

bobsleigh

British Bobsleigh Association
www.british-bobsleigh.com

The International Bobsleigh & Skeleton Federation
www.bobsleigh.com

boccia

Great Britain Boccia
www.cpsport.org

International Boccia Commission
www.bocciainternational.com

body buildings

British Amateur Weightlifters Association
www.bawla.com

British Powerlifting
www.britishpowerlifting.com

European Powerlifting
www.europowerlifting.org

International Powerlifting Federation
www.powerlifting-ipf.com

International Weightlifting Federation
www.iwf.ne

bowls

English Bowling Association
www.bowlsengland.com

International Bowling Federation
www.fiq.org

Lawn Bowls
www.lawnbowls.com

Official Lawn Bowls
www.lawnbowls.co.uk

boxing

Boxing Monthly Magazine
www.boxing-monthly.co.uk

British Boxing Board of Control
www.bbbofc.com

International Amateur Boxing Association
www.aiba.net

International Boxing Organisation
www.iboboxing.com

North American Boxing Federation
www.nabfnews.com

World Boxing Association
www.wbaonline.com

canoeing

British Canoe Union
www.bcu.org.uk

European Canoe Association
www.canoe-europe.org

International Canoe Federation
www.canoeicf.com

Irish Canoe Union
www.irishcanoeunion.com

Scottish Canoe Association
www.scot-canoe.org

Welsh Canoe Association and Union
www.welsh-canoeing.org.uk

caving

National Caving Association
www.nca.org.uk

combat

Midlands Win Chun Kuen
www.wingchun.co.uk

British Council for Chinese Martial Arts
www.bccma.demon.co.uk

British Judo Association
www.britishjudo.org.uk

British Korfball Association
www.british-korfball.org.uk/bka.htm

British Kung Fu Association
www.laugar-kungfu.com

British Shotokan Kyogi
www.bsk.cwc.net

British Traditional Karate Association
www.btka.org.uk

British United Taekwon-do Federation
www.butf.com

Budokwai Martial Arts Association
www.budokwai.com

Eikoku Nanten Shotokan Karate
Association
www.maldiamond.demon.co.uk/enska.htm

English Karate Governing Body
www.ekgb.org.uk

The English Shotokan Karate Association
www.eska.org.uk

Funakoshi Shotokan Karate International
www.fski.licomnet.com

Hampshire Shotokan Karate
www.shotokan.org.uk

International Judo Federation
www.ijf.org

Karate Union of Great Britain
www.kugb.org

Kempo Jujitsu International Budo
Association
www.kempojujitsu.com

London & District Korfball Association
www.ldka.org.uk

National Association of Karate & Martial
Arts Schools
www.nakmas.co.uk

NIMA Karate
www.nima99.co.uk/main.asp

Scottish Judo Federation
www.scotjudo.org

Shotokan Karate International of Great
Britain
www.skigb.freeserve.co.uk

Uechi-Ryu Karate Do Association (GB)
www.intbis.com/uechi.htm

UK Taekwon-do Association
www.ukta.com

Ulster School of Traditional Karate
www.ulsterkarate.com

United Kingdom Wing Chun Kung Fu
Association
www.ukwckfa.ndirect.co.uk

Welsh Karate Association
www. members.lycos.co.uk/wkahq

Wing Chun Dragon Koon Alliance
www.wingchun.dircon.co.uk/index.html

Wing Chun Kung Fu - Martial Art Institute
www.martialartinstitute.com

World Judo Organisation
www.worldjudo.org

World Karate Federation
www.wkf.net

World Kickboxing Association
www.worldkickboxing.com

cricket

Cricket World Monthly
www.cricketworld.com

Cricketer International
www.cricketer.co.uk/asp/homepage.asp

ECB
www.cricket.org/link_to_database/NATIONAL/
ENG

Clubs

Derbyshire
www.dccc.org.uk

Durham
www.durham-ccc.org.uk

Essex
www.essexcricket.org.uk

Gloucestershire County Cricket Club
www.glosccc.co.uk

Hampshire
www.hampshire.cricket.org

Kent
www.kentcountycricket.co.uk

Lancashire
www.lccc.co.uk

Leicestershire
www.leicestershireccc.com

Lincolnshire
www.btinternet.com/~Lincs.Cricket

Melbourne
www.mcc.org.au

Middlesex
www.middlesexccc.co.uk

Northamptonshire
www.nccc.co.uk

Nottinghamshire
www.trentbridge.co.uk

Somerset
www.somerset.cricket.org

Surrey
www.surreyccc.co.uk

Sussex
www.sussexcricket.co.uk

Warwickshire
www.warwickccc.org.uk

Worcestershire
www.wccc.co.uk

Yorkshire
www.yorkshireccc.org.uk

Grounds

Lord's
www.lords.org

Sydney
www.scgt.oz.au

Organisations

Australian Cricket Board
www.acb.com.au

English Cricket Board
www.ecb.co.uk

Federation of International Cricketers
www.ficahof.com

International Cricket Council
www.cricket.org/link_to_database/NATIONAL
/ICC

Minor Cricket Counties Association
www.mcca.cricket.org

New Zealand Cricket Board
www.nzcricket.co.nz

Sri Lanka Cricket Board
www.lanka.net/cricket

United Cricket Board of South Africa
www-rsa3.cricket.org

Women's Cricket
http://users.ox.ac.uk/~beth/wca.htm

Trophies

NatWest Trophy
www.natwestseries.com

Magazines & Websites

BBC Cricket
www.news.bbc.co.uk/hi/english/sport/cricket

CNN Cricket
www.cnnsi.com/cricket

Cric Info
www.cricket.org

Cricketer International Magazine
www.cricketer.com

Live from Lord's Webcam
www.cricket.org/link_to_database/NATIONAL/

ENG/CLUBS/MCC/MCCWebcam.html

Sky Sports Cricket
www.sky.co.uk/sports/cricket

Wisden
www.wisden.com

curling

Scottish Curling
www.scotcurl.co.uk

Welsh Curling Association
www.adventureholiday.com/curling.htm

cycling

Association of Cycle Traders
www.cyclesource.co.uk

Batavus
www.batavus.com

Beastway MTB
www.beastway.com

BMX
www.ebmx.com

British Cycling
www.britishcycling.org.uk

British Cycling Federation
www.bcf.uk.com

British Cyclo-Cross Association
www.cyclo-cross.co.uk

British Mountain Biking
www.bmb.org

British Pedal Car Championship
www.bpcc2000.freeserve.co.uk

Cyclists Touring Club
www.ctc.org.uk

Falcon
www.falconcycles.co.uk

London Cycling Campaign
www.lcc.org.uk

Mountain Biking UK
www.bikinguk.net

Muddy Fox
www.muddyfox.com

National Cycle Network
www.nationalcyclenetwork.org.uk

On Your Bike
www.onyourbike.com

Orbit
www.orbit-cycles.co.uk

Prutour
www.netlondon.com/sport/other/other.
894253131.html

Raleigh
www.raleighbikes.com

Road Time Trials Council
www.rttc.org.uk

Scottish Cycling
www.scuweb.com

Scottish Cyclists' Union
www.scottish.cycling.btinternet.co.uk

Sturmey Archer
www.sturmey-archer.com

Sustrans
www.sustrans.org.uk

Tour de France
www.letour.fr

Trail Cyclists Association
www.trailquest.co.uk

Union Cycliste Internationale
www.uci.ch

Wheelie Serious
www.wheelie-serious.com

darts

American Darts Organization
www.cyberdarts.com

British Darts Organisation
www.bdodarts.com

Bulls Eye Magazine
www.bullsinet.com

Embassy World Darts
www.embassydarts.com

Planet Darts
www.planetdarts.co.uk

dragon boat racing

British Dragon Boat Racing Association
www.dragonboat.org.uk

European Dragon Boat Federation
www.dragonboat.org.uk/edbf/index.htm

International Dragon Boat Federation
www.dragonboat.org.uk/idbf/index.htm

equestrianism

Association of British Riding Schools
www.equiworld.net/uk/training/

British Equestrian Federation
www.bef.co.uk/home.htm

British Horse Society
www.bhs.org.uk

exercise & fitness

Active for Life
www.active.org.uk

Creatine Store
www.creatinestore.co.uk

Exercise Fitness & Leisure
www.exercise.co.uk

Fitness Websites
www.fitnesswebsites.co.uk

Nrgize
www.nrgize.co.uk

The Keep Fit Association
www.keepfit.org.uk

extreme sports

Blue Eskimo Adventure Racing
www.blue-eskimo.com

Dangerless Aerial Sports Club
www.aerial.org

The British Elastic Rope Association
www.bungeezone.com/orgs/bersa.shtml

Xtreme Xperience
www.xtreme-xperience.com

fencing

British Academy of Fencing
www.baf-fencing.com

British Fencing Association
www.britishfencing.com

British Paraplegic Fencing Association
www.britishwheelchairsports.org/associate/
fencing.htm

Irish Amateur Fencing Federation
http://homepage.eircom.net/~iaff

Scottish Fencing
www.britsport.com/fencing

Surrey County Fencing Union
www.scfu.homestead.com

Warwickshire Fencing Union
www.warwickshirefencing.freeserve.co.uk

Welsh Fencing
www.welshfencing.org

football

Clubs

AC Fiorentina
www.acfiorentina.it

Aberdeen
www.afc.co.uk

AC Milan
www.acmilan.com

Arsenal
www.arsenal.co.uk

AS Roma
www.asromacalcio.it

Aston Villa
www.astonvilla-fc.co.uk

Barcelona
www.fcbarcelona.com/select_language.sps

Barnsley
www.barnsleyfc.co.uk

Berwick Rangers
www.brfc.mcmail.com

Birmingham City
www.bcfc.com

Blackburn Rovers
www.rovers.co.uk

Blackpool
www.blackpoolfc.co.uk

Bolton Wanderers
www.bwfc.co.uk

Bournemouth
www.afcb.co.uk

Bradford City
www.bradfordcityfc.co.uk

Bristol City
www.bcfc.co.uk

Burnley
www.clarets.co.uk

Cambridge United
www.cambridge-united.co.uk

Carlisle
www.cufconline.org.uk

Celtic
www.celticfc.co.uk

Charlton Athletic
www.charlton-athletic.co.uk

Chelsea
www.chelseafc.co.uk

Cheltenham Town
www.cheltenhamtownfc.com

Chester City
www.chester-city.co.uk

Colchester United
www.cufc.co.uk

Coventry City
www.ccfc.co.uk

Crewe Alexandra
www.s-cheshire.ac.uk/cafc

Crystal Palace
www.cpfc.co.uk

Darlington
www.darlingtonfc.co.uk

Derby County
www.dcfc.co.uk

Dunfermline Athletic
www.fife.co.uk/pars

England
www.englandfc.com

Everton
www.evertonfc.com

Fulham
www.fulhamfc.co.uk

Glasgow Rangers
www.rangers.co.uk

Heart of Midlothian
www.heartsfc.co.uk

Huddersfield Town
www.huddersfield-town.co.uk

Hull City
www.hullcity.afc.net

Ipswich Town
www.itfc.co.uk

Leeds United
www.lufc.co.uk

Leicester City
www.lcfc.com

Lincoln City
www.redimps.com

Liverpool
www.liverpoolfc.org

Macclesfield Town
www.mtfc.co.uk

Manchester City
www.mcfc.co.uk

Manchester United
www.manutd.co.uk

Middlesbrough
www.mfc.co.uk

Millwall
www.millwallfc.co.uk

Motherwell
www.motherwellfc.co.uk

Newcastle United
www.nufc.co.uk

Northampton Town
www.ntfc.co.uk

Norwich City
www.canaries.co.uk

Nottingham Forest
www.nottinghamforest.co.uk

Notts County
www.nottscounty.net

Parma AC
www.acparma.it

Peterborough United
www.theposh.com

Plymouth Argyll
www.argyll.org.uk

Queens Park Rangers
www.qpr.co.uk

Rangers
www.rangers.co.uk

Reading
www.readingfc.co.uk

Rotherham
www.themillers.co.uk

Scunthorpe United
www.scunthorpe-united.co.uk

Sheffield United
www.sufc.co.uk

Sheffield Wednesday
www.swfc.co.uk

Shrewsbury Town
www.shrewsburytown.co.uk

Southampton
www.saintsfc.co.uk

Sunderland
www.sunderland-afc.com

Tottenham Hotspur
www.spurs.co.uk

Watford
www.watfordfc.com

West Bromwich Albion
www.wba.co.uk

West Ham United
www.westhamunited.co.uk

Wimbledon
www.wimbledon-fc.co.uk

Wolverhampton Wanderers
www.wolves.co.uk

York City
www.yorkcityfc.co.uk

Magazines & Websites

Fanzine
www.soccer-fanzine.co.uk

Football 365
www.football365.com

Icons
www.icons.com

Nationwide League
www.football.nationwide.co.uk

Planet Football
www.planetfootball.com

Roy of the Rovers
www.royoftherovers.com

Soccernet
www.soccernet.com

Organisations

FIFA
www.fifa.com

Football Association
www.the-fa.org

Football League
www.football-league.co.uk

Football Supporters' Association
www.fsa.org.uk

League Managers Association
www.leaguemanagers.com

Professional Footballers' Association
www.thepfa.co.uk

Scottish Football Association
www.scottishfa.co.uk

UEFA
www.uefa.com

Tournament

England 2006
www.fa2006.org

FA Carling Premiership
www.fa-carling.com

gaelic games

British Universities Gaelic Games
www.british.unigaa.com

gliding

British Gliding Association
www.gliding.co.uk

golf

Associations

English Golf Union
www.englishgolfunion.org

Golf Foundation of Britain
www.golf-foundation.org

Golfing Union of Ireland
www.gui.ie

Ladies Golf Union
www.lgu.org

Ladies' Professional Golf Association
www.lpga.com

Professional Golf Association of America
www.pga.com

Scottish Golf
www.scottishgolf.com

Scottish Golf Schools
www.golfscotland.co.uk

US Golf Association
www.usga.org

World Amateur Golf Council
www.wagc.org

Courses

Carnoustie Golf Course Hotel & Resort
www.carnoustie-hotel.com

Gleneagles
www.gleneagles.com

Royal Birkdale
www.ukgolfer.org/clubs/royalbirkdale/index.html

Royal Troon
www.royaltroon.co.uk

St Andrews
www.standrews.org.uk

Magazines & Websites

Slazenger Golf
www.slazengergolf.co.uk

Sporting Life Golf
www.sporting-life.com/golf/news

Fore Magazine
www.scga.org/fore

Golf
www.golfonline.com

Golf Channel
www.thegolfchannel.com

Golf Digest
www.golfdigest.com

Golf Monthly
www.nexusinternet.co.uk/gm

Golf Today
www.golftoday.co.uk

Golf.com
www.golf.com

UK Golf
www.uk-golf.com

Tournaments

British Open
www.opengolf.com

European Masters
www.golf.european-masters.com

LPGA Classic
www.lpgaclassic.com

Open Championship
www.opengolf.com

PGA European Tour
www.europeantour.com

US Masters
www.masters.org

US Open
www.usopen.org

greyhounds

British Greyhound Racing Board
www.thedogs.co.uk

Greyhound Star
www.greyhoundstar.com

National Greyhound Racing Club
www.ngrc.org.uk

gymnastics

British Aerobatic Association
www.aerobatics.org.uk

British Amateur Gymnastics Association
www.baga.co.uk

Gymmedia
www.gymmedia.com

Gymnastics UEG
www.ueg-gymnastics.com

International Gymnast
www.intlgymnast.com

International Gymnastics Federation
www.fig-gymnastics.com

Scottish Gymnastics
www.scottishgymnastics.com

handball

England Handball Association
www.englandhandball.com

European Handball Association
www.eurohandball.com

International Handball Federation
www.ihf.ch

hang/paragliding

Aberdeen Hang Gliding & Para Gliding Club
www.footlaunched.com

North Wales Hang Gliding and
Para Gliding Club
www.nwhgpc.org.uk

Welsh Free Flight Association
www.wfff.co.uk

hockey

Cheshire County Hockey Association
www.ccha.net

English Hockey Association
www.fieldhockey.com

Field Hockey
www.fieldhockey.com

Field Hockey Foundation
www.fieldhockeytournament.com

Hockey Net
www.empresa.co.uk/hockeynet

International Hockey Federation
www.fihockey.org

North Hockey Association
www.northhockey.org

Scottish Hockey Union
www.parallel56.com/scottishhockey

South Hockey League
www.south-league.com

horseracing

Betting

Barry Dennis
www.barrydennis.co.uk

Blue Sq
www.bluesq.com

IG Index
www.igindex.co.uk

InterBet
www.inter-bet.com

Ladbrokes
www.bet.co.uk

Sean Graham
www.seangraham.com

Sporting Index
www.sportingindex.com

Sportingbet.com
www.sportingbet.com

Sunderlands
www.sunderlands.co.uk

Surrey Racing
www.surreyracing.co.uk

Totalbet.com
www.totalbet.com

Victor Chandler
www.victorchandler.com

William Hill
www.willhill.com

Magazines & Websites

Irish Racing
www.irish-racing.com

Race Horses.com
www.race-horses.com

Racenews
www.racenews.co.uk

Sporting Life
www.sportinglife.co.uk

Organisations

British Betting Office Association
www.bboa.co.uk

British Bloodstock Agency
www.bba.co.uk

British Horseracing Board
www.bhb.co.uk

Horserace Betting Levy Board
www.hblb.org.uk

Irish Horseracing Authority
www.iha.ie

Irish Turf Club
www.turfclub.ie

Jockey Club
www.jockeyclub.com

National Trainers Federation
www.martex.co.uk/racehorsetrainers

Racecourse Association
www.comeracing.co.uk

Tattersalls
www.tattersalls.com

Weatherbys
www.weatherbys-group.com

Racecourses

Aintree
www.aintree.co.uk

Ascot
www.ascot.co.uk

Ayr
www.ayr-racecourse.co.uk

Catterick
www.catterick.com

Cheltenham
www.cheltenham.co.uk

Chepstow
www.chepstow-racecourse.co.uk

Chester
www.chester-races.co.uk

Curragh
www.curragh.ie

Doncaster
www.britishracing.com

Down Royal
www.downroyal.com

Epsom
www.epsomderby.co.uk

Galway
www.iol.ie/galway-races

Goodwood
www.goodwood.co.uk

Hamilton Park
www.hamilton-park.co.uk

Haydock Park
www.haydock-park.com

Huntingdon
www.gg.com/huntingdon/

Kelso
www.kelso-races.co.uk

Kempton Park
www.kempton.co.uk

Market Rasen
www.marketrasenraces.co.uk

Musselburgh
www.musselburgh-racecourse.co.uk

Newbury
www.newbury-racecourse.com

Newmarket
www.newmarketracecourses.co.uk

Newton Abbot
www.newton-abbot-races.co.uk

Nottingham
www.nottinghamracecourse.co.uk

Perth
www.perth-races.co.uk

Punchestown
www.punchestown.com

Sandown Park
www.sandown.co.uk

Stratford on Avon
www.stratfordracecourse.net

Towcester
www.towcester-racecourse.co.uk

Tramore
www.tramore-racecourse.com

Uttoxeter
www.uttoxeterracecourse.co.uk

Warwick
www.warwickracecourse.co.uk

Wetherby
www.wetherby.co.uk

Wincanton
www.wincantonracecourse.co.uk

Windsor
www.windsorracing.co.uk

Wolverhampton
www.dunstallpark.co.uk

hovering

European Hovercraft Federation
www.hovercraft.org.uk/ehf/ehf.htm

Hovercraft Club of Great Britain
www.hovercraft.org.uk

hurling

Tara Camogie Hurling Club
www.taracamogieclub.freeservers.com

ice hockey

Belfast Giants
www.belfastgiants.com

British Ice Hockey UK
www.icehockeyuk.co.uk

British Ice Hockey Writers Association
www.bihwa.co.uk

British National League
www.britnatleague.co.uk

English Ice Hockey Association
www.eiha.co.uk

Face Off Magazine
www.face-off.uk.com

Ice Hockey Super League
www.iceweb.co.uk

International Ice Hockey Federation
www.iihf.com

London Knights
www.londonknights.com

Manchester Storm
www.manchesterstorm.co.uk

Power Play Magazine
www.powerplay-online.co.uk

Sekonda Ice Hockey Superleague
www.iceweb.co.uk

Sheffield Steelers
www.sheffieldsteelers.co.uk

UK Ice Hockey Superleague
www.iceweb.co.uk

inline & roller skating

Federation of Roller Skating
www.bfrs.org.uk

Inliners
www.inliners.co.uk

International Roller Skating Federation
www.rollersports.org

international games

Athens 2004 Olympics
www.athens.olympic.org/gr

British Olympic Association
www.olympics.org.uk

International Olympic Committee
www.olympic.org

International Paralympic Committee
www.paralympic.org

Manchester 2002 Sport XVII
Commonwealth Games
www.commonwealthgames2002.org.uk

Olympic Games
www.olympics.com

Sydney 2000 Olympics
www.sydney2000.co.uk

World Anti-Doping Association
www.wada-ama.org

ju jitsu

Aiuchi Ju Jitsu
www.aiuchi.org

British Kodekan Ju Jitsu Club
www.kilohana.co.uk

Go-Shin Kempo Ju Jitsu Association
www.jitsu.demon.co.uk/goshin/index.html

Ju Jitsu Scotland
www.jujitsuscotland.supanet.com

judo

BJA Bucks County
www.bucksbja.freeserve.co.uk

BJA Midlands Area
www.bjamidlandarea.org.uk

BJA Northern Home Counties
www.skybusiness.com/bjanhc

BJA Northwest Area
www.nwa.judouk.org

BJA Southern Area
www.southernareajudo.tk

BJA Southern Area - Kent
www.worldjudo.org/Kentjudo.htm

BJA Southern Area - Sussex
www.martinrivers.eurobell.co.uk/SussexCounty
Judo.htm

BJA Southern Area - Hampshire
www.hampshirejudo.org.uk

BJA Southern Area - Surrey
www.surreyweb.net/britishjudo

British Judo Association
www.britishjudo.org.uk

British Schools Judo Association
www.britishschoolsjudo.com

International Judo Federation
www.ijf.org/htmls/main.html

Peterborough & Cambs Area Judo
www.mjc.mcmail.com/CambsBJC/index.htm

Scottish Judo Federation
www.scotjudo.org

Scottish National Judo Academy
www.judoacademy.co.uk

Surrey County Judo
www.surreyweb.net/britishjudo

Welsh Judo Association
www.welshjudo.com

World Judo Association
www.worldjudo.org

Yorkshire & Humberside Judo Association
www.judo.demon.co.uk

kendo

British Kendo Association
www.kendo.org.uk

korfball

International Korfball Federation
ww.ikf.org

lacrosse

English Lacrosse Association
www.englishlacrosse.co.uk/website/home.html

Scottish Lacrosse Association
www.scottish-lacrosse.org.uk

luge

Canadian Luge Association
www.luge.ca

Great Britain Luge Association
www.gbla.org.uk

United States Luge Association
www.usaluge.org

magazines & websites

CBS Sportsline
www.sportsline.com

CNN Sports Illustrated
www.cnnsi.com

Extreme Sports
www.extremesports.com

Sports.com
www.sports.com

motor cycling

Auto Cycle Union
www.acu.org.uk/DyIndex.asp

British Racing Drivers Club
www.brdc.co.uk/flash.htm

British Touring Cars
www.btcc.co.uk

British Women's Racing Drivers Club
www.bwrdc.co.uk

Britsh Speedway Promoters Association
www.british-speedway.co.uk

Classic Racing Motorcycle Club
www.crmc.co.uk

FIA – Official Formula Racing Body
www.fia.com

Formula 3 Association (FOTA)
www.fota.co.uk

Hadley & District Light Car Club
www.hdlcc.com

Southern Autosport Association
www.southernautosport.com

motor racing

Circuits

Anglesey
www.anglesey-race-circuit.co.uk

Brands Hatch
www.brands-hatch.co.uk

Castle Combe
www.castlecombecircuit.co.uk

Donington Park
www.donington-park.co.uk

Knockhill
www.knockhill.co.uk

Mallory Park
www.mallorypark.co.uk

Monaco
www.monaco.mc/monaco/gprix

Monza
www.monzanet.it

Nürburgring
www.nuerburgring.de

Oulton Park
www.oultonpark.co.uk

Pembrey
www.barc.net/pembrey.htm

Silverstone
www.silverstone-circuit.co.uk

Drivers

Jenson Button
www.jensonbutton.com

Events

British Touring Car Championship
www.btcc.co.uk

Le Mans
www.lemans.org

World Rally Championship
www.wrc.com

Grand Prix

America
www.usgpindy.com

Austria
www.a1ring.at

Belgium
www.spa-francorchamps.be

Canada
www.grandprix.ca

France
www.magnyf1.com

Germany
www.hockenheimring.de

Italy
www.monzanet.it

Japan
www.suzukacircuit.co.jp

Malaysia
www.malaysiangp.com.my

Monaco
www.f1-monaco.com

San Marino
www.formula1.sm

Magazines & Websites

Autosport
www.autosport.com

F1 Today
www.f1today.com

F1-Live
www.f1-live.com

ITV
www.itv-f1.com

Motor Sport
www.motorsport.com

Sky Sports Formula One
www.sky.co.uk/sports/center/formula1.htm

Sporting Life Formula One
www.sporting-life.com/formula1/news

Manufacturers

Lola Cars International
www.lolacars.com

Organisations

British Trials & Rally Drivers Association
www.tcs01.demon.co.uk

Federation Internationale de l'Automobile
(FIA)
www.fia.com

Formula One Supporters Association
www.fosa.org

Teams

Arrows
www.arrows.com

BAR
www.britishamericanracing.com

Ferrari
www.shell-ferrari.com

Jaguar
www.jaguar-racing.com

Jordan
www.jordangp.com

McLaren
www.mclaren.co.uk

Minardi
www.minardi.it

Prost
www.prostgp.com

Sauber
www.sauber.ch

Williams
www.williamsf1.co.uk

mountaineering

Army Mountaineering Association
www.theama.org.uk

Association of Mountaineering Instructors
www.mycbsite.com/amiorguk

British Mountaineeing Council
www.thebmc.co.uk

netball

All England Netball Association
www.england-netball.co.uk

International Federation of Netball
Associations
www.netball.org

orienteering

Avon Schools Orienteering Association
www.geocities.com/TelevisionCity/2948

British Parachute Association
www.bpa.org.uk

Essex Stragglers Orienteering Society
www.users.globalnet.co.uk/~cordle/sos.htm

petanque

British Petanque Association
www.britishpetanque.org

British Petanque Association – Southern
Region
www.bpasouth.org.uk

Scottish Petanque Association
www.scottishpetanque.org

pentathlon

Modern Pentathlon Association of Great
Britian
www.mpagb.easynet.co.uk

personalities

Alan Shearer
www.fly.to/shearer

Andre Agassi
www.andresite.com

Anna Kournikova (Fan Club)
www.annak.org

Ayrton Senna
www.ayrton-senna.com

Babe Ruth
www.baberuth.com

Chris Bonington
www.bonington.com

Damon Hill
www.damonhill.co.uk

David Coulthard
www.davidcoulthard.com

David Ginola
www.ginola.net

David Leadbetter
www.leadbetter.com

Diego Maradona
www.diegomaradona.com

Don Bradman
www.bradman.sa.com.au

Eddie Irvine (Fan Club)
www.exclusively-irvine.com

Evander Holyfield
www.evanderholyfield.com

Evel Knieval
www.evel.com

Gary Player
www.garyplayer.com

George Best
www.georgebest.com

Heinz-Harald Frentzen
www.frentzen.de

Jack Nicklaus
www.nicklaus.com

Jacques Villeneuve
www.jacques.villeneuve.com

John Whitaker
www.john-whitaker.com

Johnny Herbert
www.johnnyherbert.co.uk

Jonny Wilkinson
www.jonny-wilkinson.co.uk

Lee Westwood
www.westy.com

Lennox Lewis
www.lennox-lewis.com

Mark Spitz
www.cmgww.com/sports/spitz

Michael Jordan
www.jordan.sportsline.com

Michael Schumacher
www.michael-schumacher.com

Mika Hakkinen
www.hakkinen.net

Mohammed Ali
www.ali.com

Nadia Comaneci (Fan Club)
www.nadiacomaneci.com

Pedro De La Rosa
www.pedrodelarosa.com

Pele
www.pele.net

Pete Sampras
www.sampras.com

Phil Mickelson
www.phil-mickelson.com

Prince Naseem Hamed
www.princenaseem.com

Ralf Schumacher
www.ralf-schumacher.de

Ronaldo
www.r9ronaldo.com

Sharron Davies
www.sharrondavies.com

Steffi Graf
www.steffi-graf.com

Steffi Graf (Fan Club)
www.cgo.wave.ca/~cskelton

Tiger Woods
www.tigerwoods.com

Tim Henman
www.henmagic.freeserve.co.uk

pigeon racing

British Homing World
www.pigeonracing.com

polo

Federation of International Polo
www.fippolo.com

Hurlingham Polo Association
www.hpa-polo.co.uk

International Women's Polo Association
www.polo.co.uk/forum

Polo World Cup on Snow
www.polostmoritz.com

Polocross Worldwide
www.polocrossworldwide.net

Schools and Universities Polo Association
www.supa.org.uk

powerboat racing

Royal Yachting Association
www.rya.org.uk

Royal Yachting Association Scotland
www.ryascotland.org.uk

Sail Scotland
www.sailscotland.co.uk

Scottish Sailing Institute
www.scottishsailinginstitute.com

The Cruising Association
www.cruising.org.uk

United Kingdom Sailing Academy
www.uk-sail.org.uk

promotion & education

Central Council of Physical Recreation
www.ccpr.org.uk

Lilleshall National Sports Centre
www.lilleshall.co.uk

National Coaching Foundation
www.ncf.org.uk

Scottish Sports Association
www.scotsport.co.uk

Sports Council (England)
www.english.sports.gov.uk

Sports Council (Northern Ireland)
www.sportscouncil-ni.org.uk

Sports Council (Scotland)
www.ssc.org.uk

Sports Council (United Kingdom)
www.uksport.gov.uk

Sports Industries Federation
www.sportslife.org.uk

SPRITO
www.sprito.org.uk

Women's Sports Foundation
www.wsf.org.uk

Youth Sport Trust
www.youthsport.net

racketball

British Racketball Website
www.racketball.co.uk

Squash UK
www.squash.uk.com/squashuk/ukdocs/rball.htm

roller skating

British Roller Skating
www.british-roller-skating.org.uk

Citiskate Inline UK
www.citiskate.com

UK Roller Skating Rink Directory
www.british-roller-skating.org.uk/rinks

roller hockey

British Inline Puck Hockey Association
www.bipha.co.uk

British Inline Skater Hocket Association
www.bisha.uk.com

Eastern Counties Roller Hockey Association
www.ecrha.org.uk

rounders

National Rounders Association
www.rounders.punters.co.uk

rowing

Amateur Rowing Association
www.ara-rowing.org

Boat Race
www.boatrace.co.uk

British Amateur Rugby League Association
www.barla.org.uk

British Rowing
www.british.rowing.org.uk

Coast Amateur Rowing Association
www.rowinguk.com

Coxless Fours
www.coxless4.com

FISA
www.fisa.org

Henley Royal Regatta
www.hrr.co.uk

International Rowing Federation
www.worldrowing.com

Ocean Rowing Society
www.oceanrowing.com

Regatta Magazine
www.regatta.rowing.org.uk

Scotland Rugby League
www.scotlandrugbyleague.org.uk

Scottish Amateur Rowing Association
www.scottish-rowing.org.uk

The Boat Race
www.theboatrace.org

rugby

British Amateur Rugby League Association
www.barla.org.uk

Great Britain Rugby League
www.uk.rleague.com

Tetley's Super League
www.superleague.co.uk

Clubs

Avondale
www.avonvalerfc.freeserve.co.uk

Ayr
www.sellitontheweb.com/ayrrfc

Bath
www.bathrugby.co.uk

Bedford
www.bedfordrugby.co.uk

Belfast Harlequins
www.belfastharlequins.com

Bristol Rugby
www.bristolrugby.co.uk

Cardiff
www.cardiffrfc.com

Coventry
www.coventryrugby.co.uk

Dungannon
www.dungannon-rugby.co.uk

Gloucester
www.kingsholm-chronicle.org.uk

Harlequins
www.quins.co.uk

Henley
www.henleyrugbyclub.org.uk

Leeds
www.leedsrugby.co.uk

Leicester
www.tigers.co.uk

Llanelli
www.scarlets.co.uk

London Irish
www.london-irish-rugby.com

London Welsh
www.london-welsh.co.uk

Manchester
www.manchester-rugby.co.uk

Moseley
www.moseleyrugby.co.uk

Neath
www.k-c.co.uk/neathrfc

Newcastle Falcons
www.newcastle-falcons.co.uk

Northampton Saints
www.northamptonsaints.co.uk

Pontypridd
www.pontypriddrfc.co.uk

Richmond
www.richmondfc.co.uk

Saracens
www.saracens.com

Shannon
www.shannonrfc.com

Swansea
www.swansearfc.co.uk

Vulcan
www.vulcanrufc.co.uk

Wakefield
www.wakefieldrugby.com

Wasps
www.wasps.co.uk

West Hartlepool
www.west-rugby.org.uk

Worcester
www.wrfc.co.uk

Magazines & Websites

ITV Rugby World Cup
www.itv-rugby.co.uk

Rugby World
www.rugbyworld.com

Scrum.com
www.scrum.com

Sporting Life Rugby League
www.sporting-life.com/rleague/news

Sporting Life Rugby Union
www.sporting-life.com/rugby/news

Organizations

English Rugby Union
www.rfu.com

International Rugby Board
www.irb.org

Irish Rugby Union
www.irfu.ie

Rugby World
www.rugbyworld.com

Scottish Rugby Union
www.sru.org.uk

Welsh Rugby Union
www.wru.co.uk

Tournaments

Allied Dunbar Premiership
www.rugbyclub.co.uk

Rugby League
www.rleague.com

rugby fives

Eton Fives Association
www.etonfives.co.uk

Rugby Fives Association
www.rfa.org.uk

sailing

Association of Northern Universities Sailing Clubs
www.salford.ac.uk/404.php

Junior Offshore Group
www.jog.org.uk

London Sailing Project
www.lsp.org.uk

Old Gaffers Association
www.oldgaffersassociation.org

Royal Yachting Association
www.rya.org.uk

Sadler & Starlight Owners Association
www.sadlerandstarlight.co.uk

Sail Scotland
www.sailscotland.co.uk

Scottish Sailing Institute
www.scottishsailinginstitute.com

The Cruising Association
www.cruising.org.uk

UK Team Racing Association
www.teamracing.org

United Kingdom Sailing Academy
www.uk-sail.org.uk

sailing & watersports
Boats & Equipment

Banks Sails
www.banks.co.uk

Corsair Marine
www.corsairuk.com

Garmin
www.garmin.com

International Coatings
www.yachtpaint.com

Laser
www.lasersailing.com

Moody
www.moody.co.uk

Nauquip
www.nauquip.com

Online Marine
www.on-line-marine.com

Oyster
www.oystermarine.com

Raytheon Marine
www.raymarine.com

Sobstad Sailmakers
www.sobstad.co.uk

Suzuki Marine
www.suzukimarine.co.uk

Tenrag
www.tenrag.com

Yamaha Motor
www.yamaha-motor.co.uk

Clubs & Organisations

Association of Sea Training Organisations
www.asto.org.uk

Attenborough Sailing Club
www.attenboroughsc.org.uk

British Disabled Water Ski Association
www.bdwsa.org.uk

British Universities Sailing Association
www.busa.co.uk

British Water Ski Federation
www.bwsf.co.uk

Coastguard Agency
www.mcga.gov.uk

International Sailing Federation
www.sailing.org

International Surfing Association
www.isa-wsg.org

International Water Ski Federation
www.iwsf.com

Jubilee Sailing Trust
www.jst.org.uk

Maritime & Coastguard Agency
www.mcagency.org.uk

National Federation of Sea Schools
www.nfss.co.uk

Ocean Youth Club
www.oyc.org.uk

Royal Institute of Navigation
www.rin.org.uk

Royal Yachting Association
www.rya.org.uk

Trinity House
www.trinityhouse.co.uk

UK Team Racing Association
www.teamracing.org

World Underwater Federation
www.cmas.org

Yacht Charter Association
www.yca.co.uk

Events, Regattas & Trophies

America's Cup
www.americascup.org

America's Cup Jubilee
www.amcup2001.com

BT Global Challenge
www.btchallenge.com

Cowes Week
www.cowesweek.co.uk

Hamble Week
www.hamble-week.org.uk

Millennium Round the World Yacht Race
www.millennium-rtw.co.uk

Sail for Gold 2000
www.sailforgold.co.uk

Holidays

Intersail
www.intersail.co.uk

Moorings
www.moorings.co.uk

Nautilus
www.nautilus-yachting.co.uk

Neilson Holidays
www.neilson.co.uk

Sunsail Holidays
www.sunsail.com

Sunvil Activity Holidays
www.activity-holidays.co.uk

Magazines & Websites

Boat Exchange
www.btx.co.uk

British Waterskiing
www.waterski-uk.com

Classic Boat Magazine
www.classicboat.co.uk

Cruising Association
www.cruising.org.uk

Dinghy Trader
www.dinghytrader.co.uk

Motor Boat & Yachting
www.ybw.co.uk

Sailing Now
www.sailingnow.com

Sailing Today
www.sailingnet.co.uk

UK Harbours Guide
www.harbours.co.uk

UK Sailing Index
www.uksail.com

Yachting & Boating World
www.ybw.co.uk

Yachting World
www.yachting-world.com

Yachts & Yachting
www.yachtsandyachting.com

shinty

Camanachd
www.shinty.com

268

shooting

British Association of Shooting & Conservation
www.basc.org.uk

British Field Target Association
www.bfta.org

Clay Pigeon Shooting Association
www.cpsa.co.uk

Muzzleloaders Association of Great Britain
www.mlagb.com

National Rifle Association of Great Britain
www.nra.org.uk

National Smallbore Rifle Association
www.nsra.co.uk

The British Shooting Sports Council
www.bssc.org.uk

Welsh Airgun Association
www.welsh-airgun.org.uk

show jumping

Equestrian Times
www.horsenews.com

Olympia Showjumping Championships
www.olympia-show-jumping.co.uk

Events

Badminton Horse Trials
www.badminton-horse.co.uk

Hickstead
www.hickstead.co.uk

Horse of the Year Show
www.hoys.co.uk

Windsor Horse Trials
www.windsor-horse-trials.co.uk

Magazines & Websites

British Dressage
www.britishdressage.co.uk

Organisations

British Endurance Riding Association
www.british-endurance.org.uk

British Equestrian Federation
www.bef.co.uk

British Horse Driving Trials Association
www.horsedrivingtrials.co.uk

British Horse Society
www.bhs.org.uk

British Horse Trials Association
www.bhta.co.uk

British Show Jumping Association
www.bsja.co.uk

International Equestrian Federation
www.horsesport.org

Pony Club
www.pony-club.org.uk

Spanish Riding School of Vienna
www.spanishridingschool.com

skeleton

British Association of Ski Instructors
www.basi.org.uk

The International Bobsleigh & Skeleton Federation
www.fibt.com

skiing

British Association of Ski Patrollers
www.basp.org.uk

British Ski & Snowboard Federation
www.complete-skier.com

Federation of Skiing
www.fis-ski.com

Scottish Ski Club
www.frogston.demon.co.uk/ssc

Ski Club of Great Britain
www.skiclub.co.uk

Snowsport Scotland
www.snsc.demon.co.uk

snooker

Embassy World Snooker
www.embassysnooker.com

English Association for Snooker & Billiards
www.easb.co.uk

The Markington & District Rural Billiards and Snooker League
www.nidderdale.fslife.co.uk

World Snooker
www.worldsnooker.com

snooker & billiards

Billiards Congress of America
www.bca-pool.com

Crucible Theatre
www.shef.ac.uk/city/theatres/crucible

EJ Riley
www.ejriley.com

Embassy World Snooker
www.embassysnooker.com

English Pool Association
www.epa.org.uk

Peradon
www.peradon.co.uk

Snooker Market
www.snookermarket.co.uk

Snooker Net
www.snookernet.com

World Professional Billiards & Snooker Association
www.wpbsa.com

World Snooker Association
www.wpbsa.com

softball

International Softball Federation
www.internationalsoftball.com

sombo

British Sombo Fedreation
www.britishsombo.co.uk

Combat Sombo
www.combatsombo.co.uk

speedway

Auto Cycle Union
www.acu.org.uk/DyIndex.asp

British Speedway Promoters Association
www.british-speedway.co.uk

sportswear & equipment

Adidas
www.adidas.com

American Golf Discount
www.americangolf.co.uk

Armour
www.armourgolf.com

Belfe
www.belfe.com

Berghaus
www.berghaus.com

Bogner
www.bogner.com

Chase Sport
www.chase-sport.com

Columbia
www.columbia.com

Couloir
www.couloir.com

Crag Hoppers
www.craghoppers.com

Fat Shaft
www.wilsonsports.com/golf

Footjoy
www.footjoy.com

Golf Pride Grips
www.golfpride.com

Gryphon
www.gryphonhockey.com

Head
www.head.com

Helly Hansen
www.hellyhansen.com

Hill Billy Powered Golf Trolleys
www.hillbilly.co.uk

Hi-Tec
www.hi-tecsports.com

JJB Sports
www.jjb.co.uk

Luhta
www.luhta.com

Maxfli
www.maxfli.com

Mitre
www.mitre.com

Mizuno
www.mizunoeurope.com

Monarch
www.monarch-hockey.com

Nevada Bob Golf Superstores
www.nevadabob.co.uk

Nike
www.nike.com

North Face
www.thenorthface.com

Oakley
www.oakley.com

O'Neill
www.oneilleurope.com

Ping
www.pingeurope.com

Pinnacle
www.pinnaclegolf.com

Powakaddy
www.powakaddy.com

Proline
www.proline-sports.co.uk

Puma
www.puma.com

Reebok
www.europe.reebok.com

Riley Leisure
www.rileyleisure.com

Schoffel
www.schoffel.com

Slazenger
www.slazenger.co.uk

Speedo
www.speedo.com

Taylor Made
www.taylormadegolf.com

TearDrop
www.teardropgolf.com

Tenson
www.tenson.com

Titleist
www.titleist.com

Top Flite
www.topflight.com

Umbro
www.umbro.com

Wilson
www.wilsonsports.com

Zoppo Hockey Sticks
www.hippo-zoppo.demon.co.uk

squash

British Squash Open Championship
www.britishopensquash.com

England Squash
www.englandsquash.com

International Racquetball Federation
www.racquetball.org

Internet Squash Federation
www.squash.org

Professional Squash Association
www.psa-squash.com

Scottish Squash
www.scottishsquash.org

Squash Player
www.squashplayer.co.uk

Squash Rackets Association
www.squashuk.com

Womens International Squash Players
Association
www.wispa.net

World Squash Federation
www.worldsquash.org

stoolball

National Stoolball Association
www.stoolball.co.uk/nsaaboutnsa.htm

sub-aqua

British Sub Aqua Club
www.bsac.com

Diver Magazine
www.divernet.com

Historical Diving Society
www.thehds.com

Sub-Aqua Association
www.saa.org.uk

surfing

British Surfing Association
www.britsurf.co.uk

International Surfing Association
www.isasurf.org

Welsh Surfing Association
www.sfsurfschool.co.uk

Welsh Surfing Federation
www.britsurf.org/wsf/surf-school.html

swimming

Amateur Swimming Association
www.britishswimming.org

Blue Rhapsody Swimming Pools Ltd
www.bluerhapsody.co.uk

British Long Distance Swimming
Association
www.bldsa.org.uk

City of Birmingham Swimming Club
www.swimbirmingham.org.uk

City of Coventry Swimming Club
www.coventry-swimming.org.uk

Easypools
www.easypools.co.uk

Federation Internationale de Natation
Amateur (FINA)
www.fina.org

Fina
www.fina.org

Institute of Swimming Teachers & Coaches
www.istc.co.uk

International Life Saving Federation
www.ilsf.org

International Swimming Schools
www.swimall.co.uk

Kelloggs / ASA Awards
www.asa-awards.co.uk

Pinelog
www.pinelog.co.uk/chaletpools.html

Royal Life Saving Society
www.lifesavers.org.uk

Speedo
www.speedo.com

Swim Scotland
www.swimscotland.co.uk

Swimming Teachers' Association
www.sta.co.uk

Swimming Websites
www.swimmingwebsites.co.uk

The Swimming Pool and Allied Trades
Association
www.spata.co.uk

table tennis

British Olympic Association Table Tennis
www.olympics.org.uk/tabletennis.htm

English Table Tennis Association
www.etta.co.uk

English Table Tennis Union
www.ettu.org

European Table Tennis Union
www.ettu.org

Guernsey Table Tennis Association
www.guernsey.net/~tabletennis

International Table Tennis Federation
www.ittf.com

Irish Table Tennis Association
www.ttireland.com

Scottish Table Tennis Association
www.sol.co.uk/t/tabletennis

Stirlingshire & Midland Counties
www.smctta.pwp.blueyonder.co.uk/index.html

Table Tennis Association of Wales
www.btinternet.com/~ttaw

taekwando

Alliance of Independent Taekwando
Schools
www.alliancetkd.cwc.net

British United Taekwando Association
www.butf.com

Elite Taekwando Association
www.e.t.a.4t.com

Ituk
www.ituk.org.uk

Moradoff Institute of Taekwan-do
www.welcome.to/taekwondo

Nicholls Tae Kwan Do Institute
www.tkd.co.uk

Tae Kwon Do Association of Great Britain
www.taekwondo.co.uk

Tae Kwon Do South
www.tkdsouth.co.uk

United Kingdom Tae Kwan Do Association
www.ukta.com

Welsh Tae Kwan Do Association
www.welshtaekwondo.co.uk

tang soo do

Dragon Tang Soo Do
www.dragontangsoodo.com

Great Britain Tang Soo Do Association
www.digitalcomfortzone.com/gbtsda

Interational Tang Soo Do Association
www.tangsoodo.co.uk

Keith Tang Soo Do
www.keith-tsd.org.uk

Scotland Tang Soo Do
www.scotland-tsd.org.uk

UK Soo Bahk Do
www.soobahkdo.co.uk

UK Tang Soo Do Association
www.uktsdf.org.uk

target sports

Airgun UK
www.airgun.org

British Shooting Sports Council
www.bssc.org.uk

Clay Pigeon Shooting Association
www.cpsa.co.uk

Clay Shooting Magazine
www.clubclayshooting.com

Grand National Archery Society
www.gnas.org

Gun Trade News
www.brucepub.com/gtn

International Archery Federation
www.archery.org

International Practical Shooting
Confederation
www.ipsc.org

International Shooting Sport Federation
www.issf-shooting.org

Muzzle Loaders' Association of Great
Britain
http://user.itl.net/~dale

National Rifle Association
www.nra.org.uk

National Small-bore Rifle Association
www.nsra.co.uk

Practical Shooting Association
www.ukpsa.co.uk

Scottish Archery
www.scottisharchery.org.uk

Scottish Rifle Association
www.hugon.demon.co.uk/sra

Scottish Smallbore Rifle Association
www.ssra.co.uk

tchoukball

Tchoukall Association of Great Britain
www.tchoukball.org.uk

ten pin bowling

Britsh Ten Pin Bowling Association
www.btba.org.uk

Scottish Ten Pin Bowling Association
www.stba.org.uk

tennis

ATP Tour
www.atptour.com

British Olympic Association Tennis
www.olympics.org.uk/tennis.htm

Champions Tennis
www.championstennis.com

International Tennis Federation
www.itftennis.com

Lawn Tennis Association
www.lta.org.uk

Real Tennis
www.real-tennis.com

Royal Tennis Court, Hampton Court Palace
www.realtennis.gbrit.com

Sporting Life Tennis
www.sporting-life.com/tennis/news

Tennis Organisation UK
www.tennis.org.uk

US Open
www.usopen.org

Wimbledon
www.wimbledon.org

WTA Tour
www.wtatour.com

Magazines & Websites

Sky Sports Tennis
www.sky.co.uk/sports/tennis

trampolining

British Trampoline Federation
www.thebtf.co.uk

triathlon

British Triathlon Association
www.britshtriathlon.co.uk

Scottish Triathlon Association
www.tri-scotland.org

Welsh Triathlon Association
www.welshtri.org.uk

tug-of-war

Scottish Tug of War Association
www.scottishtugofwar.co.uk

Tug-of-War Association
www.tugofwar.co.uk

volleyball

Association of Volleyball Professionals
www.volleyball.org

Hertfordshire Volleyball Association
www.hertsvolleyball.com

International Volleyball Federation
www.fivb.ch

Suffolk Volleyball Association
www.suffolkvolleyball.org.uk

walking

Backpackers Club
www.catan.demon.co.uk/backpack

BTA Walking Britain
www.visitbritain.com/walking

London Backpackers
www.members.tripod.co.uk/londonbackpackers

Ramblers' Association
www.ramblers.org.uk

Ramblers' Association (Lake District Area)
www.ralakedistrict.ukf.net

273

waterpolo

National Water Polo League
www.nwpl.co.uk

water skiing

British Water Ski Federation
www.bwsf.co.uk

National Water Sports Centre
www.nationalwatersports.co.uk

weightlifting

British Amateur Weightlifters Association
www.bawla.com

British Powerlifting
www.britishpowerlifting.com

European Powerlifting Federation
www.europower.org

International Powerlifting Federation
www.omniway.sm./ewf

International Weightlifting Federation
www.iwf.net

Yorkshire & North East Counties' Amateur
Weightlifters Association
www.weights.demon.co.uk/yne/index.htm

weightlifting & strength

British Amateur Weightlifters' Association
www.olympics.org.uk/weightlifting.htm

International Weightlifting Federation
www.iwf.net

Tug of War Association
www.tugofwar.co.uk

windsurfing

British Landsailing Association
www.moreair.demon.co.uk/yachts

British Windsurfing Association
www.britishwindsurfing.com

Professional Windsurfing Association
www.world-windsurfing.com

United Kingdom Boardsailing Association
www.ukwindsurfing.com

winter sports

Alpine World Cup Skiing 2000
www.irisco.net/ski

Aviemore & Cairngorms Experience
www.aviemore.co.uk

British Association of Ski Instructors
www.basi.org.uk

British Ski & Snowboard Federation
www.complete-skier.com

Cross Country Skier Magazine
www.crosscountryskier.com

Great Britain Luge Association
www.gbla.org.uk

Hockey Player Magazine
www.hockeyplayer.com

International Biathlon Union
www.ibu.at

International Bobsleigh & Tobogganing
Federation
www.bobsleigh.com

International Luge Federation
www.fil-luge.org

International Skating Union
www.isu.org

International Ski Federation
www.fis-ski.com

National Hockey League
www.nhl.com

Salt Lake City Winter Olympics 2002
www.saltlake2002.com

Scottish National Ski Council
www.snsc.demon.co.uk

Ski Club of Great Britain
www.skiclub.co.uk

Ski Magazine
www.skinet.com/ski

Ski World Cup
www.skiworldcup.org

Skier & Snowboarder Magazine
www.ski.co.uk/skimag

Tamworth Snowdome
www.snowdome.co.uk

Torino Winter Olympics 2006
www.torino2006.it

Torvill & Dean (Fan Club)
users.aol.com/tanddfanp

US Figure Skating Association
www.usfsa.org

wrestling

International Federation of Associated
Wrestling Styles
www.fila-wrestling.org

International Sports Yoga Federation
www.sportsite.com.ar/fiys.html

International Sumo Federation
www.amateursumo.com

USA Wrestling
www.usawrestling.org

WCW Wrestling
www.wcwwrestling.com

World Championship Wrestling
www.wcw.com

World Wrestling Federation
www.wwf.com

Technology

cable

Birmingham Cable
www.birmcable.co.uk

Cable London
www.cablelondon.co.uk

Cable Net
www.cablenet.net

Cable Tel
www.cabletel.co.uk

Crimptech National
www.crimptech.co.uk

Diamond Cable
www.diamond.co.uk

Inside Cable
ourworld.compuserve.com/homepages/
roger_wilson/insicab.htm

Peninsula Networks
www.peninsula.co.uk

Power Check
www.powercheck.demon.co.uk

hardware & software producers

ACER
www.acer.com

ACT
www.act.org.uk

Adobe
www.adobe.com

AMEC
www.amec.co.uk

Amiga
www.amiga.com

Amstrad
www.amstrad.com

Apple
www.apple.com

AST
www.astcomputer.com

Broderbund Europe
www.broderbund.com

Bull
www.bull.co.uk

Canon
www.canon.com

Claris
www.claris.com

Compaq
www.compaq.co.uk

DEC
www.dec.com

Dell
www.dell.com/uk

Demon
www.demon.net

Digital
www.digital.co.uk

Eidos
www.eidos.co.uk

Elonex
www.elonex.co.uk

Epson
www.epson.com

Ericsson
www.ericsson.com

Eudora
www.eudora.com

Fujitsu
www.fujitsu-pc.com

Gateway
www.gw2k.co.uk

Hewlett Packard
www.hp.com

Hitachi
www.hds.co.uk

Honeywell
www.honeywell.com

IBM
www.ibm.com

Intel
www.intel.co.uk

Iomega
www.iomega-europe.com

Lexmark
www.lexmark.co.uk

Lotus
www.lotus.com

Mesh
www.meshplc.co.uk

Microlease
www.microlease.com

Microsoft
www.microsoft.com

MISys
www.misysinc.com

Mitel
www.mitel.com

NEC
www.nec-global.com

Netcom
www.netcom.net.uk

Netscape
www.netscape.com

Nintendo
www.nintendo-europe.com

Nokia
www.nokia.com

Novell
www.novell.com

Olivetti
www.olivetti.com

Open Universal Software
www.universal.com

Oracle
www.oracle.co.uk

Packard Bell
www.packardbell.com

Playstation
http://eu.playstation.com

Psion
www.psion.com

Racal
www.racalcomm.com

Real Player
www.real.com

Shockwave
www.shockwave.com

Sibelius
www.sibelius.com

Siemens
www.siemens.com

Silicon Graphics
www.sgi.com

Sony
www.sony.com

Sunsoft
www.sunsoft.com

Texas Instruments
www.ti.com

Tiny
www.tiny.com/uk

Toshiba
www.toshiba.com

Tulip
www.tulip.com

Unisys
www.unisys.com

Universal
www.universal.com

Viglen
www.viglen.co.uk

Vitech
www.vitech.net

Vodafone
www.vodafone.co.uk

Wang
www.wang.com

Widget Software
www.widgetsoftware.com

internet companies

Cisco
www.cisco.com

Freeserve
www.freeserve.net

Hotmail
www.hotmail.com

Jellyworks
www.hemscott.co.uk/equities/company/cd03840.htm

Morse
www.morse.com

Netbenefit
www.netbenefit.com

NicNames
www.nicnames.co.uk

internet service providers

AAP Internet
www.aapi.co.uk

Aardvaak
www.aardvaak.co.uk

Abel Gratis
www.abelgratis.com

Aimity Internet
www.amity.co.uk

Airtime Internet Resources
www.airtime.co.uk

Anglianet
www.anglianet.co.uk

AOL
www.aol.co.uk

Aviators Network
www.aviators.net

Barclays
www.is.barclays.co.uk

Baynet Internet Services
www.baynet.co.uk

Bigwig
www.bigwig.net

Breathe
www.breathe.com

BT Broadband
www.bt.com/broadband

BT Click
www.btclick.com

BT Internet
www.btinternet.com

Business Serve
www.businessserve.co.uk

Cable & Wireless
www.cwcom.net

Clara.Net
www.uk.clara.net

Compuserve
www.compuserve.co.uk

Cyberphile Ltd
www.cyberphile.net

Demon
www.demon.net

Direct Connection
www.dircon.net

Easynet
www.easynet.co.uk

Entanet
www.enta.net

Enterprise
www.enterprise.net

Entweb
www.entweb.co.uk

Free UK
www.freeuk.com

Free.Net
www.thefree.net

Free4All
www.free4all.co.uk

FreeNet
www.freenet.co.uk

Freenetname
www.freenetname.co.uk

Freeserve
www.freeserve.co.uk

Freewire
www.freewire.net

FreeZone
www.freezone.co.uk

Genie
www.genie.co.uk

Global
www.global.net.uk

LineOne
www.lineone.net

Madasafish
www.madasafish.com

NetDirect
www.netdirect.net.uk

Nildram
www.nildram.net

Pipemedia
www.pipemedia.co.uk

Prestel
www.prestel.co.uk

Supanet
www.supanet.com

Talk 21
www.talk21.com

TescoNet
www.tesco.net

Tiny
www.tinyonline.net

UK Online
www.ukonline.co.uk

Virgin
www.virgin.net

WH Smith
www.whsmith.co.uk

X-Stream
www.x-stream.com

Yahoo! Online
www.yahoo.co.uk

magazines & websites

.net
www.netmag.co.uk

Acorn Gaming
www.acorn-gaming.org.uk

Bluetooth
www.bluetooth.com

British Computer Society
www.bcs.org.uk

Computer & Video Games
www.game-online.com

Computer Shopper
www.compshopper.co.uk

Computer Weekly
www.computerweekly.co.uk

Computeractive
www.computeractive.co.uk

Computing
www.vnunet.com

GameSpot UK
www.gamespot.co.uk/pcgw

IT Weekly
www.itweek.co.uk

Lara Croft
www.laracroft.com

MacUser
www.macuser.co.uk

Macworld
www.macworld.com

McAfee
www.mcafee.com

PC Advisor
www.pcadvisor.co.uk

PC Plus
www.pcplus.co.uk

PC Zone OnLine
www.pczone.co.uk

The Net
www.thenetmag.co.uk

Total Games
www.totalgames.net

search engines

About
www.about.com

All Experts
www.allexperts.com

All The Web
www.alltheweb.com

Alta Vista
www.altavista.co.uk

Ask Jeeves
www.ask.co.uk

Copernic
www.copernic.com

Daily Stocks
www.dailystocks.com

DejaNews
www.dejanews.com

Direct Hit
www.directhit.co.uk

Dogpile
www.dogpile.com

E Spotting
www.espotting.com

Electric Library
www.elibrary.com

Excite
www.excite.co.uk

Fish4
www.fish4.co.uk

Gamez
www.gamez.com

Go To
www.go2.com

Godado
www.godado.tv

Google
www.google.co.uk

Hot Bot
www.hotbot.lycos.co.uk

Inktomi
www.inktomi.com

Invisible Web
www.invisibleweb.com

Lexibot
www.lexibot.com

Looksmart
www.looksmart.co.uk

Lycos
www.lycos.co.uk

Magellan
www.mckinley.com

Mamma
www.mamma.com

Maxisearch
www.maxisearch.com

Medical World Search
www.mwsearch.com

Metacrawler
www.metacrawler.com

Mirago
www.mirago.co.uk

MSN
www.msn.co.uk

Northern Light
www.nlsearch.com

Oveture
www.overture.com

Search
www.search.com

Search Engine Websites
www.searchenginewebsites.co.uk

Search UK
www.searchuk.co.uk

Searchgov
www.searchgov.com

UK Directory
www.ukdirectory.co.uk

UK Max
www.ukmax.co.uk

UK Online
www.ukonline.co.uk

UK Plus
www.ukplus.co.uk

Web Ferret
www.zdnet.com/ferret

Webcrawler
www.webcrawler.com

Yahoo!
www.yahoo.co.uk

telecommunications

Alcatel
www.alcatel.com

Alpha Telecom
www.alphatelecom.com

Broadband-Cable
www.broadband-cable.co.uk

BT
www.bt.com

BT Cellnet
www.btcellnet.co.uk

BT Pagers
www.btmobility.com

Cable & Wireless
www.cwcom.co.uk

Cellnet
www.cellnet.co.uk

Com One
www.com1.fr/uk

Dolphin
www.dolphin-telecom.co.uk

Energis
www.energis.co.uk

Ericsson
www.ericsson.co.uk

Esprit
www.esprittelecom.com

Eurobell
www.eurobell.com

Hagenuk
www.hagenuk.de

Hutchison Telecom
www.orange.co.uk

Maxon
www.maxon.co.uk

MCI Worldcom
www.wcom.co.uk

Mercury
www.mercury.co.uk

Motorola
www.mot.com

NEC
www.euronec.com

Nokia
www.nokia.co.uk

Nortel
www.nortel.com

NTL
www.ntl.com

Nynex
www.nynex.co.uk

Odyssey
www.odysseycorp.co.uk

OFTEL
www.oftel.gov.uk

One.Tel UK
www.onetel.co.uk

Orange
www.orange.co.uk

Panasonic
www.mcuk.panasonic.co.uk

Philips
www.pcc.philips.com

Planet Talk
www.planet-talk.co.uk

Ringtones
www.ringtones.co.uk

Sagem
www.sagem.com

Samsung
www.samsungelectronics.com

Siemens
www.siemens.co.uk

Sony
www.sony-europe.com/cons/pce

Telecom UK
www.telecom.co.uk

TeleWest
www.telewest.co.uk

Thuraya
www.thuraya.com

T-mobile
www.t-mobile.co.uk

Tones 4 Fones
www.tones4fones.com

Torch
www.torch.co.uk

Virgin
www.virgin.com/mobile

Vodafone
www.vodafone.co.uk

World Online
www.worldonline.com

Your Mobile
www.yourmobile.com

web censors

Cyber Patrol
www.cyberpatrol.com

Cybersnoop
www.pearlsw.com

Net Nanny
www.netnanny.com

Surf on the Safe Side
www.surfonthesafeside.com

Xcheck
www.xcheck.net

X-Stop
www.xstop.com

airlines

AccessAir
www.accessair.com

Aer Lingus
www.aerlingus.ie

Aeroflot
www.aeroflot.org

Aerolineas Argentinas
www.aerolineas.com.ar

Aeromexico
www.aeromexico.com/ingles

Air 2000
www.air2000.co.uk

Air Afrique
www.airafrique.com

Air ALM
www.airalm.com

Air Asia
www.airasia.com

Air Atlanta Icelandic
www.atlanta.is

Air Baltic
www.airbaltic.lv

Air Berlin
www.airberlin.com

Air Caledonie
www.air-caledonie.nc

Air Canada
www.aircanada.ca

Air Caribbean
www.aircaribbean.com

Air China
www.airchina.u-net.com

Air Europa
www.air-europa.es

Air Fiji
www.airfiji.net

Air France
www.airfrance.co.uk

Air Georgia
www.air-georgia.com

Air India
www.airindia.com

Air Jamaica
www.airjamaica.com

Air Lithuania
www.airlithuania.lt

Air Macau
www.airmacau.com.mo

Air Madagascar
www.airmadagascar.info

Air Malawi
www.africaonline/airmalawi/foreword.html

Air Malta
www.airmalta.com

Air Mauritius
www.airmauritius.com

Air Moldova
www.ami.md

Air Namibia
www.airnamibia.com.na

Air Nauru
www.airnauru.com.au

Air New Zealand
www.airnz.com

Air Niugini
www.airniugini.com.pg

Air Philippines
www.airphilippines.com

Air Portugal
www.tap-airportugal.pt

Air Seychelles
www.airseychelles.it

Air Tahiti
www.airtahiti-nui.com

Air UK
www.airuk.co.uk

Air Zimbabwe
www.airzimbabwe.com

Aircalin
www.aircalin.nc

Airlanka
www.airlanka.com

Airlines of South Australia
www.asa.mtx.net

Alaska Airlines
www.alaska-air.com

Alitalia
www.alitalia.co.uk

All Nippon Airways
www.ana.co.uk

Aloha Air
www.alohaair.com

America Trans Air
www.ata.com

American Airlines
www.americanair.com

Ana Europe
www.ana-europe.com

Ansett
www.ansett.com

Ariana Afghan Airlines
www.flyariana.com

Asiana Airlines
www.flyasiana.com

Atlantic Airways
www.atlantic.fo

Atlas Air
www.atlasair.com

Austrian Airlines
www.aua.com

Azzurra Airlines
www.azzurraair.it

Bahamasair
www.bahamasair.com

Balkan Airlines
www.balkan.com

Bhoja Air
www.bhojaair.com.pk

Bouraq Indonesia Airlines
www.bouraq.com

Braathens
www.english.braathens.no

Britannia
www.britanniaairways.com

British Airways
www.british-airways.com

British European
www.british-european.com

British Midland
www.britishmidland.co.uk

British Regional Airlines
www.british-regional.com

British World Airlines
www.british-world.co.uk

Brussels Airlines
www.brussels-airlines.com

Buzz
www.buzzaway.com

BWIA
www.bwee.com

Cameroon Airlines
www.iccnet.cm/camair/accueil.htm

Cape Air
www.flycapeair.com

Cathay Pacific
www.cathaypacific.com

Cayman Airways
www.caymanairways.com

China Airlines
www.china-airlines.com

Continental
www.flycontinental.com

Corsair
www.corsair-int.com

Croatia Airlines
www.ctn.tel.hr/ctn

Crossair
www.crossair.ch

Cubana Airlines
www.cubana.cu

Cyprus Airways
www.cyprusair.com

Cyprus Turkish Airlines
www.kthy.net

Czech Airlines
www.csa.cz/en

Delta
www.delta-air.com

Dragon Air
www.dragonair.com

Eastern Airways
www.easternairways.com

EasyJet
www.easyjet.com

El Al
www.elal.co.il/worldwide/uk

Emirates (UAE)
www.ekgroup.com

EVA Air
www.evaair.com.tw/english

Finnair
www.finnair.co.uk

First Air
www.firstair.ca

Flight West Airlines
www.flightwest.com.au

Garuda Indonesia
www.garudausa.com

Ghana Airways
www.ghana-airways.com

Go
www.go-fly.com

Greek Airlines
www.cronus.gr

Greenlandair
www.greenland-guide.dk/gla

Gujarat Airways
www.gujaratairways.com

Gulf Air
www.gulfairco.com

Hapag-Lloyd Airlines
www.hapag-lloyd.com

Hawaiian Airlines
www.hawaiianair.com

Iberia
www.iberia.com

Icelandair
www.icelandair.co.uk

Indian Airlines
indian-airlines.nic.in

Japan Airlines
www.jal.co.jp

JAS Japan Air System
www.jas.co.jp

Jersey European Airways
www.jea.co.uk

Kenya Airways
www.kenyaairways.co.uk

KLM
www.klmuk.com

Korean Air
www.koreanair.com

Kuwait Airways
www.kuwait-airways.com

Lasca Airlines
www.flylatinamerica.com

Lauda Air
www.laudaair.com

LOT Polish Airlines
www.lot.com

Lufthansa
www.lufthansa.co.uk

Lynx Air International
www.lynxair.com

Malaysia Air
www.malaysiaair.com

Malaysia Airlines
www.malaysiaairlines.com.my

Malev
www.malev.hu

Manx Airlines
www.manx-airlines.com

Martin Air
www.martinairusa.com

Mexicana Airlines
www.mexicana.com

Middle Eastern Airlines
www.mea.com.lb

Midway Airlines
www.midwayair.com

Midwest Express Airlines
www.midwestexpress.com

Monarch
www.monarch-airlines.com

National Airlines
www.nationalairlines.com

North West Airlines
www.nwa.com

Olympic Airways
www.olympic-airways.gr

Pacific Coastal Airlines
www.pacific-coastal.com

Pacific Wings Hawaii
www.pacificwings.com

Pakistan International
www.piac.com

Pan Am
www.panam.org

Philippine Airlines
www.philippineair.com

Polynesian Airlines
www.polynesianairlines.co.nz

Portugália Airlines
www.pga.pt/uk

Qantas
www.qantas.com.au

Qatar Airways
www.qatarairways.com

Royal Air Maroc
www.royalairmaroc.com

Royal Brunei
www.bruneiair.com

Royal Jordanian Airlines
www.rja.com.jo

Royal Nepal Airlines
www.royalnepal.com

Ryanair
www.ryanair.com

Sahara Airlines
www.saharaairline.com

Saudi Arabian Airlines
www.saudiairlines.com

Scandanavian Airlines
www.flysas.co.uk

Shuttle America
www.shuttleamerica.com

Singapore Airlines
www.singaporeair.com

Skyways
www.skyways.se

Skywest Airlines
www.skywest.com.au

Sobelair
www.sobelair.com

Solomon Airlines
www.pacificislands.com/airlines/solomon.html

South African Airways
www.saa.co.za

Southwest Airlines
www.iflyswa.com

Spanair
www.spanair.com

Spirit Airlines
www.spiritair.com

SriLankan Airlines
www.lanka.net/Airlanka

Star Alliance
www.star-alliance.com

Sunflower Airlines
www.fiji.to

Surinam Airways
www.slm.firm.sr

Swiftair
www.swiftair.com

Swissair
www.swissair.ch

Tahiti Airlines
www.airtahitinui-usa.com

Tasmania Airlines
www.tasair.com.au

Thai Airways
www.thaiair.com

Trans States Airlines
www.transstates.net

Transmeridian Airlines
www.transmeridian-airlines.com

Turkish Airlines
www.turkishairlines.com

TWA
www.twa.com

Tyrolean Airways
www.tyrolean.at

Ukraine International Airlines
www.uia.ukrpack.net

United Airlines
www.ual.com

United Airlines Belgium
www.ual.be

US Airways
www.usairways.com

Uzbekistan Airways
www.uzbekistanairways.nl

VARIG Brasil
www.varig.com.br/english

Vietnam Airlines
www.vietnamair.com.vn

Virgin Atlantic
www.virgin-atlantic.com

World Airways
www.worldair.com

Yeman Airways
www.yemenairways.co.uk

Yugoslav Airlines JAT
www.jat.com

airports

Foreign

Albuquerque
www.cabq.gov/airport/index.html

Alicante
www.aena.es

Amsterdam
www.schiphol.nl

Atlanta
www.atlanta-airport.com

Auckland
www.auckland-airport.co.nz

Baltimore Washington
www.bwiairport.com

Bangkok
www.airportthai.or.th

Barcelona
www.aena.es/ae/bcn/homepage.htm

Berlin
www.berlin-airport.de

Boston
www.massport.com

Brisbane
www.brisbaneairport.com.au

Brussels
www.brusselsairport.be

Calgary
www.calgaryairport.com

Cape Town
www.airports.co.za

Charlotte/Douglas
www.charlotteairport.com

Chicago
www.ohare.com

Cincinnati
www.cvgairport.com

Cologne
www.airport-cgn.de

Copenhagen
www.cph.dk

Dallas Fort Worth
www.dfwairport.com

Dehli
www.delhiairport.com

Denver
www.flydenver.com

Detroit
www.metroairport.com

Dubai
www.dubaiairport.com

Dublin
www.dublin-airport.com

Dusseldorf
www.duesseldorf-international.de

Faro
www.ana-aeroportos.pt

Frankfurt
www.frankfurt-airport.de

Geneva
www.gva.ch/en

Gothenburg
www.lfv.se/site/airports/landvetter/eng/index.asp

Hannover
www.flughafen.hannover.de

Helsinki
www.ilmailulaitos.com/english/lentoase/helvan

Hong Kong
www.hkairport.com

Honolulu
www.hawaii.gov/dot/airports/visitor_info.htm

Ibiza
www.aena.es

Istanbul
www.dhmiata.gov.tr

Johannesburg
www.airports.co.za

Kansas
www.kcairports.com

Kuala Lumpur
www.klia.com.my

Madrid
www.aena.es/ae/mad/homepage.htm

Marseille
www.marseille.aeroport.fr

Melbourne
www.melbourne-airport.com.au

Memphis
www.mscaa.com

Milan
www.sea-aeroportimilano.it

Montreal
www.admtl.com

Moscow
www.sheremetyevo-airport.ru

Munich
www.munich-airport.de

Nashville
www.nashintl.com

New York (JFK)
www.panynj.gov

Newark
www.newarkairport.com

Nice
www.nice.aeroport.fr

Orlando
www.orlandoairports.net

Osaka
www.kiac.co.jp

Paris
www.adp.fr

Perth
www.perthairport.com

Rome
www.adr.it

San Diego
www.szn.org.fids/index.zsp

San Fransisco
www.sfoairport.com

Seattle
www.portseattle.org

Seoul
www.kimpo-airport.co.kr

Singapore
www.changi.airport.com.sg

Stockholm
www.arlanda.com

Stuttgart
www.flughafen-stuttgart.de

Sydney
www.sydneyairport.com.au

Taipei
www.cksairport.gov.tw

Tampa
www.tampaairport.com

Tokyo
www.narita-airport.or.jp/airport

Toronto
www.gtaa.com

Vancouver
www.yvr.ca

Venice
www.veniceairport.it

Vienna
www.viennaairport.com

Washington (Dulles)
www.mwaa.com

Zurich
www.uniqueairport.com

UK

Aberdeen
www.baa.co.uk/main/airports/aberdeen

Belfast
www.bial.co.uk

Birmingham
www.bhx.co.uk

British Airports Authority
www.baa.co.uk

British International Airports
www.bia.co.uk

Exeter
www.eclipse.co.uk/exeterair

Gatwick
www.gatwickairport.co.uk

Glasgow Prestwick
www.glasgow.pwk.com

Heathrow
www.heathrow.co.uk

Isle of Man
www.iom-airport.com

Liverpool
www.livairport.com

London City
www.londoncityairport.com

Luton
www.london-luton.com

Manchester
www.manairport.co.uk

Stansted
www.baa.co.uk/stansted

bus companies

Airbus
www.airbus.co.uk

Arriva
www.arriva.co.uk

Big Bus Tours
www.bigbus.co.uk

Blue Line
www.blueline.demon.co.uk

Bus Web
www.busweb.co.uk

Citylink
www.citylink.co.uk

Clarkes of London
www.clarkesoflondon.co.uk

Eurolines
www.eurolines.co.uk

First Group
www.firstgroup.com

Go Ahead
www.go-ahead.com

Green Line
www.greenline.co.uk

London Transport
www.londontransport.co.uk

National Express
www.gobycoach.com

Nor-Way Bussekspress
www.nbe.no

Oxford Bus
www.oxfordbus.co.uk

Redwing
www.redwing-coaches.co.uk

Speedlink
www.speedlink.co.uk

Stagecoach
www.stagecoachholdings.com

Yellow Buses
www.yellowbuses.co.uk

car hire

Alamo
www.goalamo.com

Avis
www.avis.co.uk

BCR British Car Rental
www.bcvr.co.uk

British Vehicle Rental Association
www.bbi.co.uk/bvrla

Budget
www.budget-rent-a-car.co.uk

Direct Car Hire
www.direct-car-hire.co.uk

Easy Rentacar
www.easyrentacar.com

Enterprise
www.enterprise.com

Eurodrive Car Rental
www.eurodrive.com

Europcar
www.europcar.com

Hertz
www.hertz.co.uk

Holiday Autos
www.holidayautos.co.uk

Holiday Cars Direct
www.holidaycars.co.uk

Kenning
www.kenning.co.uk

National
www.nationalcar-europe.com

Practical Car & Van Rental
www.practical.co.uk

Rent A Wreck
www.rent-a-wreck.com

Thrifty
www.thrifty.co.uk

U-Drive
www.udrive.co.uk

Woods Car Rental
www.woods.co.uk

ferries

Brittany
www.brittany-ferries.com

Calais
www.calais-port.com

Calmac
www.calmac.co.uk

Channel Hoppers
www.channelhoppers.com

Color Line
www.colorline.com

Condor
www.condorferries.co.uk

DFDS Seaways
www.dfdsseaways.co.uk

Emeraude Lines
www.emeraudelines.com

Hover Travel
www.hovertravel.co.uk

Hoverspeed
www.hoverspeed.co.uk

Irish Ferries
www.irishferries.com

P & O European
www.poferries.com

P & O Scottish
www.poscottishferries.co.uk

P & O Stena Line
www.posl.com

P&O North Sea
www.ponsf.com

Red Funnel
www.redfunnel.co.uk

Scandinavian Seaways
www.scansea.com

Sea France
www.seafrance.co.uk

Seaview
www.seaview.co.uk/ferries

Stena
www.stenaline.co.uk

Swansea Cork
www.swansea-cork.ie

Wightlink
www.wightlink.co.uk

hotels
Booking

Late Rooms.com
www.laterooms.com

Companies

British Hotel Reservation Centre
www.bhrc.co.uk

Choice
www.hotelchoice.com

Crowne Plaza
www.crowneplaza.com

Dan
www.danhotels.co.il

De Vere
www.devereonline.co.uk

Elite
www.elitehotels.co.uk

Eton Town House Group
www.etontownhouse.com

Fairmont
www.fairmont.com

Forte & Le Meridien
www.forte-hotels.com

Four Seasons
www.fourseasons.com

Goodnight Inn
www.thegoodnightinn.com

Grand Heritage
www.grandheritage.com

Hilton
www.hilton.com

Holiday Inn
www.holiday-inn.com

Intercontinental
www.interconti.com

Le Meridien
www.lemeridien-hotels.com

MacDonald
www.macdonaldhotels.com

Marriott Hotels
www.marriott.com

MKI Hotels
www.mki.ltd.uk

Novotel
www.novotel.com

Oberoi
www.oberoihotels.com

Orient Express
www.orient-expresshotels.com

Posthouse
www.posthouse-hotels.com

Queens Moat
www.queensmoat.com

Radisson
www.radisson.com

Red Carnation
www.redcarnationhotels.com

Regal
www.regal-hotels.com

Relais & Chateaux
www.relaischateaux.fr

Sheraton
www.sheraton.com

Stakis
www.stakis.co.uk

Swallow
www.swallowhotels.com

Thanos
www.thanos-hotels.com

Thistle
www.thistle.co.uk

Travel Inns
www.travelinn.co.uk

Travelodge

www.travelodge.co.uk

Virgin
www.virginhotels.com

Wyndham
www.mki.ltd.uk/wyndham.htm

Leading Hotels

Anassa
www.thanos-hotels.com

Annabelle
www.thanos-hotels.com

Elounda Beach
www.eloundabeach.gr

Gleneagles
www.gleneagles.com

Lanesborough
www.lanesborough.co.uk

Lowry Hotel
www.thelowryhotel.com

Mandarin Oriental
www.mandarin-oriental.com

Paphos Beach
www.thanos-hotels.com

Raffles Singapore
www.raffles.com

Ritz
www.theritzhotel.co.uk

San Roque Club
www.sanroqueclub.com

Savoy
www.savoy-group.co.uk

Shangri-la
www.shangri-la.com

The Manor, New Delhi
www.slh.com/themanor

magazines & websites

Conde Nast Traveller
www.cntraveller.co.uk

Fodor's Guide
www.fodors.com

Go By Coach
www.gobycoach.com

Good Holiday Guide
www.goodholidayguide.com

Good Ski Guide
www.goodskiguide.com

Holiday Which?
www.which.net/holiday

Lonely Planet
www.lonelyplanet.com

Michelin Guides
www.viamichelin.com

National Geographic
www.nationalgeographic.com

Public Transport Information
www.pti.org.uk

Rough Guides
www.roughguides.com

UK Street Map
www.streetmap.co.uk

Virgin Net Travel
www.virgin.net/travel

parking

BAA Parking
www.baa.co.uk

Britannia Parking
www.britannia-parking.co.uk

Flypark
www.flypark.co.uk

National Car Parks
www.ncp.co.uk

Parking Express, APCOA Parking
www.parkingexpress.co.uk

property hire

English Country Cottages
www.english-country-cottages.co.uk

resorts

Butlins
www.butlins.co.uk

Center Parcs
www.centerparcs.co.uk

Club Mark Warner
www.markwarner.co.uk

Club Med
www.clubmed.com

Disneyland (California)
www.disney.co.uk/usa-resorts/disneyland

Disneyland Paris
www.disneylandparis.com

Disneyworld (Florida)
www.disney.co.uk/usa-resorts/wdw

Sandals
www.sandals.com

trains

Foreign

Alaska Railroad
www.akrr.com

Amtrak
www.amtrak.com

BC Transit
www.transitbc.com

Belgian Railways
www.sncb.be

Deutsche Bahn AG
www.bahn.de

Freedom Rail
www.freedomrail.com

Inland Railway
www.inlandsbanan.se/england.html

State Railway
www.sj.se

Swiss Federal Railways
www.sbb.ch

Tranz Rail
www.tranzrail.co.nz

Union Pacific Railroad
www.uprr.com

West Coast Railway
www.wcr.com.au

UK

Alphaline Regional Railways
www.alphaline.co.uk

Anglia Railways Train Services
www.angliarailways.co.uk

ARRIVA Trains Northern
www.northern-spirit.co.uk

Association of Train Operating Companies
www.rail.co.uk/atoc

BritRail
www.britrail.net

C2C
www.c2c-online.co.uk

Central Trains
www.centraltrains.co.uk

Chiltern Railways
www.chilternrailways.co.uk

Connex
www.connex.co.uk

Docklands Light Rail
www.dlr.co.uk

English Welsh & Scottish Railways
www.ews-railway.co.uk

Eurostar
www.eurostar.com

First Great Eastern
www.ger.co.uk

First Great Western
www.great-western-trains.co.uk

First North Western
www.firstnorthwestern.co.uk

Freightliner
www.freightliner.co.uk

Gatwick Express
www.gatwickexpress.co.uk

Great Eastern Railway
www.ger.co.uk

Great North Eastern Railway
www.gner.co.uk

Heathrow Express
www.heathrowexpress.co.uk

Hull Trains
www.hulltrains.co.uk

Island Line
www.island-line.co.uk

London Transport
www.londontransport.co.uk

London Transport Season Tickets
www.tickets-on-line.co.uk

London Underground
www.thetube.com

Midland Mainline
www.midlandmainline.com

National Rail Corporation
www.nationalrail.com.au

NI Railways
www.nirailways.co.uk

Northern Spirit
www.northern-spirit.co.uk

Railtrack
www.railtrack.co.uk

Railtrack Travel Information
www.railtrack.co.uk/travel

Scotrail
www.scotrail.co.uk

Silverlink Train Services
www.silverlink-trains.com

South Central Trains
www.southcentraltrains.co.uk

South West Trains
www.swtrains.co.uk

Stansted Express
www.stanstedexpress.com

Thames Trains
www.thamestrains.co.uk

Thameslink Rail
www.thameslink.co.uk

Train Line
www.thetrainline.co.uk

Valley Lines
www.valleylines.co.uk

Virgin Trains
www.virgintrains.co.uk

Wales & West
www.walesandwest.co.uk

West Anglia Great Northern Railway
www.wagn.co.uk

travel agents, tour operators & cruises

A2b Travel
www.a2btravel.com

Abercrombie & Kent
www.abercrombiekent.co.uk

Air Miles
www.airmiles.co.uk

Airtours
www.airtours.com

Arctic Experience
www.arctic-experience.co.uk

Arctic Experience & Discover the World
www.arctic-discover.co.uk

Austravel
www.austravel.com

Bents Bicycle & Walking Tours
www.bentstours.com

Blakes Holidays
www.blakes.co.uk

British Airways Holidays
www.britishairwaysholidays.co.uk

Cadogan Holidays
www.cadoganholidays.com

Carnival
www.carnival.com

Citalia
www.citalia.co.uk

Club 18-30
www.18-30.co.uk

Club 25
www.club25.ie

Co-op Travel
www.extratravel.co.uk

Cosmos
www.cosmos-holidays.co.uk

Cresta Holidays
www.crestaholidays.co.uk

Crystal Holidays
www.crystalholidays.co.uk

Cunard
www.cunardline.com

Deckchair UK
www.deckchair.com

Destination Group
www.destination-group.com

Direct Holidays
www.directholidays.co.uk

Disney Cruises
www.disney.com/DisneyCruise

Dream Travel Africa
www.dreamtravelafrica.co.uk

E-Bookers
www.ebookers.com

Elegant Resorts International
www.elegantresorts.com

Erna Low
www.ernalow.co.uk

Expedia
www.expedia.co.uk

Festival Cruises
www.festival.gr

First Choice
www.first-choice.com

Fred Olsen
www.fredolsen.co.uk

Going Places
www.going-places.co.uk

Hayes & Jarvis Travel
www.hayesandjarvis.co.uk

Headwater
www.headwater.com

Hoseasons
www.hoseasons.co.uk

Inghams
www.inghams.com

Internet Travel Services
www.its.net

JMC
www.jmc-holidays.co.uk

Kuoni
www.kuoni.co.uk

Lastminute.com
www.lastminute.com

Lunn Poly
www.lunn-poly.co.uk

Magic Travel Group
www.magictravelgroup.co.uk

Moorings
www.moorings.co.uk

Nautilus
www.nautilus-yachting.co.uk

Neilson Holidays
www.neilson.co.uk

Norwegian Cruise Line
www.ncl.com

Orient Express Trains & Cruises
www.orient-expresstrains.com

P & O Stena Line
www.posl.com

Page & Moy
www.pagemoy.com

PGL Kids Holidays
www.pgl.co.uk

Portland
www.portland-holidays.co.uk

Portman Travel
www.portmantravel.co.uk

Powder Byrne
www.powderbyrne.com

Princess
www.princess.com

Royal Carribean Cruise Line
www.royalcaribbean.com

Saga Holidays
www.saga.co.uk

Scantours
www.scantoursuk.com

Silversea
www.silversea.com

Simply Travel
www.simply-travel.com

Skidream
www.skidream.com

Sovereign
www.sovereign.com

STA Travel
www.statravel.co.uk

Sunsail Holidays
www.sunsail.com

Sunvil Activity Holidays
www.activity-holidays.co.uk

Swan Hellenic
www.swan-hellenic.co.uk

Tenrag
www.tenrag.com

Thomas Cook
www.thomascook.co.uk

Thomson
www.thomson.co.uk

Thomson Cruising
www.thomson-holidays.com/cruises

Thomson Holidays
www.thomson-holidays.com

Tradewings
www.tradewings.co.uk

Trailfinders
www.trailfinders.co.uk

Travel for the Arts
www.travelforthearts.co.uk

Union Castle Line
www.union-castle-line.com

Virgin Holidays
www.virginholidays.co.uk

Voyages Jules Verne
www.vjv.co.uk

Wallace Arnold
www.wallacearnold.com

Windjammer
www.windjammer.com

Adventure Holidays

Adventure Holiday Websites
www.adventureholidaywebsites.co.uk

Adventure Learning
www.adventurelearning.co.uk

Andes
www.andes.org.uk

Down Under Worldwide Travel Insurance
www.duinsure.com

Exodus Holidays
www.exodus.co.uk

Galapagos Adventure Tours
www.galapagos.co.uk

Gateway To Asia
www.gateway-to-asia.co.uk

Gecko Travel
www.geckotravel.co.uk

Guiding Light Mountain Guides
www.guidinglight.org.uk

High & Wild
www.highandwild.co.uk

High Trek Snowdonia
www.hightrek.co.uk

PGL Travel Limited
www.pgl.co.uk

Tangent Expeditions International
www.tangent-expeditions.co.uk

American Holidays

American Adventures
www.americanadventures.com

American Holiday Websites
www.americanholidaywebsites.co.uk

American Round-up
www.american-roundup.co.uk

Bon Voyage
www.bon-voyage.co.uk

Disney
www.disney.go.com

Explore Worldwide
www.explore.co.uk

Premier Holidays
www.premierholidays.co.uk

Ranch America
www.ranchamerica.co.uk

South American Experience Ltd
www.sax.mcmail.com

Special Places
www.special-places.com

travel guides

Michelin
www.michelin-travel.com

Shell Geostar
www.shellgeostar.com

313

341

353